G000153649

500 FAMILY PUBS

Front cover: (top) The Bridge Hotel, (middle & bottom) The
Trout at Tadpole Bridge, Faringdon, Oxfordshire.
All other photographs: 1 AA/ Forbes Stephenson; 3 AA/Sarah
Montgomery

Printed in China by Leo Paper Products

Pub descriptions have been contributed by the following team
of writers: Phil Bryant, David Foster, David Halford, David
Hancock, Julia Hynard and Jenny White.

Directory compiled by AA Lifestyle Guides Department and
managed in the Librios Information Management System and
generated from the AA establishment database system.

Published by AA Publishing, a trading name of AA Media
Limited, whose registered office is
Fanum House, Basing View, Basingstoke RG21 4EA.
Registered number 06112600.

A CIP catalogue for this book is available from the British
Library.

ISBN: 978-0-7495-6462-9
A04301

Welcome to the Guide.

The pubs featured in this mini-guide have told us that they welcome children. Many offer children's menus or portions; some have family rooms; many have children's play areas or gardens. Many have even more child-friendly facilities, these will feature in the description. There are country pubs, city pubs, and pubs by the sea. Some are very well known and some are in stunning locations. They all offer great food and a good choice of beer for the grown ups.

Contents

❶ HURST

❷ *The Green Man* ♥

❸ Hinton Rd RG10 0BP
☎ 0118 934 2599   📠 0118 934 2939
e-mail: simon@thegreenman.uk.com
❹ dir: *Off A321, adjacent to Hurst Cricket Club*

❺ The pub gained its first licence in 1602, and Brakspear purchased a 1,000 year lease on the building in 1646. The old black beams, low in places, are still to be seen and the building has been developed to include all the old features, while newer areas reflect a similar theme. Inside you'll find open fires, hand drawn beer and good food, from sandwiches to Sunday roasts. The garden, open to fields and woodland, includes a children's play area.

❻ **Open** all wk 11-3 5.30-11 (Sun noon-10.30)
❼ **Bar Meals** food served all day **Restaurant** food
❽ served all day ⊕ BRAKSPEAR ◀ Brakspear Bitter, Hobgoblin, seasonal ales. ♥ 8 **Facilities** Children's menu Play area Garden Parking

---

❶ GUIDE ORDER Pubs are listed alphabetically by name under their village or town. Towns and villages are listed alphabetically within their county. Some village pubs prefer to be initially located under the nearest town, in which case the village name is included in the address and directions.

❷ ESTABLISHMENT NAME AND SYMBOLS If a pub's name appears in italics, it means we did not receive up-to-date information from them for 2010. See Key to symbols on page 6.

AA STARS/DESIGNATORS AA Stars and designators as appropriate are shown at the beginning of an entry.

❸ CONTACT DETAILS This gives the street name and the postcode, and if necessary the name of the village is included (see 1 above). This may be up to five miles from the named location. ☎ Telephone number, 📠 fax number, e-mail and websites as supplied by the pubs.

❹ DIRECTIONS Directions are given only when they have been supplied by the proprietor.

❺ DESCRIPTION Description of the pub and food.

❻ OPEN Indicates the hours and dates when the pub is open and closed.

7 FOOD DETAILS

BAR MEALS Indicates the times and days when proprietors tell us bar food can be ordered, and the average price of a main course as supplied by the proprietor. Please be aware that last orders could vary by up to 30 minutes.

RESTAURANT Indicates the times and days when proprietors tell us food can be ordered from the restaurant. The average cost of a 3-course à la carte meal and a 3- or 4-course fixed-price menu are shown as supplied by the proprietor. Last orders may be approximately 30 minutes before the times stated.

8 OWNERSHIP & DRINKS AVAILABLE After the 🌐, comes the name of the Brewery to which the pub is tied, or the Company which owns it. A free house is where the pub is independently owned and run.

🍺 The beer tankard symbol indicates the principal beers sold by the pub. Up to five cask or hand-pulled beers are listed. Many pubs have a much greater selection, with several guest beers each week.

🍎 The apple symbol indicates that real cider is available and listed.

🍷 The wine glass symbol followed by a number indicates the number of wines sold by the glass.

9 FACILITIES Indicates if a pub has a children's menu (which might mean children's portions), a garden, allows dogs on the premises, offers parking and has a children's play area. For further information please phone the pub.

ROOMS Only accommodation that has been inspected is indicated. In the case of AA rated accommodation only, the number of en suite bedrooms is listed. Many pubs have rooms but we only indicate those that are AA rated.

NOTES As so many establishments take one or more of the major credit cards we only indicate if a pub does not take cards.

SYMBOLS

◉ **Rosettes** – The AA's food award.
★★★ **Stars** – Accommodation rating.
⊕ **Barrel** – Name of Brewery or Company
◀ **Tankard** – Principal beers sold
◔ **Apple** – Real cider available
♀ **Wine glass** – Indicates that at least six wines are available by the glass. For the exact number of wines served this way, see notes at the bottom of each entry

AA Classifications & Awards

Many of the pubs in this Guide offer accommodation. Where a Star rating appears next to a pub's name in the Guide, the establishment has been inspected by the AA and rated either as a hotel or as guest accommodation.

The annual AA Hotel Guide and AA Bed & Breakfast Guide give further details of recognised establishments and the classification schemes. Details of AA rating schemes, as well as all AA recognised hotels, guest accommodation, restaurants and pubs are also available at theAA.com, along with a useful Route Planner.

HOTELS

The following designators indicate an establishment is rated as a Hotel by the AA: Hotel (HL);Town House Hotel (TH); Country House Hotel (CHH); Small Hotel (SHL); Metro Hotel (MET); Budget Hotel (BUD).
The AA's top hotels in Britain and Ireland are identified by red stars. (★)

GUEST ACCOMMODATION

These designators indicate that an establishment is rated as Guest accommodation by the AA: Bed & Breakfast (B&B); Guest House (GH); Farmhouse (FH); Restaurant with Rooms (RR); Guest Accommodation (GA); Inn (INN)

The very best establishments in the Guest Accommodation scheme in the 3, 4 and 5 star ratings are usually indicated by yellow stars. Because this guide is printed with only two colours, these are shown as red stars.

U Unrated - A small number of pubs have this symbol because their Star classification was not confirmed at the time of going to press

A Associate - Refers to hotels rated by another organisation, eg VisitBritain.

For an explanation of AA food & accommodation ratings see www.theaa.com/travel/accommodation_restaurants_grading.html

BEDFORD

The Three Tuns ♟

57 Main Rd, Biddenham MK40 4BD
☎ 01234 354847
dir: *On A428 from Bedford towards Northampton 1st left signed Biddenham. Into village, pub on left*

A stone-built, thatched roof pub, The Three Tuns stands in the heart of the beautiful village of Biddenham. It has a large garden with a patio and decking, and a separate children's play area with swings and a climbing frame. The old morgue, situated between the two garden areas, is the oldest building in the village and is said to be haunted. Home-cooked dishes on the regularly-changing menus include pies, steaks, curries, fish, local sausages, burgers and vegetarian specialities; all washed down with award-winning Greene King beers.

Open all wk 12-3 6-11 (Sun 12-4 7-10.30; 12-11 in summer) **Bar Meals** L served all wk 12-2 D served Mon-Sat 6-9 **Restaurant** L served all wk 12-2 booking required D served Mon-Sat 6-9 booking required ⊕ GREENE KING ◀ Greene King IPA, Abbot Ale, guest ale, Guinness. ♟ 6 **Facilities** Children's menu Play area Family room Dogs allowed Garden Parking

BROOM

The Cock

23 High St SG18 9NA
☎ 01767 314411 📄 01767 314284
dir: *Off B658 SW of Biggleswade. 1m from A1*

Unspoilt to this day with its intimate quarry-tiled rooms with latched doors and panelled walls, this 17th-century establishment is known as 'The Pub with no Bar'. Real ales are served straight from casks racked by the cellar steps. A straightforward pub grub menu includes jumbo cod, roast chicken, gammon steak, breaded lobster, and breast of Cajun chicken.

Open all wk 12-4 6-11 **Bar Meals** L served all wk 12-2.15 D served all wk 7-9 **Restaurant** L served all wk 12-2.15 D served all wk 7-9 ⊕ GREENE KING ◀ Greene King Abbot Ale, IPA, Ruddles County. **Facilities** Children's menu Play area Family room Dogs allowed Garden Parking

EATON BRAY

The White Horse ♟

Market Square LU6 2DG
☎ 01525 220231 📄 01525 222485
e-mail: davidsparrow@onetel.net
web: www.the-whitehorse.co.uk
dir: *A5 N of Dunstable onto A505, left in 1m, follow signs*

For almost 20 years, David and Janet Sparrow have built their reputation on great home cooked food at this traditional 300-year-old village inn with its oak beams and horse brasses. There's a wide ranging menu including comfort food like beef in ale pie, plus daily specials that might include sea bass fillets in lemon butter; Horton's pork with apple sausages and bubble and squeak. It's worth booking for the restaurant, but the same menu is also available in the bar.

Open all wk Closed: Sun eve Jan-Mar **Bar Meals** L served all wk 12-2.15 D served all wk 7-9.30 booking required Av main course £9.50 **Restaurant** L served all wk 12-2.15 D served all wk 7-9.30 booking required Av 3 course à la carte fr £21.50 ⊕ PUNCH TAVERNS ◀ Greene King IPA, Shepherd Neame Spitfire. ♟ 8 **Facilities** Children's menu Play area Family room Garden Parking

LINSLADE

The Globe Inn ♟

Globe Ln, Old Linslade LU7 2TA
☎ 01525 373338 📄 01525 850551
e-mail: 6458@greeneking.co.uk

Originally a farmhouse and stables, this friendly waterside inn was converted to serve passing boat crews on the Grand Union Canal. Open fires and candles set the scene for winter evenings, whilst for warmer days there's a large garden and children's play area. Expect an appetising range of light bites and mixed smoked deli board for sharing, as well as hot dishes like pan-seared Barbary duck with dauphinoise potatoes; sweet potato, chick pea and spinach curry; and daily fresh fish specials.

Open all day all wk 11-11 **Bar Meals** Av main course £8.95 food served all day **Restaurant** Av 3 course à la carte fr £20 food served all day ⊕ GREENE KING ◀ Greene King Abbot Ale, Old Speckled Hen, IPA & Ruddles County Ale, Hook Norton. ♟ 16 **Facilities** Children's menu Play area Dogs allowed Garden Parking

NORTHILL

The Crown ♥

2 Ickwell Rd SG18 9AA

☎ 01767 627337   📄 01767 627279

e-mail: info@thecrown-northill.com

dir: *Telephone for directions*

A delightful 16th-century pub with chocolate box setting between Northill church and the village duck pond. Its acre of garden includes a children's play area, and plenty of tables for alfresco eating. Inside, the unique copper-covered bar leads to an informal dining area, where the bar menu of pub favourites applies. The candlelit split-level restaurant boasts much locally sourced produce served in home-cooked dishes such as roasted lamb chump with port and rosemary jus; smoked hake fillets on tomato sauce; and pork tenderloin medallions wrapped in bacon.

Open all wk 11.30-3 6-11 (Sun 12-11 Summer Sat 11.30am-11pm) Closed: 25 Dec eve **Bar Meals** L served Mon-Sat 12-2.30, Sun 12-8 D served Mon-Sat 6.30-9.30, Sun all day Av main course £8.95 **Restaurant** L served Mon-Sat 12-2.30, Sun 12-8 booking required D served Mon-Sat 6.30-9.30, Sun all day booking required Av 3 course à la carte fr £23 ⊕ GREENE KING ◀ Greene King IPA, Abbot Ale, Old Speckled Hen, Olde Tripplus, Guest ales. ♥ 9 **Facilities** Children's menu Play area Dogs allowed Garden Parking

SOUTHILL

The White Horse ♥

High St SG18 9LD ☎ 01462 813364

e-mail: paul.e.cluett@virgin.net

dir: *Telephone for directions*

A village pub with traditional values, happily accommodating the needs of children and those who like to sit outside on cool days (the patio has heaters). Locally renowned for its chargrilled steaks from the Duke of Buccleuch's Scottish estate. Other main courses include Cajun chicken; chargrilled pork loin steaks; Whitby Bay scampi; and stuffed breaded plaice. Enjoy Greene King beers, with London Pride up from Chiswick. Recent change of management.

Open all wk **Bar Meals** L served Mon-Fri 12-2.30, Sat-Sun 12-10 booking required D served Mon-Fri 6-10, Sat-Sun 12-10 booking required Av main course £7.50 **Restaurant** L served Mon-Fri 12-2.30, Sat-Sun 12-10 booking required D served Mon-Fri 6-10, Sat-Sun 12-10 booking required Fixed menu price fr £5.50 Av 3 course à la carte fr £15 ⊕ ENTERPRISE INNS ◀ Greene King IPA, London Pride, Speckled Hen, Flowers. ♥ 8 **Facilities** Children's menu Play area Dogs allowed Garden Parking

TILSWORTH

The Anchor Inn ▾

1 Dunstable Rd LU7 9PU
☎ 01525 210289　🖷 01525 211578
e-mail: tonyanchorinn@aol.com
dir: Exit A5 at Tilsworth. In 1m pub on right at 3rd bend

The only pub in a Saxon village, the Anchor dates from 1878. The restaurant is a recent addition to the side of the pub, and the whole building has been refurbished. The licensees pride themselves on their fresh food and well-kept beers and guest ales. An acre of garden includes patio seating for alfresco dining, an adventure playground and a barbecue. Recent change of hands.

Open all day all wk noon-11.30pm **Bar Meals** Av main course £5 food served all day **Restaurant** Fixed menu price fr £10 food served all day ⊕ GREENE KING ◀ Greene King IPA, Abbot Ale, Wadworth 6X, guest ales. ▾ 12 **Facilities** Children's menu Play area Family room Garden Parking

ASHMORE GREEN

The Sun in the Wood ▾

Stoney Ln RG18 9HF
☎ 01635 42377　🖷 01635 528392
e-mail: info@suninthewood.co.uk
dir: From A34 at Robin Hood Rdbt left to Shaw, at mini-rdbt right then 7th left into Stoney Ln 1.5m, pub on left

The name promises woodland beauty and the setting delivers it, yet the centre of Newbury is surprisingly close by. Expect stone floors and plenty of wood panelling within, and a country garden, decking terrace for alfresco dining and crazy golf outside. Sample a pint of Wadworth's or one of 16 wines by the glass, and enjoy food made using local ingredients at this award-winning country pub: perhaps crisp whitebait with home-made tartare sauce, then chicken breast with wild mushroom sauce.

Open Closed: Mon **Bar Meals** L served Tue-Sat 12-2, Sun 12-4 booking required D served Tue-Sat 6-9.30 booking required Av main course £10.95 **Restaurant** L served Tue-Sat 12-2, Sun 12-4 booking required D served Tue-Sat 6-9.30 booking required Av 3 course à la carte fr £19.95 ⊕ WADWORTH ◀ Wadworth 6X, Henrys Original IPA, Badger Tanglefoot ♻ Westons Stowford Press. ▾ 16 **Facilities** Children's menu Play area Garden Parking

HERMITAGE

The White Horse of Hermitage ▼

Newbury Rd RG18 9TB ☎ 01635 200325
e-mail: thewh@btconnect.com
web: www.thewhitehorseofhermitage.co.uk
dir: 5m from Newbury on B4009. Follow signs to
Chieveley, right into Priors Court Rd, turn left at
mini-rdbt, pub approx 1m

The White Horse has achieved a solid reputation
for its pub food, using the freshest and finest
local produce to create a daily menu, including
signature dishes such as BBQ babyback ribs.
The interior bar and restaurant is contemporary
in decor, and outside you choose between the
Mediterranean-style patio or the large garden
which is equipped with swings and a football
area.

Open noon-3 5-11 Closed: Sun eve, Mon (ex BH)
Bar Meals Av main course £10 food served all day
Restaurant Av 3 course à la carte fr £15 food served
all day ⊕ GREENE KING ◀ Abbot Ale, Greene King
IPA, Guinness. ♥ 9 Facilities Children's menu Play
area Dogs allowed Garden Parking

HUNGERFORD

The Swan Inn ★★★★ INN

Craven Rd, Lower Green, Inkpen RG17 9DX
☎ 01488 668326 📄 01488 668306
e-mail: enquiries@theswaninn-organics.co.uk
web: www.theswaninn-organics.co.uk
dir: S down Hungerford High St (A338), under rail
bridge, left to Hungerford Common. Right signed
Inkpen (3m)

Organic farmers Mary and Bernard Harris
preside over this 17th-century free house, set
below Combe Gibbet and Walbury Hill. As well
as ramblers, the pub attracts cyclists, hang
gliders, shooting parties and organic food fans.
The terraced garden is in contrast to the beamed
interior with old photographic prints and open
winter fires. The menu is a feast of fresh produce;
meats are 100% organic and butchered on the
premises. The bar offers traditional English
favourites, while the restaurant serves dishes like
pan-fried breast of Barbary duck with bacon and
mushroom sauce and a range of steaks.

Open all wk 11-11 (Sun noon-10.30) Closed: 25-26
Dec Bar Meals L served all wk 12-2 D served
all wk 7-9.30 Av main course £10 Restaurant L
served Wed-Sun 12-2.30 booking required D served
Wed-Sat 7-9.30 booking required Av 3 course à la
carte fr £25 ⊕ FREE HOUSE ◀ Butts Traditional
& Jester Bitter, Butts Blackguard, guest ales.
Facilities Children's menu Play area Garden Parking
Rooms 10

11

HURST

The Green Man 🍷

Hinton Rd RG10 0BP
☎ 0118 934 2599 📠 0118 934 2939
e-mail: simon@thegreenman.uk.com
dir: *Off A321, adjacent to Hurst Cricket Club*

The pub gained its first licence in 1602, and Brakspear purchased a 1,000 year lease on the building in 1646. The old black beams, low in places, are still to be seen and the building has been developed to include all the old features, while newer areas reflect a similar theme. Inside you'll find open fires, hand drawn beer and good food, from sandwiches to Sunday roasts. The garden, open to fields and woodland, includes a children's play area.

Open all wk 11-3 5.30-11 (Sun noon-10.30) **Bar Meals** food served all day **Restaurant** food served all day ⊕ BRAKSPEAR ◖ Brakspear Bitter, Hobgoblin, seasonal ales. 🍷 8 **Facilities** Children's menu Play area Garden Parking

PALEY STREET

The Royal Oak ◎◎ 🍷

SL6 3JN ☎ 01628 620541
dir: *From Maidenhead take A330 towards Ascot for 2m, turn right onto B3024 signed White Waltham, 2nd pub on left*

Drop by for a drink and relax on one of the comfortable sofas at this traditional English dining pub, owned by Nick Parkinson, son of Sir Michael Parkinson. Fullers provide the reliable ales, but the wine list is undoubtedly the star of the drinks show; around 20 wines are served by the glass, and the main listings begin with a selection of over 20 champagnes. Meanwhile, head chef Dominic Chapman uses the best seasonal produce to create outstanding British food. Choose from a small selection of bar snacks or sample the lunch and dinner menus, which might begin with smoked haddock soup or potted Devon crab with toast. Typical mains include peppered haunch of venison with creamed spinach, Old Spot belly pork with mushy peas and braised onions, or grilled lemon sole with wild mushrooms and watercress. A beer garden completes the picture for alfresco dining.

Open 12-3 6-11 (Sun 12-4) Closed: 25 Dec & 1 Jan, Sun eve **Restaurant** L served Mon-Sat 12-3, Sun 12-4 booking required D served Mon-Thu 6.30-9.30, Fri-Sat 6.30-10 Av 3 course à la carte fr £35 ⊕ FULLERS ◖ Fuller's London Pride. 🍷 20 **Facilities** Children's menu Garden Parking

READING

The Flowing Spring ♥

Henley Rd, Playhatch RG4 9RB
☎ 0118 969 9878
e-mail: flowingspring@aol.com
dir: *3m N of Reading*

A lovely country pub on the Henley road, much favoured by walkers and cyclists. It's family friendly too, with a menu for under-12s and a small play area in the large well-kept garden. Representative dishes on the combined bar/restaurant menu include chicken goujons with chips and salad; battered cod and chips; spotted dick; and sticky toffee pudding. Being a Fullers pub, Chiswick, London Pride and ESB are all well kept on tap.

Open all wk 11-11 **Bar Meals** L served all wk D served all wk Av main course £6.95 food served all day **Restaurant** L served all wk D served all wk Av 3 course à la carte fr £12 food served all day ⊕ FULLERS ◀ London Pride, ESB, Chiswick, HSB. ♥ 7 **Facilities** Children's menu Play area Family room Dogs allowed Garden Parking

BUCKINGHAM

The Wheatsheaf ♥

Main St, Maids Moreton MK18 1QR
☎ 01280 815433 📄 01280 814631
dir: *M1 junct 13, (or M40 junct 9, A34 to Bicester) A421 to Buckingham, then A413 to Maids Moreton*

This traditional, thatched village inn has been a pub since 1750, and offers an appetising à la carte menu in the spacious conservatory overlooking the secluded beer garden. Eating options include baked cod and prawns in cream; roast aubergine stuffed with ratatouille; and home-made Thai chicken curry. Real ales and snacks can also be enjoyed in the bar, with its cosy inglenook fireplaces. Children will be delighted with the outdoor play equipment.

Open all wk **Bar Meals** L served all wk 12-2.15 D served Tue-Sat 6.45-9.30 **Restaurant** L served all wk 12-2.15 D served Tue-Sat 6.45-9.30 ⊕ FREE HOUSE ◀ John Smiths, Side Pocket For A Toad, Reverend James, Pitstop. ♥ 10 **Facilities** Children's menu Play area Family room Dogs allowed Garden Parking

CHEDDINGTON

The Old Swan ☻

58 High St LU7 0RQ
☎ 01296 668226 📠 01296 663811
e-mail: geoffrsmith@btconnect.com
dir: *From Tring towards Marsworth take B489, 0.5m. Left towards Cooks Wharf onto Cheddington, pub on left*

Formed out of three cottages in the 15th century, this delightful thatched pub is known not only for its real ales and traditional charm but also for its ghosts. A man in 18th-century dress reputedly tries to kiss ladies in the restaurant area! Food ranges from roasted half pheasant with black cherry and port sauce; sea bass fillets with pine nuts and baby spinach; to five bean, vegetable and tomato hotpot. Outside there's a large garden with a children's play area. A great choice of real ales and Westons Stowford Press cider is available.

Open all wk Mon-Fri 12-3, 5-11 (Sat-Sun 11-11) Bar Meals L served Mon-Thu 12-2, Fri-Sat 12-2.30, Sun 12-4 D served Mon-Thu 6-9, Fri-Sat 6-9.30 Av main course £10 Restaurant L served Mon-Thu 12-2, Fri-Sat 12-2.30, Sun 12-4 D served Mon-Thu 6-9, Fri-Sat 6-9.30 ⊕ PUNCH TAVERNS ◀ Courage Best, St Austell Tribute, Everard's Tiger, Shepherd Neame Spitfire, Adnams Broadside Ö Stowford Press. ♚ 12 Facilities Children's menu Play area Dogs allowed Garden Parking

HEDGERLEY

The White Horse ☻

SL2 3UY
☎ 01753 643225
dir: *Telephone for directions*

The original part of the pub is 500 years old, and over 1000 beers take their turn at the pumps during each year. At least seven real ales are always available, served by gravity. An annual beer festival is held at the end of May bank holiday. Home-made food ranges from a salad bar with pies, quiches, sandwiches and ploughman's through to curries, chilli, pasta dishes, pies and steaks.

Open all wk 11-2.30 5-11 (Sat 11-11, Sun 11-10.30) Bar Meals L served Mon-Fri 12-2, Sat-Sun 12-2.30 ⊕ FREE HOUSE ◀ Regularly changing Ö Regularly changing. ♚ 10 Facilities Children's menu Family room Dogs allowed Garden Parking

MARLOW

The Hand and Flowers ⊛⊛⊛ ▼

126 West St SL7 2BP

☎ 01628 482277 📠 01628 401913

e-mail: theoffice@thehandandflowers.co.uk

web: www.thehandandflowers.co.uk

dir: *M4 junct 9, A404 N into Marlow, A4155 towards Henley-on-Thames. Pub on outskirts on right*

Dedicated chef Tom Kerridge has been at this unassuming pub since 2005. Despite its AA rosettes, the pub is a relaxed and unpretentious place. Choices from the bar include fish and chips or roast beef and horseradish sandwich. Tom's modern Anglo-French cooking uses top produce. Served on plain, solid-wood tables are terrine of Old Spot pork and bacon with hot pickled pineapple; slow-cooked Oxford beef with bone marrow bread pudding; sea bream with braised Puy lentils, mussels and parsley; Valrhona chocolate tart with malted milk ice cream, and rhubarb crumble soufflé with stem ginger anglaise.

Open 12-2.30 6.30-9.30 (Sun 12-3.30) Closed: 24-26 Dec, 31 Dec L, 1 Jan D, Sun eve **Bar Meals** L served Mon-Sat 12-2.30 booking required D served Mon-Sat 6.30-9.30 booking required Av main course £9.80 **Restaurant** L served all wk 12-2.30 booking required D served all wk 6.30-9.30 booking required Av 3 course à la carte fr £35 ⊕ Greene King ◖ Abbot Ale, IPA. ▼ 10 **Facilities** Children's menu Garden Parking

WHITELEAF

Red Lion

Upper Icknield Way HP27 0LL

☎ 01844 344476 📠 01844 344476

e-mail: tim_hibbert@hotmail.co.uk

dir: *A4010 through Princes Risborough, turn right into The Holloway, at T-junct turn right, pub on left*

Family-owned 17th-century traditional country inn in the heart of the Chilterns, surrounded by National Trust land and situated close to the Ridgeway national trail. There are plenty of good local walks with wonderful views. A cosy fire in winter and a secluded summer beer garden add to the appeal. Hearty pub fare is served in the bar area and includes rib-eye steak, sausage and mash, vegetarian lasagne, haddock and chips, warm baguettes and jacket potatoes. You can also dine in the recently built restaurant.

Open all wk **Bar Meals** L served all wk 12-2 D served Mon-Sat 7-9 booking required Av main course £8.50 **Restaurant** L served all wk 12-2 booking required D served Mon-Sat 7-9 booking required Fixed menu price fr £9.50 ⊕ FREE HOUSE ◖ Brakspear Bitter, Hook Norton, Tribute, Guinness. **Facilities** Children's menu Family room Dogs allowed Garden Parking

CAMBRIDGE

Cambridge Blue 🍷

85 Gwydir St CB1 2LG
☎ 01223 471680
dir: *City centre*

A friendly 1860s backstreet pub with an unexpected garden. Inside are two real fires and lots of memorabilia. The tap room has seven handpumps, but there are always at least 12 real ales to choose from, such as Bishop's Farewell and Nethergate Dewdrop (the pub used to be called the Dew Drop Inn, a Victorian pun). Good value pub grub made on the premises ranges from ciabattas and jackets to curries, pies, chilli con carne and sticky toffee pudding.

Open all wk noon-2.30 5-11 (Thu-Sat noon-11 Sun noon-10.30) **Bar Meals** L served Mon-Fri 12-2, Sat-Sun 12-4 D served all wk 6-9 Av main course £7 ⊕ FREE HOUSE ◀ Woodforde's Wherry, Oakham Bishops Farewell, guest ales. ♀ 8 **Facilities** Children's menu Family room Dogs allowed Garden

CAMBRIDGE

Free Press 🍷

Prospect Row CB1 1DU
☎ 01223 368337
e-mail: craig.bickley@ntlworld.com
dir: *Telephone for directions*

Students, academics, locals and visitors rub shoulders in this atmospheric and picturesque back-street pub near the city centre. It has open fires and a beautiful walled garden - but no music, mobile phones or gaming machines. Punters are attracted by first-rate real ales and nourishing home-made food such as chilli with garlic bread; goat's cheese salad; filled toasted ciabattas; venison sausages; salmon filled with couscous and vegetables; and fresh pasta.

Open all wk noon-2.30 6-11 (Fri noon-2.30 4.30-11, Sat noon-11, Sun noon-3 7-10.30) Closed: 25-26 Dec, 1 Jan ⊕ GREENE KING ◀ Greene King IPA, Abbot Ale, Dark Mild, guest ales. ♀ 10 **Facilities** Children's menu Dogs allowed Garden

GRANTCHESTER

The Rupert Brooke ▾

2 Broadway CB3 9NQ
☎ 01223 840295 🖷 01223 841251
e-mail: info@therupertbrooke.com
dir: M11 junct 12, follow Grantchester signs

Only five minutes from the centre of Cambridge and the M11, yet set in an idyllic location overlooking the meadows close to the River Cam, sits the Rupert Brooke, named after the WWI poet. Inside, you'll find timber beams and winter log fires, with relaxing sofas and tub chairs. Using local, seasonal produce and with regularly changing menus, watch the chefs at work in the theatre-style kitchen, creating their range of modern British dishes - winter squash and sage risotto; Grasmere Farm sausages with creamy mash are typical choices. The pub provides newspapers and Wi-fi.

Open all wk 11.30-11 (Fri-Sat 11.30-mdnt) **Bar Meals** L served Mon-Sat 12-3 D served Mon-Fri 6-9.30 Av main course £11 **Restaurant** L served Mon-Sat 12-3 (Sun 12-6 (8 May-Sep)) booking required D served Mon-Sat 6-9.30 booking required Av 3 course à la carte fr £25 ⊕ ENTERPRISE INNS ◀ Harveys Sussex Best, Woodforde's Wherry, London Pride, Timothy Taylor Landlord ♂ Westons Stowford Press. ▾ 12 **Facilities** Children's menu Family room Garden Parking

STRETHAM

The Lazy Otter

Cambridge Rd CB6 3LU
☎ 01353 649780 🖷 01353 649314
e-mail: restaurant@lazy-otter.com
dir: Telephone for directions

Just off the A10 between Ely and Cambridge, the Lazy Otter stands overlooking the marina beside the River Great Ouse. There's been a pub on this site since the 18th century, but the old building was redeveloped in 1986. Today, the large beer garden and riverside restaurant are popular summer attractions. Lunchtime brings baguettes, sandwiches and jacket potatoes, whilst main course choices include ham and eggs; baked cod au gratin; and home-made spinach lasagne. Enjoy your meal with a pint of Lazy Otter best bitter or Pickled Pig cider.

Open all day all wk 11-11 (Sun noon-10.30pm) **Bar Meals** L served Mon-Sat 12-2, Sun 12-7 booking required D served Mon-Sat 6.30-9, Sun 12-7 booking required Av main course £8.50 **Restaurant** L served Mon-Sat 12-2, Sun 12-7 booking required D served Mon-Sat 6.30-9, Sun 12-7 booking required ⊕ FREE HOUSE ◀ Greene King, IPA, Guest ales ♂ Pickled Pig. **Facilities** Children's menu Play area Garden Parking

HAUGHTON MOSS

The Nags Head ♇

Long Ln CW6 9RN
☎ 01829 260265 ▤ 01829 261364
e-mail: roryk1@btinternet.com
dir: Turn off A49 S of Tarporley at Beeston/Haughton sign into Long Ln, continue for 1.75m

Set amid beautiful Cheshire countryside, this 16th-century black and white building, once a smithy, is every inch the friendly, traditional pub. Inside are low ceilings, crooked beams, exposed brickwork and real fires. Outside, there are spacious gardens and a bowling green. The extensive menu might offer moules marinière or stilton and Guinness pâté to start, followed by steak and chips or fajitas. An impressive choice of home-made desserts could include syrup and pear sponge or triple chocolate roulade.

Open all day all wk 11-mdnt Bar Meals L served all wk 12-10 D served all wk 12-10 Av main course £10 food served all day Restaurant L served all wk 12-10 D served all wk 12-10 Fixed menu price fr £8.85 Av 3 course à la carte fr £20 food served all day ⊕ FREE HOUSE ◀ Flowers IPA, Sharps Doom Bar, guest ales. ♇ 14 Facilities Children's menu Play area Dogs allowed Garden Parking

MACCLESFIELD

The Windmill Inn ♇

Holehouse Ln, Whitely Green, Adlington
SK10 5SJ
☎ 01625 574222
e-mail: mail@thewindmill.info
dir: Between Macclesfield & Poynton. Follow brown tourist signs on main road. Pub in 1.5m

Just two minutes walk from the Macclesfield Canal and close to the Middlewood Way, this former farmhouse is an ideal place to start or end a country stroll. It has an extensive landscaped garden, with children's maze, while the interior has a cosy real fire and sofas. The menu runs from tempting sandwiches and light lunches, like potted Goosnargh duck with spiced plum relish and toasted sourdough, to full meals such as smoked haddock and leek tart with hollandaise sauce followed by braised steak and onions with horseradish mash and roast parsnips.

Open all wk noon-3 5-11 (Fri-Sat noon-11, Sun noon-10.30) Bar Meals L served Mon-Fri 12-2.30, Sat-Sun 12-4 booking required D served Mon-Fri 5.30-9.30, Sat 12-9.30, Sun 12-8 booking required Av main course £10.95 Restaurant L served Mon-Fri 12-2.30, Sat 12-9.30, Sun 12-8 booking required D served Mon-Fri 5.30-9.30, Sat 12-9.30, Sun 12-8 booking required ⊕ Mitchels & Butler - Moyo Ltd ◀ Black Sheep, Old Speckled Hen, Wadworth 6X, guest ale. ♇ 14 Facilities Children's menu Dogs allowed Garden Parking

MARTON

The Davenport Arms ♥

Congleton Rd SK11 9HF
☎ 01260 224269   ▤ 01260 224565
e-mail: enquiries@thedavenportarms.co.uk
web: www.thedavenportarms.co.uk
dir: *3m from Congleton off A34*

As well as this 18th-century pub, Marton is home to a 1200 year old oak that still produces acorns. The traditional bar is very cosy, while in the restaurant all food is made on the premises from local supplies. Lunch features home-made fishcake with citrus mayo and sweet chilli dip or black pudding on sweet potato rösti with shallot purée and peppercorn sauce, followed by Cajun salmon fillets with mango, plum and salsa or home-baked ham, eggs and chips. For dinner try tiger prawn with ginger and chilli marinade or goats' cheese parcels with cranberry compote; followed by breast of pheasant in red wine sauce with red cabbage or lamb Henry with root vegetable, rosemary jus and mash.

Open noon-3 6-mdnt (Fri-Sun noon-mdnt) Closed: Mon L (ex BH) **Bar Meals** L served Tue-Sat 12-2.30, Sun 12-3 D served Tue-Sat 6-9, Sun 6-8.30 Av main course £8.95 **Restaurant** L served Tue-Sat 12-2.30, Sun 12-3 booking required D served Tue-Sat 6-9, Sun 6-8.30 booking required Av 3 course à la carte fr £22 ⊞ FREE HOUSE ◀ Copper Dragon, Storm Brewing, Directors, Weetwood, Theakstons. ♥ 9 **Facilities** Children's menu Play area Garden Parking

MOULDSWORTH

The Goshawk ♥

Station Rd CH3 8AJ
☎ 01928 740900   ▤ 01928 740965
dir: *A51 from Chester onto A54. Left onto B5393 towards Frodsham. Enter Mouldsworth, pub on left opposite rail station*

A welcoming pub with log fires and stripped pine floors, The Goshawk is conveniently located opposite the railway station in Mouldsworth, one stop from Chester. Close by are Delamere Forest and Country Park. The menu starts with light snacks of Bury black pudding with chicken and beetroot, or eggs Benedict, and shellfish starters like potted shrimps or seared scallops. There's a good choice of salads, and more substantial fare, with up to 12 fish dishes, steaks from the chargrill, and vegetarian options like stuffed roasted red peppers. House favourites are lobster thermidor and steak and kidney pudding made with Timothy Taylor's Ale, while alternatives include braised lamb shank with dauphinoise potatoes and honey roast chantenay carrots, or halibut topped with pesto and crab crust served with couscous, chickpeas and Thai asparagus.

Open all wk noon-11 (Sun noon-10.30) Closed: 25 Dec & 1 Jan **Bar Meals** food served all day **Restaurant** food served all day ◀ Timothy Taylor Landlord, Greene King IPA, Deuchars, Old Speckled Hen. ♥ 14 **Facilities** Children's menu Play area Family room Garden Parking

PLUMLEY

The Golden Pheasant Hotel 🍷

Plumley Moor Rd WA16 9RX

☎ 01565 722261   📠 01565 723804

dir: *M6 junct 19, A556 signed Chester. 2m, left at Plumley/Peover signs. Through Plumley, pub 1m opp rail station*

Set in the beautiful Cheshire countryside, The Golden Pheasant is convenient for Chester and Manchester, with trains from the station opposite hourly. This 200-year-old, traditional wayside inn is privately owned and proud of its real ales, extensive wine list and home-cooked, locally sourced food served in the dining room and lounge bar areas. Expect roaring log fires, comfy sitting areas, alfresco dining, a children's play area and a locals' bar with a darts board.

Open all day all wk 11-11 (Sun noon-10.30) **Bar Meals** Av main course £10.95 food served all day **Restaurant** Fixed menu price fr £15.95 Av 3 course à la carte fr £21.95 food served all day ⊕ J W LEES ◀ J W Lees Bitter, John Willies Bitter, Guinness. 🍷 12 **Facilities** Children's menu Play area Garden Parking

PLUMLEY

The Smoker 🍷

WA16 0TY

☎ 01565 722338   📠 01565 722093

e-mail: smoker@plumley.fsword.co.uk

dir: *From M6 junct 19 take A556 W. Pub 1.75m on left*

This 400-year-old thatched coaching inn is actually named after a white racehorse bred by the Prince Regent, although recent legislation has prompted the addition of a covered smokers' courtyard complete with heating and seating. The pub's striking wood-panelled interior of three connecting rooms provides a traditional welcoming atmosphere, with log fires, beams and copper kettles. The menu has an appealing and lengthy array of starters; main courses include Barnsley chop; deep-fried haddock; and lamb Henry.

Open all wk 10-3 6-11 (Sun 10am-10.30pm) **Bar Meals** L served Mon-Fri 10-2.30, Sun 10-9 D served Mon-Fri 6-9.30, Sun 10-9 Av main course £10 **Restaurant** L served Mon-Fri 10-2.30, Sun 10-9 booking required D served Mon-Fri 6-9.30, Sun 10-9 booking required Av 3 course à la carte fr £18.50 ⊕ FREDERIC ROBINSON ◀ Robinson's Best, Double Hop, Robinsons Smooth. 🍷 10 **Facilities** Children's menu Play area Garden Parking

SWETTENHAM

The Swettenham Arms 🍷

Swettenham Ln CW12 2LF
☎ 01477 571284 📠 01477 571284
e-mail: info@swettenhamarms.co.uk
dir: M6 junct 18 to Holmes Chapel, then A535 towards Jodrell Bank. 3m right (Forty Acre Lane) to Swettenham

Winter in this 600-year-old pub means log fires and mulled wine; summer means lavender and sunflowers in the meadow; in autumn there are the arboretum and nature reserve. And spring? Well, everywhere's lovely in spring, so just enjoy the high standards of food and service, which are year-round. Begin your meal with smoked halibut salad and quenelles of mascarpone; then 21-day roast Cheshire beef and Yorkshire pudding, or one of Chef's signature dishes; supreme of chicken, brie and spring onion in filo pastry, and white wine and basil cream sauce, perhaps. Vegetarians have a good choice.

Open all wk noon-3.30 6-11 (Sat-Sun noon-11)
Bar Meals L served Mon-Sat 12-2.30, Sun 12-9.30 booking required D served Mon-Sat 6.30-9.30, Sun 12-9.30 booking required Av main course £10 **Restaurant** L served Mon-Sat 12-2.30, Sun 12-9.30 booking required D served Mon-Sat 6.30-9.30, Sun 12-9.30 booking required Av 3 course à la carte fr £20 ⊕ FREE HOUSE ◀ Landlord, Hydes, Beartown, Pride of Pendle, guest ales ⊘ Addlestones. 🍷 8 **Facilities** Children's menu Garden Parking

BODINNICK

Old Ferry Inn 🍷

PL23 1LX
☎ 01726 870237 📠 01726 870116
e-mail: royce972@aol.com
dir: A38 towards Dobwalls, left onto A390. After 3m left onto B3359 then right to Bodinnick/Polruan for 5m

This friendly, family-run free house stands just 50 yards from the scenic River Fowey, where the car ferry still makes regular crossings to Fowey itself. Inside the 400-year-old building, old photographs and nautical bric-a-brac set the scene for sampling Sharp's Bitter and an extensive bar menu. Choices range from snacks to home-cooked food like steak and ale pie, curries, vegetarian and fish dishes.

Open all day all wk 11-11 (summer), noon-10 (winter) Closed: 25 Dec **Bar Meals** L served all wk 12-3 (summer), 12-2.30 (winter) D served all wk 6-9 (summer), 6.30-8.30 (winter) Av main course £8.50 **Restaurant** D served all wk 7-8.30 booking required Av 3 course à la carte fr £20 ⊕ FREE HOUSE ◀ Sharp's Bitter, Guinness ⊘ Stowford Press. 🍷 6 **Facilities** Children's menu Family room Dogs allowed Garden Parking

BOLVENTOR

Jamaica Inn ♟

PL15 7TS
☎ 01566 86250 ▤ 01566 86177
e-mail: enquiry@jamaicainn.co.uk
dir: *Follow A30 from Exeter. 10m after Launceston take Bolventor road, follow signs*

The setting for Daphne du Maurier's famous novel, this 18th-century inn stands high on Bodmin Moor. Its Smugglers Museum houses fascinating artefacts, while the Daphne du Maurier room honours the great writer. The place is big on atmosphere, with a cobbled courtyard, beamed ceilings and roaring fires. Lunches range from hot ciabattas to grills; the evening menu served from 3pm could start with warm melted goats' cheese bruschetta, and follow with barbecued pork ribs or poached fillet of Port Isaac salmon.

Open all day all wk 9am-11pm **Bar Meals** L served all wk Av main course £9 food served all day ⊕ FREE HOUSE ◀ Doom Bar, Tribute, Jamaica Inn Ale. ♟ 8 **Facilities** Children's menu Play area Dogs allowed Garden Parking

CALLINGTON

Manor House Inn ♟

Rilla Mill PL17 7NT
☎ 01579 362354
dir: *5m from Callington, just off B3257*

Set by the River Lynher, once a granary for the mill next door, Manor House is a traditional pub that offers real ales and ciders, and a reasonably-priced selection of home-made food. Careful attention is paid to sourcing quality local ingredients, including fresh fish. Typical choices include steak and ale pie, battered haddock and chips, chicken chasseur, and curry of the week. Lighter options include club sandwich, tuna melt, toasted sandwiches and salads.

Open Closed: Mon **Bar Meals** L served Tue-Sun 11.30-2 D served Tue-Sun 6-9 Av main course £5 **Restaurant** L served Tue-Sun 11.30-2 D served Tue-Sun 6-9 Av 3 course à la carte fr £18 ⊕ FREE HOUSE ◀ Sharp's Own & Special, Doom Bar, Betty Stogs Ŏ Thatchers Gold, Westons Scrumpy, Cornish Rattler. ♟ 8 **Facilities** Children's menu Dogs allowed Garden Parking

CONSTANTINE

Trengilly Wartha Inn ★★★ INN 🏵 🍷

Nancenoy TR11 5RP

☎ 01326 340332 📠 01326 340332

e-mail: reception@trengilly.co.uk

dir: *Follow signs to Nancenoy, left towards Gweek until 1st sign for inn, left & left again at next sign, continue to inn*

Situated in Nancenoy, not far from Constantine, this inn has six acres of gardens and meadows that include a vine-shaded pergola. There's a small bistro on one side of the inn, and plenty more space in the bar area. Everything is made from scratch using the best local produce. The bar menu offers beef stroganoff, steak, and wholetail scampi, as well as courgette and rosemary pancakes stuffed with feta, cashew nuts, spinach and cherry tomatoes, or warm fillet of lightly smoked pollack. The bistro has a good seafood selection, as well as home-made steak and kidney puddings on winter Wednesdays.

Open all wk 11-3 6-12 **Bar Meals** L served all wk 12-2.15 D served all wk 6.30-9.30 Av main course £10 **Restaurant** L served all wk 12-2.15 booking required D served all wk 6.30-12 booking required Av 3 course à la carte fr £20 ⊞ FREE HOUSE 🍺 Skinners Cornish Knocker, Betty Stogs, Sharp's Doom Bar, Sharp's Edenale, Guest Ales Ö Cornish Rattler, Thatchers Gold. 🍷 15 **Facilities** Children's menu Play area Family room Dogs allowed Garden Parking **Rooms** 8

CUBERT

The Smugglers' Den Inn 🍷

Trebellan TR8 5PY

☎ 01637 830209 📠 01637 830580

e-mail: info@thesmugglersden.co.uk

web: www.thesmugglersden.co.uk

dir: *From Newquay take B3075 to Cubert x-rds, then right, then left signed Trebellan, 0.5m*

Set in a valley leading to the coast, this thatched 16th-century pub comprises a long bar, family room, children's play area, courtyards and huge beer garden. The no-nonsense, modern menu might offer houmous and flatbread with rocket and sun-blushed tomatoes at lunch, or tempura king prawns followed by Falmouth Bay moules marinière in the evening. The impressive selection of real ales is at its best during the real ale and pie festival over the May Day weekend.

Open all day all wk 11-3 6-11 (Sat-Sun 11-3 6-mdnt, summer open all day) Closed: Jan-Mar closed Mon-Tue L **Bar Meals** L served all wk 12-2.30 (winter 12-2) D served all wk 6-9.30 (winter Sun-Thu 6-9, Fri-Sat 6-9.30) **Restaurant** L served all wk 12-2.30 (winter 12-2) booking required D served all wk 6-9.30 (winter Sun-Thu 6-9, Fri-Sat 6-9.30) booking required ⊞ FREE HOUSE 🍺 Skinner's Smugglers Ale, Sharp's Doom Bar, St Austell Tribute, Rotating Guest ales Ö Healey's Cornish Rattler. 🍷 12 **Facilities** Children's menu Play area Family room Dogs allowed Garden Parking

GUNWALLOE

The Halzephron Inn ☙

TR12 7QB

☎ 01326 240406 📠 01326 241442
e-mail: halzephroninn@gunwalloe1.fsnet.co.uk
dir: *3m S of Helston on A3083, right to Gunwalloe, through village. Inn on left*

The name of this ancient inn derives from Als Yfferin, old Cornish for 'cliffs of hell', an appropriate description of its situation on this hazardous stretch of coastline. Once a haunt of smugglers, the pub is 300 yards from the South Cornwall footpath and is the only pub on the stretch between Mullion and Porthleven. Today it offers a warm welcome, a wide selection of ales, and meals prepared from fresh local produce. Lunch brings a choice of platters accompanied by home-made rolls, plus specials such as seafood chowder. The evening menu includes beef bourguignon, whole roast partridge en croûte; or roast saddle of rabbit wrapped in prosciutto filled with mushroom and herb duxelle. An excellent Junior Menu is available.

Open all wk all wk Closed: 25 Dec Bar Meals L served all wk 12-2 D served all wk 7-9 Restaurant L served all wk 12-2 D served all wk 7-9 ⊕ FREE HOUSE 🍺 Sharp's Own, Doom Bar & Special, St Austell Tribute, Organic Halzephron Gold ♉ Cornish Rattler. ☙ 8 Facilities Children's menu Family room Garden Parking

MITCHELL

The Plume of Feathers ★★★★ INN ☙

TR8 5AX

☎ 01872 510387 📠 01637 839401
e-mail: enquiries@theplume.info
dir: *Exit A30 to Mitchell/Newquay*

Over the years, this 16th century building has welcomed various historical figures - John Wesley preached Methodism from the entrance, and Sir Walter Raleigh lived locally. The present owners have established it as a destination pub restaurant; the kitchen has an excellent reputation for its food, based on a fusion of modern European and classical British dishes, with an emphasis on fresh fish and the best Cornish ingredients. Lunch brings starters such as fishcake with sweet chilli and mixed leaves followed by a home-made beef burger with home-made relish and fries or venison stew with creamed potato and Savoy cabbage. Dinner could start with smoked mackerel fillet with houmous and toasted crostini followed by confit of Cornish duck leg with Toulouse sausage, tomato and mixed bean cassoulet. Finish with baked cheesecake with clotted cream.

Open all day all wk 9am-11/mdnt (25 Dec 11-5) Bar Meals Av main course £10 food served all day Restaurant Av 3 course à la carte fr £22 food served all day ⊕ FREE HOUSE 🍺 Doom Bar, John Smiths Smooth, Betty Stogs. ☙ 7 Facilities Children's menu Play area Dogs allowed Garden Parking Rooms 7

PORT GAVERNE

Port Gaverne Hotel ★★ HL ♀

PL29 3SQ

☎ 01208 880244   🖷 01208 880151

web: www.chycor.co.uk/hotels/port-gaverne
dir: *Signed from B3314, S of Delabole via B3267 on E of Port Isaac*

Just up the lane from a secluded cove is this 17th-century inn. In this once thriving port, women unloaded coal and other merchandise from ships then loaded them up again with slate from the Delabole quarry until, in 1893, the coming of the railway put paid to the port's prosperity. The hotel has had a long association with fishing and smuggling. As you might expect, locally supplied produce includes plenty of fresh fish. For example, along with a selection of ploughman's, you might fancy a half pint of prawns at lunchtime, or a seafood pie. At dinner expect starters like tomato, red onion and Cornish goats' cheese salad; crab soup; or lobster and monkfish Thermidor; and mains of sautéed trio of Cornish fish on vegetable rösti; pan-fried John Dory with olive oil mash; or chargrilled sirloin steak au poivre.

Open all day all wk Bar Meals L served all wk 12-2.30 D served all wk 6-9 Av main course £9 Restaurant D served all wk 7-9 Av 3 course à la carte fr £27 ⊕ FREE HOUSE ◀ Sharp's Doom Bar, Bass, St Austell Tribute. ♀ 9 Facilities Children's menu Dogs allowed Garden Parking Rooms 14

PORTHLEVEN

The Ship Inn

TR13 9JS

☎ 01326 564204   🖷 01326 564204

e-mail: cjoakden@yahoo.co.uk
dir: *From Helston follow signs to Porthleven, 2.5m. On entering village continue to harbour. Take W road by side of harbour to inn*

Dating from the 17th century, this smugglers' inn is actually built into the cliffs, and is approached by a flight of stone steps. During the winter two log fires warm the interior, while the flames of a third flicker in the separate Smithy children's room. Expect a good selection of locally caught fish and seafood, such as crab and prawn mornay, or the smoked fish platter, all smoked in Cornwall. The pub has declared itself a 'chip-free zone'.

Open all day all wk 11.30am-11.30pm (Sun noon-10.30) Bar Meals L served all wk 12-2 D served all wk 6.30-9 ⊕ FREE HOUSE ◀ Courage Best, Sharp's Doom Bar & Special, guest ales. Facilities Children's menu Family room Dogs allowed Garden

PORTREATH

Basset Arms

Tregea Ter TR16 4NG

☎ 01209 842077

e-mail: bassettarms@btconnect.com

dir: *From Redruth take B3300 to Portreath. Pub on left near seafront*

Tin-mining and shipwreck paraphernalia adorn the low-beamed interior of this early 19th-century Cornish stone cottage, built as a pub to serve harbour workers. At one time it served as a mortuary for ill-fated seafarers, so there are plenty of ghost stories! The menu makes the most of local seafood, such as mussels and fries, and home-made fish pie, but also provides a wide selection of alternatives, including half chicken in barbecue sauce; 12oz gammon steak; curry of the day; and salads including crab, when available.

Open all day all wk 11am-11pm (Fri-Sat 11am-mdnt, Sun 11-10.30) Bar Meals L served all wk 12-2 D served all wk 6-9 Av main course £9.50 Restaurant L served all wk 12-2 D served all wk 6-9 Av 3 course à la carte fr £18 ⊕ FREE HOUSE ◀ Sharp's Doom Bar, Courage, John Smith's Smooth. Facilities Children's menu Play area Dogs allowed Garden Parking

ST BREWARD

The Old Inn & Restaurant🍷

Churchtown, Bodmin Moor PL30 4PP

☎ 01208 850711 🖨 01208 851671

e-mail: theoldinn@macace.net

dir: *A30 to Bodmin. 16m, right just after Temple, follow signs to St Breward. B3266 (Bodmin to Camelford road) turn to St Breward, follow brown signs*

Located high up on Bodmin Moor, one of Cornwall's oldest inns is now owned and run by local man Darren Wills, the latest licensee in its 1,000-year history. The solid granite pub has slate flagstone floors and two huge granite fireplaces with real fires in winter. It is well-known throughout this glorious area for its wholesome home-cooked food, frequented by many regulars who are drawn by its Moorland Grills and Sunday roasts. Check out the local Cornish wines as well. There is also a large beer garden with a children's pet corner.

Open all day all wk 11-11 Bar Meals L served Sun-Fri 11-2, Sat 11-9 D served Sun-Fri 6-9, Sat 11-9 Av main course £8.95 Restaurant L served Mon-Fri 11-2, Sat-Sun 11-9 booking required D served Mon-Fri 6-9, Sat-Sun 11-9 booking required Av 3 course à la carte fr £19 ⊕ FREE HOUSE ◀ Sharp's Doom Bar & Special, guest ales. 🍷 20 Facilities Children's menu Family room Dogs allowed Garden Parking

ST JUST (NEAR LAND'S END)

The Wellington ★★ INN

Market Square TR19 7HD
☎ 01736 787319 📠 01736 787906
e-mail: wellingtonhotel@msn.com
dir: *Take A30 to Penzance, then A3071 W of Penzance to St Just*

Standing in the market square of an historic mining town, this family-run inn makes an ideal base for exploring the spectacular beaches and countryside of West Penwith. Low ceilings, Cornish stonework and a secluded walled garden help to evoke the atmosphere of old Cornwall. The blackboard menu features fresh crab, local fish and daily home-cooked specials: Stilton and vegetable crumble; smoked mackerel salad; country ham, eggs and chips; and a prize-winning ploughman's are typical selections.

Open all day all wk **Bar Meals** L served all wk 12-2 D served all wk 6-9 (winter 6-8.30) Av main course £8 **Restaurant** D served all wk 6-9 (summer) ⊕ ST AUSTELL BREWERY ◾ St Austell Tinners, St Austell Tribute, HSD ☼ Cornish Rattler. **Facilities** Children's menu Play area Dogs allowed Garden **Rooms** 11

TREBARWITH

The Mill House Inn ♥

PL34 0HD
☎ 01840 770200 📠 01840 770647
e-mail: management@themillhouseinn.co.uk
web: www.themillhouseinn.co.uk
dir: *From Tintagel take B3263 S, right after Trewarmett to Trebarwith Strand. Pub 0.5m on right*

Originally known as Treknow Mill, the building dates from 1760, and became a pub in 1960. Set in seven acres of gardens, this stone inn has log fires in the lounge and slate-floored bar. Meals can be enjoyed outside on the terraces, while dinner in the restaurant over the millstream is a particular treat. At lunchtime, favourites, such as sausage and mash or haddock and chips, appear alongside more exotic dishes, like Tuscan bean cassoulet with dressed leaves, Parmesan and ciabatta. In the restaurant, try lobster and sea trout terrine with herb salad and asparagus cream; then honey-glazed duck breast with fondant potatoes and carrot and maple purée. Live music Friday or Saturday night every week.

Open all wk 11-11 (Fri-Sat 11am-mdnt) (Sun noon-10.30) Closed: 25 Dec **Bar Meals** L served Mon-Sat 12-2.30, Sun 12-3 D served all wk 6.30-8.30 **Restaurant** D served all wk 6.30-9 ⊕ FREE HOUSE ◾ Sharp's Doom Bar, Red Stripe, Skinners Cornish Knocker ☼ Inch's Stonehouse, Stowford Press. ♥ 7 **Facilities** Children's menu Play area Family room Dogs allowed Garden Parking

TREBURLEY

The Springer Spaniel ♟

PL15 9NS

☎ 01579 370424

e-mail: enquiries@thespringerspaniel.org.uk
web: www.thespringerspaniel.org.uk
dir: *On A388 halfway between Launceston &
Callington*

This country pub's creeper-clad walls conceal a
cosy bar with wooden settles, farmhouse-style
chairs and a wood-burning stove. Children are
welcome, and their own 'Little Jack Russell' menu
serves up organic sausages, burgers and chips,
and vegetable pasta bake. The restaurant is full
of plants and flowers, and is candle-lit in the
evenings. In summer, relax in the garden. Food-
wise, beef from the owners' own organic farm as
a speciality, from burgers and sausages to fine
steaks. Stilton beef is a particular favourite: pan-
fried strips of beef in a Stilton and brandy sauce.
Daily specials are strong on fish and game, like
chargrilled tuna steak or braised rabbit.

Open all wk noon-2.30 6-10.30 **Bar Meals** L
served all wk 12-1.45 D served all wk 6.15-8.45
Av main course £8.95 **Restaurant** L served all wk
12-1.45 D served all wk 6.15-8.45 Av 3 course à
la carte fr £22 ⊕ FREE HOUSE ◀ Sharp's Doom
Bar, Skinner's Betty Stogs, St Austell Tribute, guest
ale ♂ Rattler, Cornish Orchard's Black & Gold. ♟ 7
Facilities Children's menu Family room Dogs allowed
Garden Parking

ZENNOR

The Tinners Arms ♟

TR26 3BY

☎ 01736 796927

e-mail: tinners@tinnersarms.com
dir: *Take B3306 from St Ives towards St Just. Zennor
approx 5m*

The only pub in the village, this 13th-century,
granite-built free house is close to the South
West coastal path and is particularly popular
with walkers. It has changed very little over the
years, with its stone floors and low ceilings.
The main bar has open fires at both ends and
outside there is a large terrace with sea views.
A sample menu features sirloin steak, chicken
pie, slow-cooked duck leg, and butternut squash
risotto. For a lighter bite enjoy a fresh Newlyn
crab sandwich.

Open all wk **Bar Meals** L served all wk 12-2 D served
all wk 6.30-9 ⊕ FREE HOUSE ◀ Zennor Mermaid,
Tinners Ale, Sharps Own ♂ Burrow Hill. ♟ 12
Facilities Children's menu Family room Dogs allowed
Garden Parking

AMBLESIDE

Drunken Duck Inn
★★★★★ INN ⊛⊛ ♑

Barngates LA22 0NG
☎ 015394 36347 📄 015394 36781
e-mail: info@drunkenduckinn.co.uk
web: www.drunkenduckinn.co.uk
dir: *From Kendal on A591 to Ambleside, then follow Hawkshead sign. In 2.5m inn sign on right, 1m uphill*

With fabulous views towards Lake Windermere, this 17th-century inn stands in glorious Lakeland countryside. In the same ownership for over 30 years and constantly evolving, the traditional whitewashed inn continues to offer outstanding food and service. Barngates Brewery is next door and its ales are served in the oak-floored and beamed bar. Local food is served in the informal restaurant areas, from lunchtime dishes like braised beef and dumplings; lamb hotpot; or confit duck leg with bean casserole, to dinner dishes like partridge with spiced cabbage and pan jus, duck with confit garlic risotto and duck jus, and roast halibut with red wine reduction.

Open all wk Closed: 25 Dec Bar Meals L served all wk 12-4 Av main course £20 Restaurant D served all wk 6-9.30 booking required Av 3 course à la carte fr £40 ⊞ FREE HOUSE ◀ Barngates Cracker Ale, Chesters Strong & Ugly, Tag Lag, Catnap, Mothbag, guest ale. ♑ 20 Facilities Children's menu Garden Parking Rooms 17

BOOT

The Boot Inn

CA19 1TG
☎ 019467 23224 📄 019467 23337
e-mail: enquiries@bootinn.co.uk
web: www.bootinn.co.uk
dir: *From A595 follow signs for Eskdale then Boot*

The village of Boot boasts England's oldest working watermill, some fine walking country, and the delightful Boot Inn slap bang in the middle. The beamed Burnmoor Room restaurant dates back to 1578, but there's also a modern conservatory, and an eating area in the bar. Local produce is taken very seriously. Sandwiches, jacket potatoes and ploughman's platters on the lunch menu are supported by options such as Cumberland sausage with chips or home-made pies. In the evening the range includes starters of mozzarella and tomatoes or prawn cocktail; main courses such as curry or gammon, chips and peas. The children's menu has small versions of several dishes from the main menu, or the likes of sausages and chips. The beer garden has two children's play areas.

Open all wk Closed: 25 Dec Bar Meals Av main course £7.95 food served all day Restaurant D served all wk 6-8.30 booking required ⊞ ROBINSONS ◀ Double Hop, Unicorn, Dizzy Blonde, Dark Hatters Ŏ Westons Stowford Press Organic. Facilities Children's menu Play area Family room Dogs allowed Garden Parking

BORROWDALE

The Langstrath Country Inn ♥

CA12 5XG

☎ 017687 77239

e-mail: info@thelangstrath.com

dir: *B5289 past Grange, through Rosthwaite, left to Stonethwaite. Inn on left after 1m*

Refurbishments over the years at this 16th-century, family-run inn, include the addition of a restaurant with spectacular views up the Langstrath valley. A meal here could start with Cumbrian cheese soufflé or smoked Borrowdale trout and avocado salad; continue with Goosnargh chicken breast on olive oil mash or Cumbrian sirloin steak; and wind up with some delicious sticky toffee pudding. The bar offers decent ales and an extensive wine list. Set on the coast-to-coast and Cumbrian Way walks, this is an ideal spot for hikers.

Open noon-10.30 Closed: Dec-Jan, Mon Bar Meals L served Tue-Sun 12-2.30 D served Tue-Sun 6-9 Av main course £12 Restaurant L served Tue-Sun 12-2.30 D served Tue-Sun 6-9 Av 3 course à la carte fr £21 ⊕ FREE HOUSE ◀ Jennings Bitter, Black Sheep, Hawkshead Bitter, Cocker Hoop ♂ Thatchers Gold. ♥ 8 Facilities Children's menu Garden Parking

BRAITHWAITE

Coledale Inn

CA12 5TN

☎ 017687 78272   📄 017687 78272

e-mail: info@coledale-inn.co.uk

dir: *M6 junct 50, A66 towards Cockermouth for 18m. Turn to Braithwaite then towards Whinlatter Pass. Follow sign on left, over bridge to Inn*

Set in a peaceful spot above Braithwaite village, this inn is ideal for exploring the footpaths that begin nearby. The building started life as a woollen mill in the 1820s, and is full of attractive Victorian prints, furnishings and antiques. Home-made meals, such as Cumberland sausage with mash or home-made steak and kidney pie, are backed by an impressive wine list. Don't expect an explanation of the strange-shaped tree in the garden, because no-one knows.

Open all day all wk 11-11 Bar Meals L served all wk 12-2 D served all wk 6-9 Av main course £8.95 ⊕ FREE HOUSE ◀ Yates, Theakstons, Jennings Best, John Smiths. Facilities Children's menu Play area Dogs allowed Garden Parking

BRAMPTON

Blacksmiths Arms ★★★★ INN ♥

Talkin Village CA8 1LE

☎ 016977 3452   📄 016977 3396

e-mail: blacksmithsarmstalkin@yahoo.co.uk

dir: *From M6 take A69 E, after 7m straight over rdbt, follow signs to Talkin Tarn then Talkin Village*

This attractive family-run village inn stands in some of northern Cumbria's most scenic countryside; the Borders, Hadrian's Wall and the Lakes are all close by. The original smithy, dating from 1700, remains part of inn along with the bar, restaurant and accommodation. Enjoy the warm hospitality and a pint of ale from Brampton Brewery, while choosing from the menus that range from bar snacks to full à la carte offerings. Dishes typically include lasagne, assorted pies, Cumberland sausages, and fresh local trout.

Open all wk noon-3 6-mdnt **Bar Meals** L served all wk 12-2 D served all wk 6-9 Av main course £9.95 **Restaurant** L served all wk 12-2 D served all wk 6-9 Av 3 course à la carte fr £15.95 ⊕ FREE HOUSE ◄ Yates, Brampton, Black Sheep. ♥ 20 **Facilities** Children's menu Garden Parking **Rooms** 8

BROUGHTON-IN-FURNESS

The Old Kings Head ★★★★ INN

Church St LA20 6HJ

☎ 01229 716293

e-mail: russell@clar7jw.freeserve.co.uk

dir: *Telephone for directions*

With a history spanning 400 years, the spick-and-span former coaching inn is one of the oldest buildings in the town. Perfectly located for exploring the southern Lakes, the pub offers comfortable en suite rooms and freshly prepared food using local ingredients. Look to the chalkboard for daily fish specials, perhaps hot potted prawns, and whole bass with lemon and lime cream, or tuck into winter lamb casserole, rack of lamb, or a classic steak and ale pie.

Open all wk noon-3 5-mdnt **Bar Meals** L served all wk 12-2 booking required D served all wk 5-9 booking required **Restaurant** L served all wk 12-2 booking required D served all wk 5-9 booking required ⊕ ENTERPRISE INNS ◄ Beckstones, Black Sheep, IPA, Black Dog. **Facilities** Children's menu Play area Garden Parking **Rooms** 6

BUTTERMERE

Bridge Hotel ★★★ CHH 🍷

CA13 9UZ

☎ 017687 70252 📄 017687 70215

e-mail: enquiries@bridge-hotel.com

web: www.bridge-hotel.com

dir: *Take B5289 from Keswick*

An 18th-century former coaching inn set between Buttermere and Crummock Water in an outstandingly beautiful area, surrounded by the Buttermere Fells. There are wonderful walks right from the front door. Good food and real ales are served in the character bars (Cumberland sausage, rainbow trout or Scottish salmon), and a four-course dinner in the dining room - including, perhaps, roast Lakeland lamb with Cumberland sauce and crispy leeks, or venison braised with mushrooms and Old Peculier jus.

Open all day all wk all wk 10.30am-11.30pm Bar Meals food served all day Restaurant D served all wk 6-8.30 Av 3 course à la carte fr £31.50 ⊕ FREE HOUSE ◀ Theakston's Old Peculier, Black Sheep Best, Buttermere Bitter, Boddingtons, Hawkshead Gold. 🍷 12 Facilities Children's menu Garden Parking Rooms 21

CONISTON

The Black Bull Inn & Hotel 🍷

1 Yewdale Rd LA21 8DU

☎ 015394 41335 & 41668

📄 015394 41168

e-mail: i.s.bradley@btinternet.com

dir: *M6 junct 36, A590. 23m from Kendal via Windermere & Ambleside*

A cosy refuge in the heart of the Lake District, set at the foot of the Old Man of Coniston mountain and adjacent to Coniston Water, this 400-year-old coaching inn has been run by the same family for nearly 30 years. Back in the 1990s the owners' son started a micro-brewery behind the inn, which has gone from strength to strength; the award-winning real ales are not only sold behind the bar, but shipped out to neighbouring hostelries. There is also a good range of real ciders available. For hungry ramblers calling in at lunchtime, there is an excellent range of snacks including toasted sandwiches, soups and jacket potatoes. Alternatively, the restaurant menu runs from hearty winter warmers such as home-made chilli through to a salad of local Esthwaite trout fillets.

Open all wk Closed: 25 Dec Bar Meals food served all day Restaurant D served all wk 6-9 booking required ⊕ FREE HOUSE ◀ Coniston Bluebird, Old Man Ale, Opium, Blacksmith, XB, Oatmeal Stout. 🍷 10 Facilities Children's menu Family room Dogs allowed Garden Parking

GRASMERE

The Travellers Rest Inn 🍷

Keswick Rd LA22 9RR

☎ 015394 35604 📠 017687 72309

e-mail: stay@lakedistrictinns.co.uk

dir: *From M6 take A591 to Grasmere, pub 0.5m N of Grasmere*

Located on the edge of picturesque Grasmere and handy for touring and exploring the ever-beautiful Lake District, the Travellers Rest has been a pub for more than 500 years. Inside, a roaring log fire complements the welcoming atmosphere of the beamed and inglenooked bar area. An extensive menu of traditional home-cooked fare is offered, ranging from Westmorland terrine and eggs Benedict, to wild mushroom gratin and rump of Lakeland lamb.

Open all day all wk **Bar Meals** food served all day FREE HOUSE Jennings Bitter & Cocker Hoop, Cumberland Ale, Sneck Lifter, guest ales. 🍷 10 **Facilities** Children's menu Family room Dogs allowed Garden Parking

HAWKSHEAD

Queens Head Hotel ★★ HL 🍷

Main St LA22 0NS

☎ 015394 36271 📠 015394 36722

e-mail: enquiries@queensheadhotel.co.uk

web: www.queensheadhotel.co.uk

dir: *M6 junct 36, A590 to Newby Bridge, 1st right, 8m to Hawkshead*

Behind the 16th-century Queen's Head's flower-bedecked exterior are oak-beamed ceilings, wood-panelled walls, a slate floor and welcoming fire. The menus and specials board draw on a wealth of quality local produce: trout, pheasant, hams, sausages and slow-maturing lamb. For lunch try sandwiches, salads or light bites like steamed, smoked haddock fillet with mixed leaves or chicken liver pâté with orange and tequila and toasted brioche. Heartier lunch options include a 'pot of fish' in lemon and parsley cream sauce; or Thai curry. Evening meals include game and wild mushroom terrine with juniper berry oil, followed by venison casserole; lamb cutlets; or pan-fried sea bass fillet.

Open all wk 11am-11.45pm Sun 12-11.45 **Bar Meals** L served 12-2.30 Sun 12-5 D served all wk 6.15-9.30 Av main course £12.95 **Restaurant** L served 12-2.30 Sun 12-5 booking required D served all wk 6.15-9.30 booking required FREDERIC ROBINSON Hartleys Cumbria Way, Double Hop, Guest Ale. 🍷 11 **Facilities** Children's menu Family room Garden **Rooms** 13

KESWICK

The Horse & Farrier Inn ♥

Threlkeld Village CA12 4SQ
☎ 017687 79688 📄 017687 79823
e-mail: info@horseandfarrier.com
web: www.horseandfarrier.com
dir: *M6 junct 40 follow Keswick (A66) signs, after 12m turn right signed Threlkeld. Pub in village centre*

This inn stands at the foot of 868-metre Blencathra. Within its thick, whitewashed stone walls are slate-flagged floors, beamed ceilings and all the features of a 300 year old inn. The Horse & Farrier has an excellent reputation for food, form hearty breakfasts to home-cooked meals served in the bar or restaurant. Lunchtime features open sandwiches and baguettes, as well as favourites like scampi, and steak and kidney pie. Dinner may begin with salmon escalope with asparagus and lemon oil; or duck liver and brandy pâté with beetroot chutney. Then follow with pan-roasted chicken breast with tomato and herb risotto; sea bass on tagliatelle verdi; or fillet steak with shallot and port wine sauce. Swiss ice creams range from pink grapefruit and orange sorbet to chocolate mint parfait.

Open all day all wk 7.30am-mdnt **Bar Meals** food served all day **Restaurant** food served all day ⊕ JENNINGS BROTHERS PLC ◀ Jennings Bitter, Cocker Hoop, Sneck Lifter, Cumberland Ale, guest ale. ♥ 9 **Facilities** Children's menu Family room Dogs allowed Garden Parking

LITTLE LANGDALE

Three Shires Inn ★★★★ INN

LA22 9NZ
☎ 015394 37215 📄 015394 37127
e-mail: enquiry@threeshiresinn.co.uk
web: www.threeshiresinn.co.uk
dir: *Turn off A593, 2.3m from Ambleside at 2nd junct signed 'The Langdales'. 1st left 0.5m. Inn in 1m*

This Victorian Cumbrian slate and stone inn enjoys a stunning location, and has been run by the Stephensons since 1983. The bars boast bare beams and slate walls warmed in winter by log fires. On fine days, head for the picnic tables by the stream with magnificent fell views. Light lunches start with sandwiches, baguettes, soups and ploughman's. Hot food includes Angus steak burger and beef and ale pie. Hearty evening choices take in marinated rump of lamb with garlic and herb mash and port and redcurrant sauce, and steak with all the trimmings.

Open all wk 11-3 6-10.30 Dec-Jan, 11-10.30 Feb-Nov (Fri-Sat 11-11) Closed: 25 Dec **Bar Meals** L served all wk 12-2 (ex 24 Dec) D served all wk 6-8.45 (ex mid wk Dec-Jan) booking required Av main course £12.95 **Restaurant** D served all wk 6-8.45 (ex mid wk Dec-Jan) booking required Fixed menu price fr £18.95 Av 3 course à la carte fr £18 ⊕ FREE HOUSE ◀ Jennings Best & Cumberland, Coniston Old Man, Hawkshead Bitter, Blacksheep Bitters. **Facilities** Children's menu Garden Parking **Rooms** 10

LOWESWATER

Kirkstile Inn ★★★★ INN ?

CA13 0RU

☎ 01900 85219 📄 01900 85239

e-mail: info@kirkstile.com

dir: From A66 Keswick take Whinlatter Pass at Braithwaite. Take B5292, at T-junct left onto B5289. 3m to Loweswater. From Cockermouth B5289 to Lorton, past Low Lorton, 3m to Loweswater. At red phone box left, 200yds

Standing in the shadow of Melbreak, the Inn has offered hospitality for 400 years. The dining room dates back to 1549 and is the oldest part of the inn. There is plenty of choice from regular menus and blackboard specials. There are baguettes, sandwiches and jacket potatoes, as well as hot dishes like pan-fried chicken with salad and wild rice; Cumberland tattie pot; and cream cheese tart. At dinner begin with black pudding in beer batter with red wine sauce; or smoked chicken salad. Follow with hake fillet with sweet potato; goats' cheese, spinach and vegetable lasagne; or lamb shoulder with rosemary mash.

Open all wk Closed: 25 Dec **Bar Meals** L served all wk 12-3 booking required D served all wk 6-9 booking required Av main course £10.25 **Restaurant** D served all wk 6-9 booking required Av 3 course à la carte fr £21 ⊕ FREE HOUSE ◀ Kirkstile Gold, Yates Bitter, Melbreak, Grasmoor Ale ♻ Stowford Press. ? 10 **Facilities** Children's menu Family room Dogs allowed Garden Parking **Rooms** 8

RAVENSTONEDALE

The Fat Lamb Country Inn ★★ HL

Crossbank CA17 4LL

☎ 015396 23242 📄 015396 23285

e-mail: enquiries@fatlamb.co.uk

dir: On A683 between Sedbergh & Kirkby Stephen

Modern amenities blend with old fashioned hospitality at this 350 year-old free house. The former coaching inn is built of local stone, and stands in open countryside. An open fire on the traditional Yorkshire range warms the bar in winter; this is the oldest part of the building, and here, visitors and locals can mingle without a pool table or electronic entertainment intruding. Snacks and meals are served here and in the relaxed restaurant. The table d'hôte menu might feature dishes such as local lamb cutlets in mint jus; pan-fried tuna steak with black olive and red onion dressing; or roast guinea fowl with caramelised onion and apple sauce. The inn stands in informal gardens with a patio and picnic tables, and you might also like to visit the adjoining nature reserve, a unique wildlife haven.

Open all wk **Bar Meals** L served all wk 12-2 booking required D served all wk 6-9 booking required Av main course £9.60 **Restaurant** L served all wk 12-2 booking required D served all wk 6-9 booking required Fixed menu price fr £22 Av 3 course à la carte fr £12.50 ⊕ FREE HOUSE ◀ Black Sheep Bitter. **Facilities** Children's menu Play area Dogs allowed Garden Parking **Rooms** 12

WINDERMERE

The Angel Inn ♓

Helm Rd LA23 3BU
☎ 015394 44080 📄 015394 46003
e-mail: rooms@the-angelinn.com
dir: *From Rayrigg Rd (parallel to lake) into Crag Brow, then right into Helm Rd*

City chic style is offered at this sophisticated gastro-pub in a great location five minutes' from Lake Windermere in the centre of Bowness-on-Windermere. Local ales vie with international beers at the bar, and good food based on local produce is available throughout the day from a choice of menus: breakfast/brunch; sandwiches and light lunches; starters, nibbles and salads; main courses - braised Cumbrian farmed pork belly with parmentier potatoes, carrot purée and black pudding - desserts and a children's menu. In warmer weather head for the garden terrace where there are great views.

Open all day all wk 9am-11pm Closed: 25 Dec **Bar Meals** L served all wk 11.30-4 D served all wk 5-9 **Restaurant** L served all wk 11.30-4 D served all wk 5-9 ⊕ FREE HOUSE ◀ Coniston Bluebird Bitter, Hawkshead Bitter. ♓ 12 **Facilities** Children's menu Garden Parking

WINDERMERE

Eagle & Child Inn ★★★ INN ♓

Kendal Rd, Staveley LA8 9LP
☎ 01539 821320
e-mail: info@eaglechildinn.co.uk
web: www.eaglechildinn.co.uk
dir: *M6 junct 36, A590 towards Kendal then A591 towards Windermere. Staveley approx 2m*

The rivers Kent and Gowan meet at the gardens of this friendly inn, and it's surrounded by miles of excellent walking, cycling and fishing country. Several pubs in Britain share the same name, which refers to a legend of a baby found in an eagle's nest. Dishes include Fleetwood mussels in tomato, garlic and white wine sauce, local rump steak braised with onions; and roast cod loin in anchovy and parsley butter. There is comfortable accommodation available.

Open all wk all wk 11am-11pm **Bar Meals** L served Mon-Fri 12-2.30, Sat-Sun 12-3 D served Mon-Fri 6-8.45, ◀ Black Sheep Best Bitter, Coniston, Hawkshead Bitter, Dent Ales, Yates Bitter, Tirril Brewery ⚲ Westons. ♓ 10 **Facilities** Children's menu Dogs allowed Garden Parking **Rooms** 5

BAKEWELL

The Bull's Head

Church St, Ashford-in-the-Water DE45 1QB
☎ 01629 812931
e-mail: bullshead.ashford@virgin.net
dir: *Off A6, 2m N of Bakewell, 5m from Chatsworth
Estate*

A family affair for several generations, the Bull's
Head has seen the London and Manchester
coaches come and go. Everything about this
cosy pub is smartly turned out, from the roses
climbing round the door to the shiny brassware
in the bar. The interior is unpretentious, with
dark wooden beams, open brick fires and comfy
banquettes. There is no restaurant as such;
dishes from a frequently changing menu are
cooked to order and served in the small lounge
bar. Lunchtime sees a range of sandwiches on
offer, or delicious home-made soups such as
tomato and lovage; or yellow split pea. Steak
and Old Stockport ale pie served with braised
red cabbage and dripping-roasted potatoes is
a popular main course choice, with blueberry
crumble pie and vanilla ice cream to finish.

Open all wk 11-3 (summer) noon-3 (winter) 6-11
(Sun noon-3 7-10.30) **Bar Meals** L served all wk
12-2 D served Mon-Sat (ex Thu in winter) 6.30-9,
Sun 7-9 ⊕ ROBINSONS ◄ Old Stockport, Unicorn,
Double Hop. **Facilities** Children's menu Family room
Dogs allowed Garden Parking

BARLOW

The Trout at Barlow

33 Valley Rd S18 7SL
☎ 0114 289 0893   🖹 0114 289 0893
e-mail: mikenorie@btconnect.com
dir: *From Chesterfield follow the Newbold Rd B619
for 4.5m*

This country pub, a few miles outside Chesterfield
at the start of the Peak District, has recently
changed hands. It is strong on food and jazz,
with Jazz Club every Saturday night and Jazz
Dining the first Monday of the month. There is
also a quiz on a Wednesday night. A weekly-
changing choice of two real ales is offered and
freshly prepared, home-cooked food. All special
occasions are catered for, such as weddings and
parties.

Open all wk 12-3 6-11 (Sun noon-9.30) **Bar
Meals** booking required Av main course £10.95
Restaurant L served Mon-Sat 12-2, Sun 12-4
booking required D served Mon-Sat 6-9 booking
required ⊕ MARSTON'S ◄ Marston's Pedigree,
Mansfield Smooth, Marston's Finest Creamy, Guest.
Facilities Children's menu Garden Parking

BARROW UPON TRENT

Ragley Boat Stop ♈

Deepdale Ln, Off Sinfin Ln DE73 1HH
☎ 01332 703919
e-mail: ragley@king-henry-taverns.co.uk
dir: *Please telephone for directions*

When King Henry's Taverns bought this canalside pub, its outbuildings were in a dangerous condition, there was no sewerage, and three acres of overgrown garden sloped down to the waterside. But now it offers pub grub to satisfy the appetites of boaters hungry after hours sitting motionless at the tiller. Traditional favourites include bangers and mash; fisherman's pie; and for the truly ravenous a Mighty Man mixed grill. Pan-fried swordfish and steaks in different guises, such as fillet steak fajitas, are other tempting choices.

Open all day all wk noon–11 **Bar Meals** Av main course £3 food served all day **Restaurant** food served all day ⊕ KING HENRY TAVERNS ◀ Greene King IPA, Marstons Pedigree, Guinness. ♈ 15 **Facilities** Children's menu Play area Family room Garden Parking

BRADWELL

The Old Bowling Green Inn ♈

Smalldale S33 9JQ
☎ 01433 620450
e-mail: dalesinns@aol.com
dir: *Off A625 onto B6049 towards Bradwell. Turn right onto Gore Lane up side of park. Through bottleneck into Smalldale. Pub 150 yds on the right*

A 16th-century coaching inn with impressive views over glorious countryside. Traditional country cooking and good value daily specials supplemented by weekly changing ales produce grilled goats' cheese with sun-dried tomatoes and caramelised onions; chicken breast in mushroom, white wine and mustard grain cream sauce; sea bass fillets on celeriac mash; and meat and potato pie. Bakewell tart and apple crumble feature among a range of tempting home-made puddings.

Open all day all wk **Bar Meals** L served Mon-Sat 12-2.30, Sun 12.30-4 D served Mon-Sat 6-9 Av main course £7.50 **Restaurant** L served Mon-Sat 12-2.30, Sun 12.30-4 D served Mon-Sat 6-9 ⊕ ENTERPRISE INNS ◀ Stones, Tetleys, Copper Dragon, Black Sheep, John Smiths. ♈ 6 **Facilities** Children's menu Garden Parking

BRASSINGTON

Ye Olde Gate Inne

Well St DE4 4HJ

☎ 01629 540448 🖹 01629 540448

e-mail: theoldgateinn@supanet.com

dir: *2m from Carsington Water off A5023 between Wirksworth & Ashbourne*

Built in 1616 out of local stone and timbers allegedly salvaged from the wrecked Armada fleet, this venerable inn stands beside an old London to Manchester turnpike in the heart of Brassington, a hill village on the southern edge of the Peak District. Oak beams, black cast iron log burner, an antique clock, charmingly worn quarry-tiled floors and a delightful mishmash of polished furniture give the inn plenty of character. The menu offers firm lunchtime favourites, such as home-roasted ham, egg and home-made chips; and Cumberland sausages with creamed mash and onion gravy. In the evening, start with crevettes cooked in garlic butter and choose from the likes of roast pheasant breast wrapped in bacon with a port sauce, or pan-fried fillet of beef served with an oxtail broth.

Open Closed: Mon (ex BH), Tue L **Bar Meals** L served Wed-Sat 12-2, Sun 12-2.30 D served Tue-Sat 6.30-8.45 Av main course £9 ⊕ MARSTON'S ◀ Marston's Pedigree, Jennings Cumberland, guest ales. **Facilities** Children's menu Family room Dogs allowed Garden Parking

HARTSHORNE

The Mill Wheel ★★★★ INN ☙

Ticknall Rd DE11 7AS

☎ 01283 550335 🖹 01283 552833

e-mail: info@themillwheel.co.uk

dir: *A511 from Burton-on-Trent towards Leicester. Left at island signed A514/Derby. Pub a short distance*

This old building's huge mill wheel has survived for some 250 years. In 1945 a dispute over water rights cut off the supply and the site became derelict. Since being restored in 1987, the wheel has been slowly turning once again, and is very much the focus of attention in the bar and restaurant. Here dishes such as pan-fried Cornish mackerel with tapenade bruschetta are served, followed perhaps by roast loin of lamb with dauphinoise potatoes. If you want to stay over, there are modern bedrooms available.

Open all wk **Bar Meals** food served all day **Restaurant** L served 12-2.30 (Sun 12-8.30) D served 6-9.15 Mon-Thu (6-9.30 Fri-Sat, 12-8.30 Sun) ⊕ FREE HOUSE ◀ Abbot Ale, Oakham Ale, Summer Lightning, Bass, Pedigree. ☙ 8 **Facilities** Children's menu Garden Parking **Rooms** 4

HATHERSAGE

The Scotsmans Pack Country Inn ★★★★ INN ☙

School Ln S32 1BZ
☎ 01433 650253 ▤ 01433 650712
web: www.scotsmanspack.com
dir: Hathersage is on A625 8m from Sheffield

This historic inn in the beautiful Hope Valley is located on one of the old packhorse trails used by Scottish 'packmen' or travelling drapers. Just a short walk away from Hathersage church and Little John's Grave, the inn is ideally placed for walking and touring the Peak District, with five individually designed en suite bedrooms. Hearty pub dishes include braised steak in red wine sauce, home-made lasagne and salad, and lamb's liver and bacon with onion gravy. Wash you meal down with a great choice of real ales.

Open all day all wk 11-3 6-mdnt (all day Fri-Sun) **Bar Meals** L served Mon-Fri 12-2 booking required D served Mon-Fri 6-9, Sat-Sun 12-9 booking required ⊕ MARSTONS PLC ◗ Jennings Cumberland, Pedigree, Mansfield Bitter. ☙ 7 **Facilities** Children's menu Family room Garden Parking **Rooms** 5

MELBOURNE

The Melbourne Arms ★★★ INN ☙

92 Ashby Rd DE73 8ES
☎ 01332 864949 & 863990
▤ 01332 865525
e-mail: info@melbournearms.co.uk

This restaurant on the village outskirts was tastefully converted from an 18th-century pub about 13 years ago. There are two bars, a coffee lounge and the restaurant itself, traditionally decorated, - no, not red flock wallpaper - where an extensive menu of authentic Indian dishes is offered. With a range of English dishes and a children's menu too, there's no reason why the whole family can't find plenty to enjoy. You can stay over in one of the modern bedrooms.

Open all day all wk 11.30am-11.30pm **Bar Meals** Av main course £6.99 food served all day **Restaurant** Fixed menu price fr £12.99 Av 3 course à la carte fr £19 food served all day ⊕ FREE HOUSE ◗ Pedigree, Tetley's Smooth, Guinness. ☙ 12 **Facilities** Children's menu Play area Family room Garden Parking **Rooms** 7

SHARDLOW

The Old Crown Inn

Cavendish Bridge DE72 2HL

☎ 01332 792392

e-mail: the.oldcrowninn@btconnect.com
dir: M1 junct 24 take A6 towards Derby. Left before
river, bridge into Shardlow

A family-friendly pub on the south side of the
River Trent, where up to seven guest ales are
served. It was built as a coaching inn during
the 17th century, and retains its warm and
atmospheric interior. Several hundred water
jugs hang from the ceilings, while the walls
display an abundance of brewery and railway
memorabilia. Traditional food is lovingly prepared
by the landlady, including sandwiches, jackets,
omelettes, ham and eggs, and Cumberland
sausages.

Open all day all wk 11am-mdnt (Fri-Sat 11am-
1am) **Bar Meals** L served Mon-Fri 12-2, Sat
12-8, Sun 12-3 D served Mon-Fri 5-8, Sat 12-8
Av main course £6.50 **Restaurant** L served Mon-
Fri 12-2, Sat 12-8, Sun 12-3 D served Mon-Fri
5-8, Sat 12-8 Fixed menu price fr £9.25 (Sun L
only) ⊕ MARSTONS ◀ Marston's Pedigree, Jennings
Cocker Hoop, Guest ales. **Facilities** Children's menu
Play area Dogs allowed Garden Parking

ASHBURTON

The Rising Sun ★★★★ INN ♥

Woodland TQ13 7JT

☎ 01364 652544

e-mail: admin@therisingsunwoodland.co.uk
dir: From A38 E of Ashburton take lane signed
Woodland/Denbury. Pub on left, approx 1.5m

A former drovers' inn, largely rebuilt following a
fire in 1989, The Rising Sun is set in beautiful
Devon countryside, convenient for Exeter,
Plymouth and Torbay. Regularly changing real
ales are served. Owner Paul is the chef and is
dedicated to using local and seasonal produce
on his menus. There's a good choice of fish
from Brixham – baked Brixham sea bass - and
excellent West Country cheeses; children's
menu too. As well as dishes like roasted rack of
Woodland lamb or belly of Tamworth pork, the
pub is also well known for its home-made pies
(available to take home). There are five en suite
bedrooms available.

Open all wk noon-3 6-11 (Sun noon-3 6.30-11, all
day mid Jul-mid Sep) Closed: 25 Dec **Bar Meals** Av
main course £8.50 food served all day **Restaurant**
Av 3 course à la carte fr £17 food served all
day ⊕ FREE HOUSE ◀ Princetown Jail Ale, IPA,
Teignworthy Reel Ale, guest ales ♂ Thatchers. ♥ 10
Facilities Children's menu Play area Family room
Dogs allowed Garden Parking **Rooms** 5

41

AVONWICK

The Avon Inn ♟

TQ10 9NB

☎ 01364 73475

e-mail: dfreresmith@yahoo.co.uk

dir: *Telephone for directions*

There's a change of ownership at this handsome whitewashed free house, just off the busy Exeter to Plymouth trunk road. The focus is on great home-cooked food using fresh local produce, with fruit and vegetables from the owners own allotment. Warm and cosy in winter, the large beer garden is perfect for the warmer weather with its three areas – lawn and flowers, new family area and a secluded section that goes down to the river Avon. Look out for barbecues at weekends.

Open all day all wk 10.30am-11.30pm (Sun 10.30am-11pm) **Bar Meals** Av main course £7 food served all day **Restaurant** Av 3 course à la carte fr £20 food served all day ⊕ FREE HOUSE ◀ Otter Bitter, Otter Bright, Blackawton 44 Special, Guinness Ŏ Thatchers Gold. ♟ 6 **Facilities** Children's menu Play area Dogs allowed Garden Parking

AXMOUTH

The Harbour Inn

Church St EX12 4AF

☎ 01297 20371

e-mail: theharbourinn@live.co.uk

dir: *Main street opposite church, 1m from Seaton*

The River Axe meanders through its valley into Lyme Bay, but just before they meet is Axmouth harbour, which accounted for one sixth of Devon's trade during the 16th century. This cosy, oak-beamed, harbourside inn was built four centuries earlier, however. Gary and Graciela Tubb have maintained three principles - local ingredients bought from small family businesses, nothing frozen, and everything home made. A bar and bistro menu offers scampi and chips, lasagne, sausages or faggots with mash and gravy, jacket potatoes, baguettes and sandwiches. From a daily updated blackboard menu, you might want to consider pork tenderloin with prunes and bacon; swordfish steak with niçoise salad; or tagliatelle, wild mushrooms and spicy tomato sauce. The Harbour makes a great stop if you are walking the South West Coast Path between Lyme Regis and Seaton.

Open all wk **Bar Meals** L served 12-2 D served 6.30-9 (Sun 7-9) **Restaurant** L served 12-2 D served 6.30-9 (Sun 7-9) ⊕ HALL & WOODHOUSE ◀ Badger 1st Gold, Tanglefoot, Sussex Ŏ Stowford Press, Applewood. **Facilities** Children's menu Play area Dogs allowed Garden Parking

AXMOUTH

The Ship Inn ☻

EX12 4AF

☎ 01297 21838

dir: *1m S of A3052 between Lyme & Sidmouth. Signed to Seaton at Boshill Cross*

There are long views over the Axe estuary from the beer garden of this creeper-clad family-run inn. It was built soon after the original Ship burnt down on Christmas Day 1879, and is able to trace its landlords back to 1769; the current ones have been there for over 40 years. Well kept real ales complement an extensive menu including daily blackboard specials where local fish and game feature, cooked with home-grown herbs.

Open all day all wk 11am-11pm Bar Meals L served all wk 12-2.30 booking required D served all wk 6-9 booking required Restaurant L served all wk 12-2.30 booking required D served all wk 6-9 booking required ⊕ PUNCH TAVERNS ◀ Otter Bitter, Guinness, 6X ♂ Stowford Press. ☻ 10 Facilities Children's menu Play area Family room Dogs allowed Garden Parking

BICKLEIGH

Fisherman's Cot ☻

EX16 8RW

☎ 01884 855237 ▤ 01884 855241

e-mail: fishermanscot.bickleigh@marstons.co.uk

dir: *Telephone for directions*

Well-appointed thatched inn by Bickleigh Bridge over the River Exe with food all day and large beer garden, just a short drive from Tiverton and Exmoor. The Waterside Bar is the place for snacks and afternoon tea, while the restaurant incorporates a carvery and à la carte menus. Sunday lunch is served, and champagne and smoked salmon breakfast is optional.

Open all day all wk 11am-11pm (Sun noon-10.30pm) Bar Meals L served all wk 12-9 booking required D served all wk 12-9 booking required food served all day Restaurant L served all wk 12-9 booking required D served all wk 12-9 booking required food served all day ⊕ ELDRIDGE POPE ☻ 8 Facilities Children's menu Garden Parking

BRAMPFORD SPEKE

The Lazy Toad Inn 🍷

EX5 5DP

☎ 01392 841591 📠 01392 841591

e-mail: thelazytoadinn@btinternet.com
dir: *From Exeter take A377 towards Crediton 1.5m, right signed Brampford Speke*

Substantial renovation at this Grade II listed 19th-century free house has created a series of cosy, beamed rooms in which to enjoy good food, real ales and traditional ciders. Winter fires and a new walled beer garden mark the passage of the seasons, whilst home-grown herbs complement meat and fish cured in the pub's own smokery. Menu choices might include steamed port and pigeon pudding; or Gloucester Old Spot sausages with bubble and squeak. There is a great selection of real ales and ciders to choose from.

Open 11.30-2.30 6-11 (Sun 12-3) Closed: 2 wks Jan, Sun eve & Mon **Bar Meals** L served Tue-Sun 12-2 booking required D served Tue-Sat 6-9 booking required Av main course £11.50 **Restaurant** Av 3 course à la carte fr £24 ⊕ FREE HOUSE ◀ St Austell Tribute, Exmoor Fox, Otter Ale & Bitter, Exe Valley Exeter Old Ŏ Sandford Devon Red, Traditional Farmhouse, Old Kirton. 🍷 12 **Facilities** Children's menu Family room Dogs allowed Garden Parking

CHERITON BISHOP

The Old Thatch Inn 🍷

EX6 6HJ

☎ 01647 24204

e-mail: mail@theoldthatchinn.f9.co.uk
dir: *0.5m off A30, 7m SW of Exeter*

This charming 16th-century free house is in Dartmoor National Park, and is popular with travellers on their way to and from Cornwall. For a time during its long history, the inn passed into private hands and then was a tea room, before its licence was renewed in the early 1970s. All the food is prepared using fresh ingredients from the southwest, with seafood featuring strongly. Examples include grilled whole sardines with garlic herb butter; pan-seared breast of duck with dauphinoise potatoes; or baked fillet of sea bass with a crayfish tail, lemon and thyme risotto. Look out for the speciality pumpkin and sunflower seed mini loaf sandwich filled with a variety of choices such as Somerset brie, smoked chicken and redcurrant sauce.

Open all wk 11.30-3 6-11 Closed: 25-26 Dec, Sun eve **Bar Meals** L served all wk 12-2.30 D served Mon-Sat 6.30-9 Av main course £12 **Restaurant** L served all wk 12-2.30 D served Mon-Sat 6.30-9 Av 3 course à la carte fr £22.50 ⊕ FREE HOUSE ◀ Otter Ale, Port Stout, O'Hanlon's Royal Oak, Skinners Betty Stogs, Yellowhammer Ŏ Thatchers Scrumpy Jack. 🍷 9 **Facilities** Children's menu Family room Dogs allowed Garden Parking

CLAYHIDON

The Merry Harriers ♈

Forches Corner EX15 3TR
☎ 01823 421270 📠 01823 421270
e-mail: peter.gatling@btinternet.com
dir: *Wellington A38, turn onto Ford Street (marked by brown tourist sign). At top of hill turn left, 1.5m on right*

The Merry Harriers is a 15th-century inn that stands high on the Blackdown Hills, with plenty of space for a beer garden and skittle alley. Inside the bar are beamed ceilings, a cosy inglenook and attractive dining areas. More than 90 per cent of kitchen ingredients are from the West Country. Menus include pork chop with apple sauce; pan-fried lamb's liver and bacon; grilled fillets of rainbow trout; smoked duck breast served on a mixed leaf and pomegranate salad; or chicken korma. The children's menu includes kiddie curry, steak and kidney pie, and organic pork and apple sausages and chips.

Open noon-3 6.30-11 Closed: Sun eve & Mon **Bar Meals** L served Tue-Sat 12-2, Sun 12-2.15 booking required D served Tue-Sat 6.30-9 booking required Av main course £9 food served all day **Restaurant** L served Tue-Sat 12-2, Sun 12-2.15 booking required D served Tue-Sat 6.30-9 booking required food served all day ⊕ FREE HOUSE 🍺 Otter Head, Cotleigh Harrier, Exmoor Gold, St Austell Tinners ♉ Thatchers Gold. ♈ 14 **Facilities** Children's menu Play area Family room Dogs allowed Garden Parking

COLYFORD

The Wheelwright Inn ♈

Swanhill Rd EX24 6QQ
☎ 01297 552585
dir: *Please telephone for directions*

This pretty thatched inn has earned a reputation for outstanding food and service since Gary and Toni Valentine took over in 2007. The 17th-century pub has undergone substantial refurbishment, but the low beams, wooden floors and log fire ensure that it retains its authentic country feel. Expect a varied contemporary menu, including well-filled sandwiches on locally baked bread; local pork cutlet with creamy potato and swede mash; and moules marinière with crusty bread.

Open all day all wk **Bar Meals** food served all day **Restaurant** food served all day ⊕ HALL & WOODHOUSE 🍺 Badger First Gold, Tanglefoot, Hopping Hare, Guinness ♉ Stowford Press. ♈ 8 **Facilities** Children's menu Family room Dogs allowed Garden Parking

CORNWORTHY

Hunters Lodge Inn ♀

TQ9 7ES

☎ 01803 732204

dir: *Off A381, S of Totnes*

Built in 1740, this country local is at the hub of
village life, sponsoring a football team, charity
events and a dog show (it's a dog friendly pub).
There's even a Christmas party for children. Other
notable features are the real log fire and resident
ghost. An extensive menu offers dishes from the
sea (sesame battered Brixham cod fillet), and
from the land (gammon steak, Cornworthy hens'
eggs) as well as a selection of pasta dishes
(spaghetti carbonara).

Open all wk 11.30am-2.30 6.30-close (Closed
Mon L) **Bar Meals** L served Tue-Sun 11.30-2
booking required D served all wk 6.30-9 booking
required **Restaurant** L served Tue-Sun 11.30-2
booking required D served all wk 6.30-9
booking required ⊕ FREE HOUSE ◀ Teignworthy
Reel Ale, Sharp's Doom bar, Guest ales. ♀ 14
Facilities Children's menu Play area Dogs allowed
Garden Parking

EXETER

The Twisted Oak ♀

Little John's Cross Hill EX2 9RG

☎ 01392 273666

e-mail: info@twistedoakpub.com

dir: *A30 to Okehampton, follow signs for pub*

Set in a beautiful part of Ide just outside Exeter,
this large pub has been turned into a quality,
food-driven venue in the last few years. There
is a choice of dining areas - an informal place
where you can relax on the leather sofas and eat;
a separate lounge bar restaurant; and a more
formal conservatory area, which is adult only in
the evenings. During the summer months the
huge garden provides seating and a children's
play area.

Open all wk 11am-3 5-11pm (Fri-Sun 11am-mdnt)
Bar Meals L served Mon-Thu 12-2.30, Fri-Sun all day
D served Mon-Thu 6-9, Fri-Sun all day **Restaurant** L
served Mon-Thu 12-2.30, Fri-Sun all day D served
Mon-Thu 6-9, Fri-Sun all day ◀ Sharp's Doom Bar,
Exmoor Ale. ♀ 7 **Facilities** Children's menu Play area
Family room Dogs allowed Garden Parking

HORNS CROSS

The Hoops Inn & Country Hotel ★★★ HL 🏵 ▯

Clovelly EX39 5DL
☎ 01237 451222 📄 01237 451247
e-mail: sales@hoopsinn.co.uk
web: www.hoopsinn.co.uk
dir: *On A39 between Bideford & Clovelly*

Having made their way along tortuous footpaths to evade the revenue men, smugglers would share out their spoils in this 13th-century inn, set in 16 acres of gardens and meadows on the rugged Atlantic coast. Menus are based on the freshest produce Devon can offer, including herbs, fruit and vegetables from the garden. Guests may dine in the bar, morning room or restaurant, where tables set with crisp white napkins create just the right level of formality. Seasonal menus focus on local producers and suppliers, and house specialities include terrine of Devon game with home-made piccalilli, and Exmoor venison with griottine cherry sauce.

Open all day all wk 7am-11pm (Sun 8.30am-10.30pm) **Bar Meals** L served all wk 12-6 D served all wk 6-9 Av main course £13.50 food served all day **Restaurant** D served all wk 7-9 booking required Fixed menu price fr £20 Av 3 course à la carte fr £27.50 ⊕ FREE HOUSE ◀ Hoops Old Ale & Best, Golden Pig, Doom Bar ♉ Thatchers Gold, Winkleigh. ▯ 20 **Facilities** Children's menu Play area Family room Dogs allowed Garden Parking **Rooms** 13

KINGSTON

The Dolphin Inn

TQ7 4QE
☎ 01548 810314 📄 01548 810314
e-mail: info@dolphininn.eclipse.co.uk
web: www.dolphin-inn.co.uk
dir: *From A379 (Plymouth to Kingsbridge road) take B3233 for Bigbury-on-Sea. Follow brown inn signs*

The Dolphin is just a mile from the beaches of the South Hams and the beautiful Erme Estuary, ideal for walkers, golfers and surfers. The inn dates from the 16th century and was originally built as cottages for stone masons working on the village church next door. All the food is home made and the menu includes pies, crab bake, lobster bisque, lamb stew, and stuffed chicken breast. Specials provide daily fish and game dishes.

Open noon-3 6-11 (Sun 7-10.30) Closed: Sun eve Winter **Bar Meals** L served Mon-Fri 12-2 (Sat-Sun 12-2.30) D served all wk 6-9 (closed Sun & Mon eve winter) Av main course £8.95 **Restaurant** L served Mon-Fri 12-2 (Sat-Sun 12-2.30) D served all wk 6-9 (closed Sun & Mon eve winter) ⊕ PUNCH TAVERNS ◀ Teignworthy Spring Tide, Courage Best, Sharp's Doom Bar, Otter. **Facilities** Children's menu Play area Family room Dogs allowed Garden Parking

MODBURY

California Country Inn

California Cross PL21 0SG
☎ 01548 821449 📄 01548 821566
e-mail: california@bellinns.entadsl.com
web: www.californiacountryinn.co.uk
dir: *Telephone for details*

Oak beams and exposed stonework are features of this whitewashed 14th-century free house. Brass, copper and old photographs decorate the interior, and there's a landscaped garden for summer use. Menus are created from only locally supplied produce, with prime meats from the chargrill, and dishes ranging from lasagne and beer-battered cod in the bar to roast monk fish with Yealm mussels, or loin of Plympton venison in the restaurant.

Open all day all wk 11-11 **Bar Meals** L served Mon-Sat 12-2, Sun 12-8 D served Mon-Sat 6-9, Sun 12-8 Av main course £9 **Restaurant** L served Sun 12-2 D served Wed-Sun 6-9 booking required Av 3 course à la carte fr £20 ⊕ FREE HOUSE ◀ Guinness, Abbot Ale, London Pride, Doom Bar. **Facilities** Children's menu Family room Dogs allowed Garden Parking

MOLLAND

The London Inn

EX36 3NG
☎ 01769 550269
dir: *Telephone for directions*

New owners at this 15th-century inn passionately believe that Exmoor needs to retain at least one of its traditional pubs. The London has many historic features and remains a centre for the shooting and hunting crowd. Home-made locally sourced food and ale straight from the cask are served, and the latest venture is a micro-brewery. Typical dishes include wood pigeon salad, venison sausages with bubble and squeak and gravy, and jam roly poly.

Open 12-3 6.30-11.30 (Sun 12-5) Closed: Sun eve **Bar Meals** L served Mon-Sat 12-2, Sun 12-3 D served Mon-Sat 7-9 Av main course £7 **Restaurant** L served Mon-Sat 12-2, Sun 12-3 booking required D served Mon-Sat 7-9 booking required ⊕ FREE HOUSE ◀ Exmoor Ale, Cotleigh Tawny Bitter Ŏ Winkleigh Cider. **Facilities** Children's menu Family room Dogs allowed Garden Parking **Notes** no credit cards

MORETONHAMPSTEAD

The White Hart Hotel ★★★ HL 🏵 ▾

The Square TQ13 8NF

☎ 01647 441340 📠 01647 441341

e-mail: enquiries@Whitehartdartmoor.co.uk

dir: *From A30 at Whiddon Down take A382 for Chagford & Moretonhampstead. Pub in village centre. Parking in 20yds*

Set in the heart of Dartmoor, this Grade II listed building dates from 1639 and has a recently refurbished bar, lounge and brasserie restaurant area for informal dining and drinking. Locally brewed ales are served alongside locally sourced food and dishes include rump of Dartmoor lamb with mini moussaka and feta cheese, and steamed stone bass with scallop and mushroom fricassee. Customers can also call in for morning coffee or afternoon tea.

Open all day all wk 11-11 **Bar Meals** L served all wk 12-2.30 D served all wk 6-9.30 Av main course £7.95 **Restaurant** L served all wk 12-2.30 booking required D served all wk 6-9.30 booking required Fixed menu price fr £15.95 Av 3 course à la carte fr £25 ⊕ HART INNS LTD ◀ St Austell Tribute, Otter, Doom Bar Ö Thatchers. ▾ 18 **Facilities** Children's menu Dogs allowed Garden **Rooms** 28

NORTH BOVEY

The Ring of Bells Inn ▾

TQ13 8RB

☎ 01647 440375 📠 01647 440746

e-mail: info@ringofbellsinn.com

dir: *1.5m from Moretonhampstead off B3212. 7m S of Whiddon Down junct on A30*

The Ring of Bells is one of Dartmoor's most historic inns, an attractive thatched property located just off the village green. It was built in the 13th century as lodgings for the stonemasons working on the construction of the nearby church. Visitors too are attracted by the good Devon pub food and West Country ales, and there is certainly plenty to do and see in the area. The short daily menus are full of interesting options – to start perhaps Jerusalem artichoke soup; or a warm salad of goats' cheese, parmesan and olive oil. The main courses could feature loin of venison with celeriac and braised lentils; or grilled fillet of brill with asparagus and roast lobster sauce. Leave a little room for crème brûlée with figs or a home-made crumble.

Open all day all wk Closed: 25 Dec **Bar Meals** L served all wk all day Etr-Oct, all wk 12-2.30 Nov-Etr D served all wk all day Etr-Oct, all wk 6.30-9.30 Nov-Etr Av main course £10 **Restaurant** D served all wk 6.30-9.30 booking required ⊕ FREE HOUSE ◀ Otter Ale, St Austell Tribute, Sharps Doom Bar. ▾ 12 **Facilities** Children's menu Family room Dogs allowed Garden

NOSS MAYO

The Ship Inn ⏑

PL8 1EW ☎ 01752 872387　📄 01752 873294
e-mail: ship@nossmayo.com
web: www.nossmayo.com
dir: *5m S of Yealmpton on River Yealm estuary*

Made from reclaimed English oak and local stone, this 16th-century waterfront in is spacious, but cosy thanks to wooden floors, bookcases, log fires and pictures. The inn is popular with sailing fans, who can tie up their boats right outside. Home-made dishes are served from noon until 9:30pm, and majors on local produce. Devon Cheddar, Cornish Yarg and local ham are among the choices with a ploughman's. Alternatives include baguettes and dishes such as sausages and mash with onion gravy, and breaded scampi. Three-course meals start with grilled goats' cheese on mixed salad, and crayfish cocktail with Marie rose sauce, followed by pan-fried duck breast on potato rösti; rib eye steak with peppercorn sauce; or sea bass fillet on stir-fried vegetables with noodles and hoi sin. Round off with crème brûlée; bread and butter pudding; or sticky toffee pudding.

Open all day all wk **Bar Meals** Av main course £12 food served all day **Restaurant** Av 3 course à la carte fr £23 food served all day ⊕ FREE HOUSE ◀ Tamar, Jail Ale & Butcombe Blonde, Dartmoor IPA. ⏑ 10 **Facilities** Children's menu Dogs allowed Garden Parking

SIDMOUTH

The Blue Ball ★★★★ INN ⏑

Stevens Cross, Sidford EX10 9QL
☎ 01395 514062　📄 01395 519584
e-mail: rogernewton@blueballinn.net
web: www.blueballinn.net
dir: *M5 junct 30 exit to A3052. Through Sidford towards Lyme Regis, on left after village, approx 13m*

The Newton family has run this 14th-century thatched, cob-and-flint pub since 1912, although much of it had to be rebuilt after a 2006 fire. The inn is a lovingly maintained building, with hanging baskets in summer, and cosy in winter. Settle down in one of the fireside seats and peruse the extensive menus, which begin at 8am with breakfast – smoked salmon and scrambled eggs, croissants and coffee. Pub classics feature on the main menu, from fishcakes with tartare sauce and deep-fried whitebait for starters, to steak and kidney pud; cod and chips; steak with peppercorn sauce and all the trimmings, and jacket potatoes; salads; and sandwiches. Puddings include chocolate and walnut sponge pudding and range of Salcombe ice creams.

Open all day all wk **Closed**: 25 Dec eve **Bar Meals** L served all wk 12-3 D served all wk 6-9 Av main course £9.50 **Restaurant** L served all wk 12-3 D served all wk 6-9 ⊕ PUNCH TAVERNS ◀ Otter Bitter, Tribute, John Smiths, Guest Ale ♉ Stowford Press. ⏑ 10 **Facilities** Children's menu Play area Family room Dogs allowed Garden Parking **Rooms** 9

TOTNES

The Durant Arms ★★★★ INN ♥

Ashprington TQ9 7UP ☎ 01803 732240
dir: Exit A38 at Totnes junct, to Dartington & Totnes, at 1st lights right for Kingsbridge on A381, in 1m left for Ashprington

The Durant Arms is situated in the village of Ashprington, just outside Totnes. Proprietors Graham and Eileen Ellis uphold British values of hospitality at this 18th-century hostelry. The small bar is fitted out in traditional style, with work by local artists on display. All produce is sourced locally if possible, so local fish and seafood figure in dishes such as smoked salmon with black pepper; or whole prawns with garlic dip, to start, and main courses of sea bass fillet on roasted vegetables with pepper sauce; or fillets of lemon sole roulade. Alternatives might be devilled kidneys with brandy and cream; and roast half pheasant with port wine sauce. Desserts range from chocolate fondant with clotted cream to treacle sponge pudding with vanilla ice cream. Hand-made English cheeses from nearby Sharpham's organic dairy are another speciality. The courtyard to the rear is the place to linger over a summer meal.

Open all wk **Bar Meals** L served all wk 12-2 D served all wk 7-9.15 **Restaurant** L served all wk 12-2 D served all wk 7-9.15 ⊕ FREE HOUSE ◀ Dartmoor Bitter, Tetley, Tribute. ♟ 8 **Facilities** Children's menu Family room Dogs allowed Garden Parking **Rooms** 8

TRUSHAM

Cridford Inn ♥

TQ13 0NR ☎ 01626 853694
e-mail: reservations@vanillapod-cridfordinn.com
web: www.cridfordinn.co.uk
dir: A38 take junct for Teign Valley, turn right follow signs Trusham for 4m

The rough stone walls, fireplaces and mosaic floor, have all been here for a very long time. This thatched former longhouse has its origins in the mid-9th century, rebuilt in the late 11th. One of the windows may be the earliest surviving domestic example in Britain. Try smoked Dartmouth salmon; game pie, (braised wild boar, venison, pheasant and rabbit); baked field mushrooms with smoked applewood and herb crust; steak and kidney pie; honey-baked ham and eggs; seafood mornay; or one of a selection of chargrills. A three-course dinner may feature pan-fried red mullet with red wine, beetroot, creamed leeks and crispy bacon; followed by roast guinea fowl; and chocolate pudding.

Open all wk 11-3 6-11 (Sat 11-11 Sun noon-10.30) **Bar Meals** L served all wk 12-2 D served all wk 7-9.30 Av main course £8.95 **Restaurant** L served Sun 12-1.30 booking required D served Mon-Sat 7-9.30 booking required Fixed menu price fr £21.95 Av 3 course à la carte fr £23.45 ⊕ FREE HOUSE ◀ Doom Bar, Otter Ale ♻ Thatchers. ♟ 8 **Facilities** Children's menu Family room Garden Parking

TUCKENHAY

The Maltsters Arms ♚

TQ9 7EQ ☎ 01803 732350 📄 01803 732823
e-mail: pub@tuckenhay.demon.co.uk
dir: *A381 from Totnes towards Kingsbridge. 1m, at hill top turn left, follow signs to Tuckenhay, 3m*

Accessible only along high-banked lanes, or by boat either side of high tide, this old stone country inn on Bow Creek off the River Dart was once owned by TV chef, Keith Floyd. The daily changing menu may feature pan-fried skate wing, beef and bell pepper balti, mushroom tortelloni, stone bass fillet and salmon in white wine sauce, or T-bone steak with mushroom and tarragon sauce. Famous for summer barbecues and occasional music events.

Open all day all wk 11-11 (25 Dec 12-2) **Bar Meals** L served all wk 12-3 D served all wk 7-9.30 Av main course £11 food served all day **Restaurant** L served all wk 12-3 booking required D served all wk 7-9.30 booking required Av 3 course à la carte fr £20 ⊕ FREE HOUSE ◀ Princetown Dartmoor IPA, Young's Special, Teignworthy Maltsters Ale, Sharps Doom Bar, Skinners Betty Stoggs Ö Westons Perry. ♚ 18 **Facilities** Children's menu Family room Dogs allowed Garden Parking

WINKLEIGH

The Kings Arms ♚

Fore St EX19 8HQ
☎ 01837 83384 📄 01834 83055
e-mail: kingsarmswinkleigh@googlemail.com
dir: *Village signed from B3220 (Crediton to Torrington road)*

Scrubbed pine tables and traditional wooden settles set the scene at this ancient thatched country inn in Winkleigh's central square. Wood-burning stoves keep the beamed bar and dining rooms warm in chilly weather, and traditional pub games are encouraged. Generous servings of freshly-made food include sandwiches and hot snacks, as well as steak and kidney parcel, loin of lamb with rosemary and redcurrant sauce, and Lucy's fish pie. Booking is recommended at weekends.

Open all day all wk 11-11 (Sun noon-10.30) **Bar Meals** food served all day **Restaurant** food served all day ⊕ ENTERPRISE INNS ◀ Butcombe Bitter, Sharp's Doom Bar, Cornish Coaster Ö Winkleigh Cider. ♚ 9 **Facilities** Children's menu Dogs allowed Garden

YEALMPTON

Rose & Crown ☻

Market St PL8 2EB
☎ 01752 880223   📠 01752 881058
e-mail: info@theroseandcrown.co.uk

From the classic brown and cream décor to the comfy leather sofas and open fire, the interior of this stylish bar restaurant reflects a perfect balance between contemporary and traditional features. The head chef regularly changes his tempting à la carte and set menus, and sources his ingredients locally wherever possible. Many dishes are traditional classics with an extra touch of class, whilst others feature a Pacific Rim twist with exotic Indonesian and Malaysian flavours. 'Lite bites' are served in the sunken lounge, whilst the restaurant menu might include options like pan-seared pork with mustard potatoes and roasted carrots; wild sea bass on mussel chowder with chargrilled new potatoes; or courgette cannelloni with Parmesan and rocket.

Open all wk **Bar Meals** L served all wk 12-2.30 D served all wk 6.30-9.30 Av main course £11 **Restaurant** L served all wk 12-2.30 booking required D served all wk 6.30-9.30 booking required Fixed menu price fr £9.95 Av 3 course à la carte fr £24 ⊞ INNTRA WEST LTD ◀ Doom Bar, London Pride, Courage Best, IPA Greene King, Otter, Tribute. ♟ 8 **Facilities** Children's menu Family room Dogs allowed Garden Parking

BUCKHORN WESTON

Stapleton Arms ☻

Church Hill SP8 5HS ☎ 01963 370396
e-mail: relax@thestapletonarms.com
dir: 3.5m from Wincanton in village centre

A stylish but unstuffy pub in a pretty village, with a spacious bar, elegant dining room and secluded garden. Expect simple, innovative food based on quality produce from small local suppliers. For starters try winter vegetable and thyme soup with a hunk of freshly delivered bread; or pan-fried scallops with celeriac purée, crispy Parma ham and toasted fennel seeds. Main courses include slow-roasted belly pork with apple mash and a cider sauce; and ruby red beetroot and fresh horseradish risotto. Fish caught off Dorset's south coast is delivered daily. You can even decide on your Sunday joint and the pub will prepare and cook it for you. Typical desserts are gooey chocolate pudding with chocolate ice cream; and classic crème brûlée with a tuile biscuit.

Open all wk 11-3 6-11 (Sun noon-10.30) **Bar Meals** L served all wk 12-3 D served all wk 6-10 Av main course £12 **Restaurant** L served all wk 12-3 booking required D served all wk 6-10 booking required Av 3 course à la carte fr £23 ⊞ FREE HOUSE ◀ Butcombe, Hidden Brewery, Moor's Revival ⚫ Thatchers Cheddar Valley, Butcombe's Ashton Press, Orchard Pig. ♟ 12 **Facilities** Children's menu Dogs allowed Garden Parking

BUCKLAND NEWTON

Gaggle of Geese 🍸

DT2 7BS ☎ 01300 345249
e-mail: gaggle@gaggleofgeese.co.uk
dir: *On B3143 N of Dorchester*

Mark and Emily Hammick have breathed new life into this now thriving community local since taking over in 2008. Fresh flowers and fat candles top scrubbed tables in the spruced-up bar, where you can sup West Country ales and local ciders, and tuck into some cracking pub food. Prepared from local seasonal produce, including meat from Mark's family farm, dishes include pork terrine with apple chutney, roasted butternut squash risotto, and rib-eye steak and peppercorn sauce. Well worth the diversion off the A352 south of Sherborne. In May and September, poultry auctions are held for charity.

Open all wk 11.30-3 6 11.30 (Sun 11.30-11.30, Sat 11.30-11.30 in summer) Closed: 1 wk Jan, 25 Dec Bar Meals L served Mon-Sat 12-2, Sun 12-3 booking required D served Sun-Thu 7-9, Fri-Sat 7-9.30 booking required Av main course £10 Restaurant L served Mon-Sat 12-2, Sun 12-3 booking required D served Sun-Thu 7-9, Fri-Sat 7-9.30 booking required Av 3 course à la carte fr £25 ⊕ FREE HOUSE ◀ Ringwood, Proper Job, Tribute, Butcombe Bitter, Hop Back Summer Lightning Ö Thatchers Gold, Lulworth Skipper, Bridge Farm Traditional. 🍷 10 Facilities Children's menu Play area Dogs allowed Garden Parking

CATTISTOCK

Fox & Hounds Inn

Duck St DT2 0JH
☎ 01300 320444 📄 01300 320444
e-mail: lizflight@yahoo.co.uk
web: www.foxandhoundsinn.com
dir: *On A37, between Dorchester & Yeovil, follow signs to Cattistock*

This attractive 16th-century inn is set in the beautiful village of Cattistock. Original features include beams, open fires in winter and huge inglenooks, one with an original bread oven. It is a fascinating building, full of curiosities, such as the hidden cupboard reached by a staircase that winds around the chimney in one of the loft areas. Traditional home-made meals include locally made faggots; mushroom stroganoff; steak and kidney pudding; and Dorset apple cake. A superb garden is available in the summer. Recent change of ownership.

Open noon-2.30 7-11 (Thu-Sat 12-2.30 6-11) Closed: Mon L Bar Meals L served Tue-Sun 12-2 D served Tue-Sat 7-11 booking required Av main course £8.95 Restaurant L served Tue-Sun 12-2 D served Tue-Sat 7-11 booking required ⊕ PALMERS ◀ Palmers IPA, Copper Ale, Palmers 200, Dorset Gold Ö Thatchers Traditional. Facilities Children's menu Play area Dogs allowed Garden Parking

CORFE CASTLE

The Greyhound Inn ☂

The Square BH20 5EZ
☎ 01929 480205 ▤ 01929 480205
e-mail: eat@greyhoundcorfe.co.uk
dir: *W from Bournemouth, take A35 to Dorchester, after 5m left onto A351, 10m to Corfe Castle*

A classic coaching inn, set beneath the ruins of Corfe Castle, the Greyhound has a large beer garden with views of Swanage Steam Railway. A full diary of events features two annual beer festivals in May and August and a West Country sausage and cider festival in October half term. The convivial atmosphere embraces families, cyclists and walkers enjoying local food and ale, including winter game and summer shellfish from Swanage, Weymouth or Lulworth.

Open all wk 11-11 **Bar Meals** L served all wk 11-3 D served all wk 6-9 Av main course £10.75 ⊕ ENTERPRISE INNS ◀ Fuller's London Pride, Timothy Taylor Landlord, Black Sheep, Ringwood Best, Purbeck Brewery Fossil Fuel, Marston's Pedigree ♂ Westons Organic, Stowford Press. ☂ 6 **Facilities** Children's menu Play area Family room Dogs allowed Garden

EVERSHOT

The Acorn Inn ★★★★ INN ◉ ☂

DT2 0JW ☎ 01935 83228 ▤ 01935 83707
e-mail: stay@acorn-inn.co.uk
web: www.acorn-inn.co.uk
dir: *A303 to Yeovil, Dorchester Rd, on A37 right to Evershot*

Immortalised as the Sow and Acorn in Thomas Hardy's *Tess of the D'Urbervilles*, this 16th-century free house stands in an Area of Outstanding Natural Beauty. Two oak-panelled bars are warmed by log fires, blazing in carved hamstone fireplaces. Most of the food is locally sourced, and the interesting menus might include starters such as chicken, wild mushroom and herb terrine. Typical main course choices include roasted butternut squash, Parmesan, cherry tomato and pine nut tagliatelle; sea bass on herb crushed new potatoes with basil pesto; and West Country sausages with grain mustard mash and rosemary jus. Finish with raspberry and Amaretto crème brulée; or creamed mango fool with sesame tuile biscuit and blackberries.

Open all day all wk 11-11 **Bar Meals** L served all wk 12-2 D served all wk 7-9 **Restaurant** L served all wk 12-2 booking required D served all wk 7-9 booking required ⊕ FREE HOUSE ◀ Draymens, guest ale ♂ Thatchers Gold, Thatchers Scrumpy. ☂ 7 **Facilities** Children's menu Family room Dogs allowed Garden Parking **Rooms** 10

GILLINGHAM

The Kings Arms Inn ♥

East Stour Common SP8 5NB
☎ 01747 838325
e-mail: nrosscampbell@aol.com
dir: *4m W of Shaftesbury on A30*

A family-run, 200-year-old free house, this village inn makes a great base for exploring Dorset's countryside and coast. There is a public bar with a log fire, the Mallard and Garden Room and an enclosed acre of attractive beer garden. The menus offer an extensive choice of restaurant fare and traditional pub grub. Popular choices include chicken breast stuffed with haggis on black pudding mash in a Drambuie sauce, or steak and kidney pudding with red onion marmalade. A separate menu is available for children and there is an eat lunch for a fiver deal.

Open all wk **Bar Meals** L served Mon-Sat 12-2.30, Sun 12-9.15 booking required D served Mon-Sat 5.30-9.15, Sun 12-9.15 booking required **Restaurant** L served Mon-Sat 12-2.30, Sun 12-9.15 booking required D served Mon-Sat 5.30-9.15, Sun 12-9.15 booking required ⊕ FREE HOUSE ◀ London Pride, Copper Ale, Tribute, Wadworth 6X. ♥ 8 **Facilities** Children's menu Family room Dogs allowed Garden Parking

MARSHWOOD

The Bottle Inn ♥

DT6 5QJ ☎ 01297 678254 📄 01297 678739
e-mail: thebottleinn@msn.com
dir: *On B3165 (Crewkerne to Lyme Regis road) 5m from the Hunters Lodge*

In the 18th century the Bottle Inn was the first pub in the area to serve bottled beer rather than beer from the jug - hence the name. Standing on the edge of Marshwood Vale, its rustic interior has wooden settles, scrubbed tables and a blazing fire. The lunch menu keeps it simple with jacket potatoes, grilled paninis, burgers like wild boar and apple, ploughman's, baguettes, lite bites (perhaps crab cakes; pâté; or deep fried brie) plus haddock and chips; chilli; and gammon steak. At dinner the choices could be smoked duck with raspberry coulis or king prawns in garlic and cream, followed by steak and kidney pudding or supreme of chicken stuffed with smoked salmon with whisky and mustard cream sauce. The pub is home to the annual World Stinging-Nettle Eating Championships.

Open all wk noon-3 6-11 **Bar Meals** L served all wk 12-2 booking required Av main course £8 **Restaurant** L served all wk 12-2 booking required D served all wk 6-9 booking required Fixed menu price fr £9.50 ⊕ FREE HOUSE ◀ Otter Ale, Otter Bitter, Stargazer, guest ale ♂ Stowford Press, Thatchers Gold. ♥ 7 **Facilities** Children's menu Play area Family room Garden Parking

MOTCOMBE

The Coppleridge Inn 🅰 ★★★ INN ⛊

SP7 9HW ☎ 01747 851980 🖹 01747 851858
e-mail: thecoppleridgeinn@btinternet.com
web: www.coppleridge.com
dir: *Take A350 towards Warminster for 1.5m, turn left at brown tourist sign. Follow signs to inn*

Previously a dairy farm, this 18th-century building retains plenty of traditional features, including flagstone floors and log fires. Run by the Goodinge family for nearly 20 years, it offers a good range of real ales and a daily-changing menu of sophisticated pub food, ranging from roasted lamb rump on sweet potato mash with sage jus to grilled lemon sole with dill velouté. For sunny days there is a large garden and terrace with Blackmore Vale views, a secure children's playground and 10 bedrooms if you would like to stay over.

Open all wk 11-3 5-11 (Sat 11am-mdnt Sun noon-11) **Bar Meals** L served all wk 12-2.30 D served all wk 6-9 Av main course £11.50 **Restaurant** L served all wk 12-2.30 D served all wk 6-9 Av 3 course à la carte fr £22 ⊕ FREE HOUSE 🍺 Butcombe Bitter, Greene King IPA, Wadworth 6X, Fuller's London Pride, Sharp's Doom Bar. ⛊ 10 **Facilities** Children's menu Play area Family room Dogs allowed Garden Parking **Rooms** 10

OSMINGTON MILLS

The Smugglers Inn ⛊

DT3 6HF ☎ 01305 833125
e-mail:
smugglers.weymouth@hall-woodhouse.co.uk
dir: *7m E of Weymouth towards Wareham, pub signed*

Set on the cliffs at Osmington Mills with the South Coast Footpath running through the garden, the inn has beautiful views across Weymouth Bay. In the late 18th century (the inn dates back to the 13th century) it was the base of infamous smuggler Pierre La Tour who fell in love with the publican's daughter, Arabella Carless, who was shot dead while helping him to escape during a raid. Things are quieter now and you can enjoy a pint of Tanglefoot or one of the guest ales like Pickled Partridge. On the menu typical dishes are chicken and bacon salad, chargrilled rump steak, and Sussex smokey (fish pie).

Open all wk 11-11 (Sun noon-10.30) **Bar Meals** L served all wk 12-9.30 D served all wk 12-9.30 Av main course £9 food served all day **Restaurant** L served all wk 12-9.30 D served all wk 12-9.30 food served all day ⊕ HALL & WOODHOUSE 🍺 Badger, Tanglefoot, guest ale. ⛊ 12 **Facilities** Children's menu Play area Dogs allowed Garden Parking

PUNCKNOWLE

The Crown Inn 🍷

Church St DT2 9BN ☎ 01308 897711
e-mail: crownpuncknowle@btinternet.com
dir: *From A35, into Bridevally, through Litton Cheney. From B3157, inland at Swyre*

There's a traditional atmosphere within the rambling, low-beamed bars at this picturesque 16th-century thatched inn, which was once the haunt of smugglers on their way from nearby Chesil Beach to visit prosperous customers in Bath. Food ranges from light snacks and sandwiches to home-made dishes like lamb chops with mint sauce; mushroom and nut pasta with French bread; and tuna steak with basil and tomato sauce. Recent change of hands.

Open 12-3 6-11 Closed: Sun eve **Bar Meals** L served all wk 12-2 D served Mon-Sat 6-9 Av main course £8 **Restaurant** L served all wk 12-2 D served Mon-Sat 6-9 Av 3 course à la carte fr £18 ⊕ PALMERS ◣ Palmers IPA, 200 Premium Ale, Copper, Tally Ho! ♨ Thatchers Gold. 🍷 10 **Facilities** Children's menu Family room Dogs allowed Garden Parking

SHERBORNE

Queen's Head

High St, Milborne Port DT9 5DQ
☎ 01963 250314
e-mail: info@queenshead.co.uk
dir: *On A30, 2.5m W of Sherborne towards Salisbury*

Milborne Port has no facilities for shipping, the suffix being Old English for 'borough', a status it acquired in 1249. The building came much later, in Elizabethan times, although no mention is made of it as a hostelry until 1738. Charming and friendly bars, restaurant, beer garden and skittle alley combine to make it a popular free house in these parts.

Open all wk 11-2.30 5.30-11.30 (Fri-Sat 11am-mdnt) **Bar Meals** L served all wk 12-2.30 booking required D served all wk 5.30-9.30 booking required Av main course £7.50 **Restaurant** L served all wk 12-2.30 booking required D served all wk 5.30-9.30 booking required ⊕ ENTERPRISE INNS ◣ Butcombe Bitters, Fuller's London Pride, Hopback Summer Lightning. **Facilities** Children's menu Dogs allowed Garden Parking

SYDLING ST NICHOLAS

The Greyhound Inn ★★★★ INN 🏵 ♗

DT2 9PD ☎ 01300 341303
e-mail: info@thegreyhounddorset.co.uk
dir: *Off A37 (Yeovil to Dorchester road), turn off at Cerne Abbas/Sydling St Nicholas*

A 17th-century inn with a walled garden, The Greyhound is set in a picturesque village complete with stream. Food is served in the bar or cosy restaurant, ranging from snacks to the full dining experience. Local seafood is a speciality, with dishes such as pan-fried monkfish with chorizo, fresh basil, cherry tomatoes and sherry, and there is a good choice of meat and game. Stylish and well-equipped accommodation is available, including ground floor rooms.

Open all wk 11-2.30 6-11 Closed: Sun eve **Bar Meals** L served all wk 12-2 booking required D served Mon-Sat 6-9 booking required **Restaurant** L served all wk 12-2 booking required D served Mon-Sat 6-9 booking required ⊕ FREE HOUSE ◀ Palmer IPA, Wadworth 6X, St Austell Tinners, Old Speckled Hen, Spitfire ♂ Thatchers Gold. ♗ 7 **Facilities** Children's menu Play area Dogs allowed Garden Parking **Rooms** 6

TARRANT MONKTON

The Langton Arms ★★★★ INN ♗

DT11 8RX
☎ 01258 830225 📄 01258 830053
e-mail: info@thelangtonarms.co.uk
dir: *A31 from Ringwood, or A357 from Shaftesbury, or A35 from Bournemouth*

Occupying a peaceful spot close to the village church, this 17th-century thatched inn serves real ales from four pumps, including the house beer, Hidden Pint, which comes from the Hidden Brewery at Dinton, near Salisbury. The Stables restaurant and conservatory offers the sort of fulfilling meal that on a weekday might comprise marinated crispy beef from the Tarrant Valley, followed by real ale battered haddock, and then home-made mango, pineapple and passion fruit parfait. Or at lunchtime on Sunday, the same degree of satisfaction could well be derived from home-cured gravadlax; roast loin of pork and caramelised onion gravy; and a selection of West Country cheeses. A comprehensive bar menu is also available.

Open all day all wk **Bar Meals** L served Mon-Fri 12-2.30, Sat-Sun all day D served Mon-Thu 6-9.30, Fri 6-10, Sat-Sun all day **Restaurant** L served Mon-Fri 12-2.30, Sat-Sun all day D served Mon-Thu 6-9.30, Fri 6-10, Sat-Sun all day ⊕ FREE HOUSE ◀ Guest ales (all local). ♗ 7 **Facilities** Children's menu Play area Family room Dogs allowed Garden Parking **Rooms** 6

TRENT

Rose & Crown Trent ♟

DT9 4SL ☎ 01935 850776 📄 01935 850776
e-mail: hkirkie@hotmail.com
web: www.roseandcrowntrent.com
dir: *Just off A30 between Sherborne & Yeovil*

You'll find this thatched, ivy-clad inn tucked away in the conservation village of Trent, opposite the church. Part 14th century, part 18th century, and recently refurbished, the inn has a massive open fire and plenty of seating. Owners Heather and Stuart have established an impressive reputation for home-cooked food. The lunch menu brings ploughman's and tapas, as well as heartier offerings such as salmon, crab and coriander fishcake with sweet chilli dressing, followed by roast chicken breast with black pudding and a tarragon cream sauce. Dinner may comprise grilled goats' cheese bruschetta with a beetroot and pear dressing followed by rump of lamb with a herb crust. Puddings are a treat.

Open 12-3 6-11 (Sat-Sun 12-11) Closed: Mon **Bar Meals** L served Tue-Sun 12-3 booking required D served Tue-Sat 6-9 booking required Av main course £8.95 **Restaurant** L served Tue-Sun 12-3 D served Tue-Sat 6-9 booking required Fixed menu price fr £12.95 Av 3 course à la carte fr £26.95 ⊕ WADWORTH ◖ 6X, Henry's IPA, Horizon, Bishops Tipple, guest ale ♻ Stowford Press, Thatchers Gold. ♟ 8 **Facilities** Children's menu Family room Dogs allowed Garden Parking

WEST LULWORTH

The Castle Inn ♟

Main Rd BH20 5RN
☎ 01929 400311 📄 01929 400415
e-mail: office@lulworthinn.com
dir: *Follow village signs from A352 (Dorchester to Wareham road). Inn on right on B3070 through West Lulworth. Car park opposite*

In a delightful setting near Lulworth Cove, this family-run thatched village inn lies close to plenty of good walks. The friendly bars offer a traditional atmosphere in which to enjoy a pint of well-kept Isle of Purbeck. Outside, you'll find large tiered gardens packed with plants, and in summer there's a giant outdoor chess set. The wide-ranging menu includes chicken stroganoff, seafood stew, sirloin steak grill, and tuna steak. There's also a good vegetarian choice.

Open all wk Closed: 25 Dec **Bar Meals** L served all wk 12-2 D served all wk 7-10 Av main course £8.50 ⊕ FREE HOUSE ◖ John Smiths, Sharps, Isle of Purbeck, Piddle Ales, Palmers. ♟ 8 **Facilities** Children's menu Dogs allowed Garden Parking

BARNARD CASTLE

The Morritt Arms Hotel ★★★ HL ⛾

Greta Bridge DL12 9SE
☎ 01833 627232 📠 01833 627392
e-mail: relax@themorritt.co.uk
dir: *At Scotch Corner take A66 towards Penrith, after 9m turn at Greta Bridge. Hotel over bridge on left*

Situated in rural Teesdale, The Morritt Arms has been an inn for two centuries. Full of character, the bar has a very interesting Dickensian mural. Here the carte offers starters of pressed ham, black pudding, Wensleydale cheese and home-made chutney; chilli and garlic tiger prawns with soft egg noodles, spring onions and coriander; wild mushrooms on toast with poached Neasham egg, truffle and tarragon dressing. Main courses include slow roasted belly pork with bubble and squeak, roasted roots and mustard jus; pan-fried trout, saffron and pea risotto, parsley oil; Teesdale lamb rack, leek and mustard mash, parsnips and redcurrant jus; and Mediterranean vegetables, sun blushed tomatoes, goats' cheese and tomato sauce. You can also dine in the oak-panelled hotel restaurant, Pallatt's bistro, or the landscaped gardens.

Open all day all wk 7am-11pm **Bar Meals** food served all day **Restaurant** L served all wk 12-3 D served all wk 7-9.30 ⊕ FREE HOUSE ◀ John Smith's, Timothy Taylor Landlord, Black Sheep Best. ⛾ 20 **Facilities** Children's menu Play area Family room Dogs allowed Garden Parking **Rooms** 27

COTHERSTONE

The Fox and Hounds ⛾

DL12 9PF ☎ 01833 650241
e-mail: foxenquiries@tiscali.co.uk
dir: *4m W of Barnard Castle. From A66 onto B6277, signed*

This delightful 18th-century coaching inn in the heart of Teesdale is a perfect holiday base. Both the restaurant and the heavily beamed bar boast welcoming winter fires in original fireplaces. Fresh local ingredients are the foundation of home-made food such as a warm salad of Wensleydale cheese, bacon, cranberries and apple; steak, black pudding and Black Sheep ale pie; or pan-fried crown of Holwick pheasant on bubble and squeak mash with rich gravy.

Open all wk 12-2.30 6.30-11 (Sun 6.30-10.30) Closed: 25-26 Dec **Bar Meals** L served all wk 12-2 D served all wk 6.30-9 **Restaurant** D served all wk 6.30-9 ⊕ FREE HOUSE ◀ Black Sheep Best, Village Brewer Bull Bitter, Black Sheep Ale, Daleside Special, Yorkshire Terrier. ⛾ 10 **Facilities** Children's menu Garden Parking

MIDDLESTONE

Ship Inn ⚲

Low Rd DL14 8AB ☎ 01388 810904
e-mail: tony.theshipinn@googlemail.com
dir: *On B6287 (Kirk Merrington to Coundon road)*

Beer drinkers will appreciate the string of real ale-related accolades received by this family-run pub on the village green. In the last five years regulars could have sampled well over 800 different beers. Home-cooked food is served in the bar and restaurant, using beef, pork and lamb reared locally. The Ship has three unique attributes – it is 23 miles from the sea, 550 feet above sea level and the cellar is 9 feet above the bar! The rooftop patio has spectacular views over the Tees Valley and Cleveland Hills.

Open all wk 4-11 (Fri-Sun noon-11) Bar Meals L served Fri-Sun 12-2 D served all wk 6-9 Av main course £4.95 ⊕ FREE HOUSE ◀ 6 guest ales. ⚲ 13 Facilities Children's menu Play area Family room Dogs allowed Parking

NEWTON AYCLIFFE

Blacksmiths Arms ⚲

Preston le Skerne, (off Ricknall Lane) DL5 6JH
☎ 01325 314873

A former smithy dating from the 1700s, and still relatively isolated in its farmland setting. Enjoying an excellent reputation locally as a good dining pub, it offers starters of hot smoked mackerel and potato salad; cod and prawn brandade; chicken fillet goujons; and potted mushrooms. Requiring their own page on the menu are fish dishes such as grilled halibut steak with risotto, and gingered salmon. Chef's specialities include Gressingham duck breast, and pork au poivre.

Open Closed: 1 Jan, Mon ⊕ FREE HOUSE ◀ Ever changing selection of real ales. ⚲ 10 Facilities Children's menu Play area Garden Parking

CASTLE HEDINGHAM

The Bell Inn ♟

Saint James St CO9 3EJ ☎ 01787 460350
e-mail: bell-castle@hotmail.co.uk
web: www.hedinghambell.co.uk
dir: *On A1124 N of Halstead, right to Castle Hedingham*

Run by the same family for over 40 years, this unspoilt pub began life in the 15th century as a coaching inn. Today it oozes traditional charm, from log fires in winter to a huge orchard garden and vine-covered patio for summer lounging. Food from quality local suppliers is home cooked and largely traditional, although the Turkish chef offers interesting specials such as grilled lamb meatballs. Fish is hand-picked from Billingsgate or delivered fresh from Colchester. Summer and winter beer festivals are a feature.

Open all wk 11.45-3 6-11 (Fri-Sat noon-mdnt Sun noon-11) Closed: 25 Dec eve Bar Meals L served Mon-Fri 12-2, Sat-Sun 12-2.30 D served Sun-Mon 7-9, Tue-Sat 7-9.30 Av main course £8.50 ⊕ GRAYS ◀ Maldon Gold Mighty Oak, Adnams Bitter, Mighty Oak IPA, guest ale Ŏ Stowford Press. ♟ 8 Facilities Children's menu Play area Family room Dogs allowed Garden Parking

CLAVERING

The Cricketers ♟

CB11 4QT
☎ 01799 550442 📄 01799 550882
e-mail: info@thecricketers.co.uk
dir: *From M11 junct 10, A505 E. Then A1301, B1383. At Newport take B1038*

With landlords called Sally and Trevor Oliver, it comes as no surprise to learn that this 16th-century village pub is where celebrity chef Jamie started his career. Cricket memorabilia decorates the beamed bar and restaurant, both of which offer their own menus and specials. Typical are meat and vegetarian antipasti; braised rabbit with gnocchi and mixed wild mushrooms; pavé of Scottish salmon on crab spaghetti; sautéed calf's liver and bacon with Szechuan spiced potatoes; and spinach and feta filo pastry pie. There's always plenty of fish, and a roast on Sunday. Jamie himself supplies some produce from his organic garden nearby. Sensible children's menu.

Open all day all wk Closed: 25-26 Dec Bar Meals L served all wk 12-2 booking required D served all wk 6.30-9.30 booking required Av main course £13 Restaurant L served all wk 12-2 booking required D served all wk 6.30-9.30 booking required Av 3 course à la carte fr £29.50 ⊕ FREE HOUSE ◀ Adnams Bitter, Tetley Bitter, Greene King IPA, Adnams Broadside, Woodforde's Wherry, Nog Ŏ Aspall. ♟ 10 Facilities Children's menu Play area Family room Garden Parking

DEDHAM

Marlborough Head Inn 🍷

Mill Ln CO7 6DH ☎ 01206 323250
e-mail: jen.pearmain@tiscali.co.uk
dir: *E of A12, N of Colchester*

Tucked away in glorious Constable Country, a
16th-century building that was once a clearing-
house for local wool merchants. In 1660, after
a slump in trade, it became an inn. Today it
is as perfect for a pint, sofa and newspaper
as it is for a good home-cooked family meal.
Traditional favourites such as steak, Guinness
and mushroom pie; and lamb shank with red
wine and rosemary appear on the menu, plus fish
is given centre stage on Fridays.

Open all wk 11.30-11 **Bar Meals** Av main course
£8.95 food served all day **Restaurant** food served
all day ∰ PUNCH ◀ Adnams Southwold, Greene King
IPA ♂ Aspall. 🍷 8 **Facilities** Children's menu Family
room Dogs allowed Garden Parking

HORNDON ON THE HILL

Bell Inn & Hill House 🍷

High Rd SS17 8LD
☎ 01375 642463 🖹 01375 361611
e-mail: info@bell-inn.co.uk
dir: *M25 junct 30/31 signed Thurrock*

The Bell is a 15th-century coaching inn, as
the archway through to the courtyard testifies.
Once inside, look for the original king post that
supports the inn's roof timbers. The bar menu
offers sandwiches and light meals such as
fishcakes with poached egg and hollandaise;
and braised lamb's liver with mustard mash. In
the restaurant start with smoked salmon with
scrambled egg and cheddar rarebit; or cream of
parsnip soup. For a main course, try roast duck
with balsamic roast fig and cranberry compote;
or wild mushroom ravioli with sauté of wild
mushroom. Desserts include apple, sultana
and cinnamon filo millefeuille with caramel ice
cream; or caramelised pannacotta with rhubarb
compote, ginger ice cream and lemon shortbread.

Open all wk Closed: 25-26 Dec **Bar Meals** L served
all wk 12-1.45 D served all wk 6.30-9.45 Av main
course £15.95 **Restaurant** L served Mon-Sat
12-1.45, Sun 12-2.30 booking required D served all
wk 6.30-9.45 booking required Av 3 course à la carte
fr £23 ∰ FREE HOUSE ◀ Greene King IPA, Interbrew
Bass, Crouchvale Brewers Gold, Ruddles County,
Spitfire. 🍷 16 **Facilities** Children's menu Dogs
allowed Garden Parking

LITTLE CANFIELD

The Lion & Lamb 🍷

CM6 1SR

☎ 01279 870257 📄 01279 870423

e-mail: info@lionandlamb.co.uk

dir: *M11 junct 8, B1256 towards Takeley & Little Canfield*

A favourite for business or leisure, this traditional country pub restaurant is handy for Stansted airport and the M11. Inside you'll find oak beams, winter log fires, and an extensive food selection. From the bar menu choose sandwiches, steak and ale pie, Lion & Lamb beef burger, lasagne or sausage and mash. In the restaurant sample vegetable moussaka of red lentils and aubergine, Thai red beef curry, or a kangaroo fillet from the grill!

Open all wk 11-11 Bar Meals Av main course £9 food served all day Restaurant Av 3 course à la carte fr £25 food served all day ⊕ GREENE KING ◀ Old Speckled Hen, Greene King IPA, Old Bob, guest ales. 🍷 10 Facilities Children's menu Play area Garden Parking

NORTH FAMBRIDGE

The Ferry Boat Inn

Ferry Ln CM3 6LR ☎ 01621 740208

e-mail: sylviaferryboat@aol.com

dir: *From Chelmsford take A130 S then A132 to South Woodham Ferrers, then B1012. right to village*

Owned by the same family for 26 years, this 500-year-old traditional weatherboard inn has beams, log fires and a resident ghost. It is tucked away at the end of a lovely village on the River Crouch, next to the marina, and was once a centre for smugglers. These days it is understandably popular with the sailing fraternity. In addition to the extensive menu and chef's specials, dishes might include minted lamb chop, grilled sea bass, chicken korma or beef chilli.

Open all wk 11.30-3 6.30-11 (Sun 12-4 6.30-10.30 & all day in summer) Bar Meals food served all day Restaurant food served all day ⊕ FREE HOUSE ◀ Greene King IPA, Abbot Ale, Morland. Facilities Children's menu Family room Dogs allowed Garden Parking

PATTISWICK

The Compasses at Pattiswick ☻

Compasses Rd CM77 8BG
☎ 01376 561322 ▤ 01376 564343
e-mail: info@thecompassesatpattiswick.co.uk
web: www.thecompassesatpattiswick.co.uk
dir: *From Braintree take A120 E towards Colchester. After Bradwell 1st left to Pattiswick*

Set in beautiful countryside and made from two estate workers' cottages, is this award-winning dining pub, where a passion for good food turns into superbly cooked dishes, jam-packed with local produce. At lunchtime try potted shrimps; local pork pie with piccalilli; grilled plaice with scallop butter and cavolo nero. The dinner menu offers dishes like sweet potato and parsnip curry with braised rice and raita; rib-eye steak with sautéed mushrooms and peppercorn butter; and sea bass fillets with anchovy mash and chive clotted cream. The desserts list offers apple and rhubarb crumble; and spotted dick.

Open all wk 11-3 5.30-11 (Sat 5.30-mdnt, Sun noon-4.30, Sun eve in Summer) Bar Meals L served all wk 12-3 D served Mon-Thu 6-9.30, Fri-Sat 6-9.45 Restaurant L served Mon-Sat 12-3, Sun 12-4.30 booking required D served Mon-Thu 6-9.30, Fri-Sat 6-9.45 booking required ⊕ FREE HOUSE ◀ Woodforde's Wherry, Adnams, Adnams Broadside, St Austell Tribute Ŏ Aspalls. ☻ 12 Facilities Children's menu Play area Dogs allowed Garden Parking

STOCK

The Hoop ☻

21 High St CM4 9BD ☎ 01277 841137
e-mail: thehoopstock@yahoo.co.uk
dir: *On B1007 between Chelmsford & Billericay*

This 15th-century free house on Stock's village green is every inch the traditional pub. Expect a warm welcome, real ales and a pleasing lack of music or fruit machines. The annual beer festival enjoys growing popularity, but the food is also a major draw. In keeping with the gorgeously traditional interior, a meal might include potted shrimps with brown bread; calves' liver with bacon, mash and onion rings; and bread and butter pudding for dessert.

Open all wk 11-11 (Sun 12-10.30) Bar Meals L served Mon-Sat 12-2.30, Sun 12-5 D served Mon-Sat 6-9 Av main course £9 Restaurant L served Tue-Fri 12-2.30, Sun 12-5 booking required D served Tue-Sat 6-9 booking required Av 3 course à la carte fr £25 ⊕ FREE HOUSE ◀ Adnams Bitter, 4 guest ales Ŏ Westons, Thatchers. ☻ 10 Facilities Children's menu Dogs allowed Garden

WOODHAM MORTIMER

Hurdle Makers Arms ♟

Post Office Rd CM9 6ST
☎ 01245 225169 ▤ 01245 225169
e-mail: gary@hurdlemakersarms.co.uk
dir: *From Chelmsford A414 to Maldon/Danbury. 4.5m, through Danbury into Woodham Mortimer. Over 1st rdbt, 1st left, pub on left. Behind golf driving range*

A Grade II listed building dating back 400 years, the Hurdle Makers Arms has been a pub since 1837. Right at the heart of village life, it has live music, quiz nights and regular themed food evenings. Real ale lovers who like to discover new ales will be delighted by the wide range of micro-brewery products on offer. There are even guest ciders. Home-made pub food is served seven days a week, and in summer there are weekend barbecues in the large beer garden.

Open all wk all day summer (winter Mon-Thu noon-3 5.30-11 Fri-Sat all day Sun 12-9) **Bar Meals** L served Mon-Fri 12-3, Sat 12-9.30, Sun 12-8 D served Mon-Fri 6-9.30, Sat 12-9.30, Sun 12-8 **Restaurant** L served Mon-Fri 12-3, Sat 12-9.30, Sun 12-8 D served Mon-Fri 6-9.30, Sat 12-9.30, Sun 12-8 ⊕ GRAY & SONS ◀ Abbot, Mighty Oak, Crouch Vale, Farmers ales, Guest ales ♉ Old Rosie. ♟8 **Facilities** Children's menu Play area Garden Parking

ALDERTON

The Gardeners Arms ♟

Beckford Rd GL20 8NL ☎ 01242 620257
e-mail: gardeners1@btconnect.com
dir: *Please telephone for directions*

This family-run, 16th-century thatched free house is in a quiet Cotswolds village. You can play boules in the large beer garden, and shove ha'penny or other traditional bar games in the stone-walled bar. Seasonal local produce and daily fresh fish underpin simple dishes such as home-made beef lasagne; tiger prawn Thai green curry; liver, bacon and onions; broccoli and cauliflower cheese gratin; and Mediterranean vegetable Wellington. Monthly-changing specials include slow-braised Cotswold lamb shoulder; and pan-fried halibut steak. Two beer festivals are held, one in May and the other at Christmas.

Open all wk 10-2 5-10 (Sun all day, Fri till mdnt) **Bar Meals** L served all wk 12-2 D served all wk 5.30-9 Av main course £4.50 **Restaurant** L served Mon-Sat 12-2, Sun all day booking required D served all wk 5.30-9.30 booking required Fixed menu price fr £10 Av 3 course à la carte fr £15 ⊕ FREE HOUSE ◀ Doom Bar, Butcombe Best, Courage Best, Local Guest Ales ♉ Westons GWR. ♟8 **Facilities** Children's menu Dogs allowed Garden Parking

67

BIBURY

Catherine Wheel

Arlington GL7 5ND ☎ 01285 740250
dir: *Telephone for directions*

This low-beamed 15th-century pub is situated in a Cotswold village, which was described by William Morris as 'the most beautiful in England'. Inside is an original ship's timber beam, as well as various prints and photographs of Old Bibury, and blazing log fires in winter. Traditional pub food includes fresh Bibury trout, salmon and prawns, and tuna steak. Alongside a range of real ales, look out for Weston's Stowford Press, a traditional English cider.

Open all day all wk 10am-11pm (Mon-Fri 3-6 closed during winter) **Bar Meals** L served all wk 12-2.30 D served all wk 6-9.30 Av main course £10 **Restaurant** L served all wk 12-2.30 D served all wk 6-9.30 Av 3 course à la carte fr £20 ⊕ BARNSLEY HOUSE LTD ◀ Hook Norton, Sharps Doom Bar ♻ Westons Stowford Press. **Facilities** Children's menu Dogs allowed Garden Parking

BIRDLIP

The Golden Heart ♥

Nettleton Bottom GL4 8LA
☎ 01242 870261 📄 01242 870599
e-mail: cathstevensgh@aol.com
dir: *On A417 Gloucester to Cirencester. 8m from Cheltenham. Pub at base of dip in Nettleton Bottom*

This centuries-old Cotswold stone inn has glorious views from its terraced gardens. It probably started life as a drovers' inn, and retains plenty of original features. Excellent local ales and traditional ciders are the focus of the bar, while the extensive menus show an equal commitment to local produce, particularly prize-winning meat from livestock markets and shows. On the other hand, it also makes room for exotic meats including a low fat ostrich casserole or a crocodile, zebra and rattlesnake mixed grill.

Open all wk 11-3 5.30-11 (Fri-Sun open all day) Closed: 25 Dec **Bar Meals** L served Mon-Sat 12-3, Sun all day D served Mon-Sat 6-10, Sun all day Av main course £11.25 **Restaurant** L served Mon-Sat 12-3, Sun all day D served Mon-Sat 12-3, Sun all day ⊕ FREE HOUSE ◀ Otter Bitter, Wickwar, Cotswolds Way, Wye Valley, Otter, Gold Festival ♻ Westons, Henney, Thatchers. ♥ 10 **Facilities** Children's menu Family room Dogs allowed Garden Parking

CHEDWORTH

Hare & Hounds ☻

Foss Cross GL54 4NN ☎ 01285 720288
e-mail: stay@hareandhoundsinn.com
dir: *On A429 (Fosse Way), 6m from Cirencester*

A 14th-century inn with various interconnecting dining areas often described as a rabbit warren. Open fires, beams and stone and polished wood floors add to the charm. It's ideally placed for touring the Cotswolds or attending Cheltenham race meetings. There's a daily changing blackboard, along with a menu typically listing breast of Gressingham duck; baked fillet of cod; and Burmese vegetable tofu curry.

Open all wk 11-3 (Sat 6-close Sun 7- close) **Bar Meals** L served all wk 12-2.30 booking required D served Mon-Sat 6.30-9.30, Sun 7-9 booking required **Restaurant** L served all wk 12-2.30 booking required D served Mon-Sat 6.30-9.30, Sun 7-9 booking required ⊕ ARKELLS ◀ Arkells 2B, 3B, Moonlight ○ Stowford Press. ☻ 10
Facilities Children's menu Family room Dogs allowed Garden Parking

CHIPPING CAMPDEN

The Bakers Arms ☻

Broad Campden GL55 6UR ☎ 01386 840515
dir: *1m from Chipping Campden*

There is a friendly family atmosphere at this country Cotswold inn, where you can expect to find exposed stone walls, beams and an inglenook fireplace. A choice of four to five real ales is offered alongside reasonably priced meals. Choose from sandwiches, warm baguettes and filled giant Yorkshire puddings, or dishes such as mariner's pie, Thai red vegetable curry, and liver, bacon and onions with rich gravy.

Open all wk 11.30-2.30 4.45-11 (Fri-Sun 11.30-11 Apr-Oct all wk 11.30-11) Closed: 25 Dec **Bar Meals** L served Mon-Fri 12-2, Sat 12-2.30, Sun 12-6 D served Mon-Sat 6-9 Av main course £7.50 **Restaurant** L served Mon-Fri 12-2, Sat 12-2.30, Sun 12-6 D served Mon-Sat 6-9 ⊕ FREE HOUSE ◀ Stanway Bitter, Bombardier, Donnington BB. ☻ 6
Facilities Children's menu Play area Garden Parking
Notes no credit cards

CHIPPING CAMPDEN

Eight Bells 🍷

Church St GL55 6JG
☎ 01386 840371 📠 01386 841669
e-mail: neilhargreaves@bellinn.fsnet.co.uk
dir: *8m from Stratford-upon-Avon, M40 Junct 15*

Located just off the High Street, the Eight Bells was built in the 14th century to house stonemasons working on the nearby church and to store the eight bells. A cobbled entranceway leads into two atmospheric bars, with oak beams, open fireplaces and a priest's hole. In summer, guests spill out into the courtyard or the terraced garden that overlooks the almshouses and church. Lunchtime sandwiches on ciabatta bread are available Monday to Saturday, and dishes range through home-made soup, bruschetta, traditional fish and chips, monkfish tail wrapped in Parma ham, and Mr Lashford's sausage of the day. Home-made desserts take in hot ginger sponge or poached pear in a brandy-snap basket.

Open all day all wk noon–11 (Sun noon–10.30) Closed: 25 Dec **Bar Meals** L served Mon–Thu 12-2, Fri-Sun 12-2.30 D served Mon–Thu 6.30-9, Fri-Sat 6.30-9.30, Sun 6.30-8.45 **Restaurant** L served Mon–Thu 12-2, Fri-Sun 12-2.30 D served Mon–Thu 6.30-9, Fri-Sat 6.30-9.30, Sun 6.30-8.45 ⊕ FREE HOUSE ◀ Hook Norton Best & guest ales, Goff's Jouster, Marston Pedigree, Purity UBU Ò Old Rosie. ☌ 8 **Facilities** Children's menu Family room Dogs allowed Garden

CLIFFORD'S MESNE

The Yew Tree 🍷

Clifford's Mesne GL18 1JS
☎ 01531 820719 📠 01531 820912
e-mail: cass@yewtreeinn.com
dir: *From Newent High Street follow signs to Clifford's Mesne. Pub at far end of village on road to Glasshouse*

Sitting on the slopes of May Hill, the county's highest point, from which you can see across seven counties, and once used as a cider press, the Yew Tree features quarry-tiled floors, log fires and a well-stocked bar. Free-range chickens provide eggs for the kitchen and many of the greens are home grown. Starters include gravadlax with dill dressing; and chargrilled courgette and sun-dried tomato risotto. Daily specials complement old favourites such as pork belly with caramelised celeriac, and rabbit and bacon pudding. Other mains include duck breast with blackberry and shallot compote; and mushroom, spinach and mascarpone roulade.

Open Closed: Mon, Tue L, Sun eve **Bar Meals** L served Wed-Sat 12-2 booking required D served Tue-Sat 6-9 booking required Av main course £12 **Restaurant** L served Sun 12-4 booking required Av 3 course à la carte fr £20 ⊕ FREE HOUSE ◀ Wye Valley HPA, Cotswold Spring Brewery Glory, Local Ales Ò Stowford Press, Old Rosie. ☌ 16 **Facilities** Children's menu Play area Dogs allowed Garden Parking

COATES

The Tunnel House Inn

GL7 6PW ☎ 01285 770280 📄 01285 700040
e-mail: bookings@tunnelhouse.com
web: www.tunnelhouse.com
dir: *From Cirencester on A433 towards Tetbury, in 2m turn right towards Coates, follow brown signs to Canal Tunnel & Inn*

Lying between Coates and Tarlton, the Tunnel House enjoys a glorious rural location. Depending on the weather, relax in the garden or the log fire-warmed bar. Food is served here or in the restaurant area. At lunchtime try a bacon and brie sandwich or a ploughman's, or choose from the monthly changing menu, featuring dishes such as beer-battered cod and chips; ham, eggs and chips; and rump steak. Dinner could include chicken liver parfait, Melba toast and red onion confit; then braised lamb shank in Madeira sauce; blackened fillet of mackerel with horseradish cream; or wild mushroom, chilli, pine nut and cream cheese tagliatelle.

Open all wk Closed: 25 Dec **Bar Meals** L served all wk 12-2.15 D served all wk 6.45-9.15 Av main course £10 **Restaurant** L served all wk 12-2.15 D served all wk 6.45-9.15 Fixed menu price fr £10 Av 3 course à la carte fr £22 ⊕ FREE HOUSE ◗ Uley Old Spot, Uley Bitter, Wye Valley Bitter, Hook Norton, Budding, Butcombe Ö Cornish Rattler, Black Rat, Westons Organic. **Facilities** Children's menu Play area Family room Dogs allowed Garden Parking

HINTON

The Bull Inn 🍷

SN14 8HG ☎ 0117 937 2332
e-mail: diserwhite@aol.com
web: www.thebullathinton.co.uk
dir: *From M4 junct 18, A46 to Bath 1m, turn right 1m, down hill. Pub on right*

Since it was built in the 17th century, The Bull has been an inn, a farm and a dairy, and following some of that tradition the owners now rear their own pigs for the restaurant table. Inside it retains two inglenook fireplaces and original flagstone flooring, while outside there's a front-facing terrace and a large rear garden with a children's play area. Food served draws on locally supplied produce and home-grown fruit and vegetables. Look out for Royal Gloucester steak and ale pie with horseradish pastry; and deep fried cod in soda and lime batter.

Open noon-3 6-11.30 (Sat-Sun & BH open all day) Closed: Mon L (ex BH) **Bar Meals** L served Tue-Sat 12-2, Sun 12-3.30 D served Mon-Thu 6-9, Fri-Sat 6-9.30 Av main course £12 **Restaurant** L served Tue-Sat 12-2, Sun 12-3.30 booking required D served Mon-Thu 6-9, Fri-Sat 6-9.30 booking required ⊕ WADWORTH ◗ Wadworth 6X & Henrys IPA, Wadworth Bishops Tipple, Wadworth Summersault, guest ale. 🍷 12 **Facilities** Children's menu Play area Dogs allowed Garden Parking

LOWER APPERLEY

The Farmers Arms 🍷

Ledbury Rd GL19 4DR ☎ 01452 780307
e-mail: danieljrpardoe@googlemail.com
dir: *From Tewkesbury take A38 towards Gloucester/
Ledbury. 2m, right at lights onto B4213 (signed
Ledbury). 1.5m, pub on left*

A popular, 16th-century, timber-framed pub on
the village fringe and close to the River Severn.
Low beams, an open fire, regular guest ales
and an extensive menu are to be found within.
Home-made dishes using locally sourced produce
include steak and kidney pie; honey roast ham
with free range eggs and chips; and luxury fish
pie. Look lout for special themed nights - Italian,
French, Irish.

Open all wk 11-3 6-12 (Sat-Sun & summer 11-mdnt)
Bar Meals L served all wk 12-2 D served all wk
6-9.30 Av main course £7.50 **Restaurant** L served
all wk 12-2 D served all wk 6-9.30 Av 3 course à
la carte fr £22.50 ⊕ WADWORTH 🍺 Wadworth 6X,
Henry's Original IPA, guest ales ♂ Stowford Press,
Thatchers Gold. 🍷 12 **Facilities** Children's menu Play
area Dogs allowed Garden Parking

MARSHFIELD

The Lord Nelson Inn ★★★ INN 🍷

1 & 2 High St SN14 8LP ☎ 01225 891820
e-mail: thelordnelsoninn.@btinternet.com
dir: *On A420 between Bristol & Chippenham. M4
Junct 19 Bath then travel along A46 towards railway
stations, Bath & Chippenham.*

Located in a village at the edge of the Cotswolds,
this 17th-century coaching inn is family run and
has a good reputation for its home-made food
and quality cask ales. There is a spacious bar,
candlelit restaurant, log fires in winter and a
patio for summer use. Dishes range from home-
made burger with hand cut chips, to collops of
monkfish with saffron and red pepper dressing,
and timbale of white and wild rice. There are
three en suite bedrooms available.

Open all day all wk noon-11 (Fri-Sun all day) **Bar
Meals** L served Mon-Sat 12-2, Sun 12-3 D served
Mon-Sat 6.30-9, Sun 6-8 booking required Av
main course £10.95 **Restaurant** L served Mon-Sat
12-2, Sun 12-3 D served Mon-Sat 6.30-9, Sun
6-8 booking required Av 3 course à la carte fr
£14.95 ⊕ ENTERPRISE INNS 🍺 Courage Best, Bath
Gem, 6X ♂ Stowford Press. 🍷 12 **Facilities** Children's
menu Play area Dogs allowed Garden **Rooms** 3

MEYSEY HAMPTON

The Masons Arms ♀

28 High St GL7 5JT
☎ 01285 850164 📄 01285 850164
dir: *6m E of Cirencester off A417, beside village green*

New landlords have taken over this 17th-century stone pub beside the green in a charming village on the southern edge of the Cotswolds near Cirencester. The hub of the community, expect to find a log fire in the big inglenook, straightforward pub food, and local Hooky and changing guest ales on tap in the convivial beamed bar. Worth noting if visiting the Cotswold Water Park nearby.

Open all wk **Bar Meals** L served all wk 12-3 D served all wk 3-6 **Restaurant** L served all wk 12-3 D served all wk 3-6 ⊕ FREE HOUSE ◀ Hook Norton Best, Butcombes, Theakstons, guest ales. ♀ 14 **Facilities** Children's menu Play area Dogs allowed Garden Parking

MINCHINHAMPTON

The Weighbridge Inn ♀

GL6 9AL ☎ 01453 832520 📄 01453 835903
e-mail: enquiries@2in1pub.co.uk
dir: *Between Nailsworth & Avening on B4014*

This 17th-century inn stands on the old London to Bristol packhorse trail. Inside is memorabilia from the old Longfords Mill, alongside rural artefacts and rustic furnishings. Outside, the patios and garden offer good views of the Cotswolds. Owner Howard Parker prides himself on the quality of the food, all cooked from scratch. Famous '2 in 1' pies, served straight from the oven on a wooden board, have been made here for years. The filling of your choice (such as pork, bacon and celery, or salmon in a creamy sauce) topped with cauliflower cheese and a pastry lid. The regular menu may list moules marinière, corned beef hash, salmon fishcakes with parsley and chive sauce, and almond and pear tart with Amaretto custard.

Open all day all wk noon-11 (Sun noon-10.30) Closed: 25 Dec & 10 days Jan **Bar Meals** L served all wk 12-9.30 booking required D served all wk 12-9.30 booking required Av main course £10 food served all day **Restaurant** L served all wk 12-9.30 booking required D served all wk 12-9.30 booking required food served all day ⊕ FREE HOUSE ◀ Wadworth 6X, Uley Old Spot, Laurie Lee Ò Wicked Witch, Westons Bounds Brand. ♀ 16 **Facilities** Children's menu Family room Dogs allowed Garden Parking

SHEEPSCOMBE

The Butchers Arms ♟

GL6 7RH ☎ 01452 812113 🖃 01452 814358

e-mail: mark@butchers-arms.co.uk

dir: 1.5m S of A46 (Cheltenham to Stroud road), N of Painswick

Set on the sunny side of Sheepscombe valley, this award-winning pub has a garden terrace with lovely views of beech-wooded slopes on all sides. Deer hunted by Henry VIII in his royal park used to hang in the bar - hence the pub's name. Light meals and salads are augmented by traditional favourites such as cottage pie, chef's turkey curry, tomato and mushroom risotto, fish and chips, and grilled steaks. Specials may include sea bass, scallops, pork belly, or local shoot pheasant. The 'Young Person's Menu' keeps children happy, or an adult-sized main course can be divided in two. An ever-changing specials board above the fireplace completes the choice.

Open all wk 11.30-2.30 6.30-11 (Sat 11.30-11.30 Sun noon-10.30) Bar Meals L served all wk 12-2.30 booking required D served Mon-Sat 6.30-9.30, Sun 6.30-9 booking required Av main course £9.50 Restaurant L served all wk 12-2.30 booking required D served Mon-Sat 6.30-9.30, Sun 6.30-9 booking required Av 3 course à la carte fr £17.50 ⊕ FREE HOUSE ◀ Otter Bitter, Goffs Jouster, Butcombe Gold, St Austell Tribute ♻ Westons Stowford Press, Westons Bottled Ciders. ♟ 10 Facilities Children's menu Dogs allowed Garden Parking

SOMERFORD KEYNES

The Bakers Arms ♟

GL7 6DN ☎ 01285 861298

dir: Exit A419 signed Cotswold Water Park. Cross B4696, 1m, follow signs for Keynes Park & Somerford Keynes

A beautiful chocolate box pub built from Cotswold stone, with low-beamed ceilings and inglenook fireplaces. Dating from the 15th century, the building was formerly the village bakery and stands in mature gardens ideal for al fresco dining. Discreet children's play areas and heated terraces add to its broad appeal. Somerford Keynes is in the Cotswold Water Park, and the man-made beach of Keynes Park is within easy walking distance, while the nearby Thames Path and Cotswold Way make the pub popular with walkers.

Open all day all wk 11-11 (Sun 12-10.30) Bar Meals L served Mon-Fri 12-2.30, Sat-Sun 12-9 D served Mon-Fri 6-9, Sat-Sun 12-9 Restaurant L served Mon-Fri 12-2.30, Sat-Sun 12-9 D served Mon-Fri 6-9, Sat-Sun 12-9 ⊕ ENTERPRISE INNS ◀ Courage Best, Butcombe Bitter, Stroud Budding. ♟ 8 Facilities Children's menu Play area Family room Dogs allowed Garden Parking

STONEHOUSE

The George Inn

Peter St, Frocester GL10 3TQ

☎ 01453 822302   📠 01453 791612

e-mail: info@georgeinn.co.uk

dir: *M5 junct 13, onto A419 at 1st rdbt 3rd exit
signed Eastington, left at next rdbt signed Frocester.
Approx 2m on right in village*

An award-winning 18th-century coaching inn,
unspoiled by juke box or fruit machine. Instead,
crackling log fires and a sunny courtyard
garden give the place all-year-round appeal.
The Cotswold Way and a network of leafy paths
and lanes are on the doorstep. Expect a warm
welcome, a selection of real ales including three
local brews, and good home-cooked food from
nearby suppliers. Tuck in to half a roast chicken,
or Frocester Fayre faggots with mash, peas and
gravy.

Open all day all wk 7.30am-mdnt **Bar Meals**
food served all day **Restaurant** food served all
day ⊕ FROCESTER BEER CO LTD ◀ Deuchars IPA,
Blacksheep, 3 guest ales. **Facilities** Children's menu
Play area Family room Dogs allowed Garden Parking

STROUD

The Ram Inn

South Woodchester GL5 5EL

☎ 01453 873329   📠 01453 873329

e-mail: raminnwoodchester@hotmail.co.uk

dir: *A46 from Stroud to Nailsworth, right after 2m
into South Woodchester, follow brown tourist signs*

From the plentiful seating on terrace of the
17th-century Cotswold stone Ram Inn, there
are splendid views over five valleys, although
proximity to the huge fireplace may prove more
appealing in winter. Rib-eye steak, at least two
fish dishes, home-made lasagne and Sunday
roasts can be expected, washed down by
regularly changing real ales such as Uley Old
Spot, Stroud Budding and Stroud Organic. The
Stroud Morris Men regularly perform.

Open all day all wk 11-11 **Bar Meals** L served
all wk 12-2 D served all wk 6-9 Av main course
£7.50 **Restaurant** L served all wk 12-2 D served
all wk 6-9 ⊕ FREE HOUSE ◀ Uley Old Spot,
Stroud Budding, Butcombe Bitter, Guests.
Facilities Children's menu Family room Dogs allowed
Garden Parking

STROUD

The Woolpack Inn ₹

Slad Rd, Slad GL6 7QA
☎ 01452 813429 🖷 01452 813429
e-mail: info@thewoolpackinn-slad.com
dir: *2m from Stroud, 8m from Gloucester*

The Woolpack is a friendly local, situated in the beautiful Slad Valley close to the Cotswold Way, an area immortalised by Laurie Lee in his book Cider with Rosie. Indeed, the author was a regular at the pub. Not surprisingly, the place is popular with walkers. Walking boots and wellies aren't frowned upon here, and children and dogs are made welcome. Honest, straightforward food is freshly prepared from the best local produce, all washed down with a pint of Uley bitter.

Open all day all wk noon-mdnt (Sun noon-11pm) **Bar Meals** L served Mon-Sat 12-2, Sun 12-3.30 booking required D served Tue-Sat 6.30-9 booking required Av main course £11.50 **Restaurant** L served Mon-Sat 12-2, Sun 12-3.30 booking required D served Tue-Sat 6.30-9 booking required Av 3 course à la carte fr £18 ⊕ FREE HOUSE ◀ Uley Pig's Ear, Old Spot, Uley Bitter, guest ale ♻ Old Rosie, Stowfords Press. ₹ 8 **Facilities** Children's menu Family room Dogs allowed Garden Parking

TETBURY

Gumstool Inn ₹

Calcot Manor GL8 8YJ
☎ 01666 890391 🖷 01666 890394
e-mail: reception@calcotmanor.co.uk
dir: *3m W of Tetbury*

The Gumstool Inn is part of Calcot Manor Hotel, set in 220 acres of Cotswold countryside. The hotel is a converted 14th-century stone farmhouse built by Cistercian monks, set around a courtyard. Typical starters from monthly menus include crisp goats' cheese parcel, roasted beetroot salad; or Cajun spiced calamari salad with chilli jam. Starters include warm Cornish crab and leek tart with rocket and frisée salad; crispy Asian duck noodle salad with Thai dressing; and grilled haloumi cheese, polenta and wood-roasted Mediterranean vegetables. Among the mains, roast pheasant with bacon, bread sauce and potato gratin; or Moroccan spiced lamb tagine with lemon, rose harissa and coriander.

Open all wk 11.30-2.30 5.30-11 **Bar Meals** L served all wk 11.30-2 booking required D served all wk 7-9.30 booking required Av main course £8 **Restaurant** L served all wk 12-2 booking required D served all wk 7-9.30 booking required Av 3 course à la carte fr £35 ⊕ FREE HOUSE ◀ Atlantics Sharp's IPA, Matthews Bob Wool, Wickwar Cotswold Way, Butcombe Blonde. ₹ 12 **Facilities** Children's menu Play area Family room Garden Parking

UPPER ODDINGTON

The Horse and Groom Inn ♥

GL56 0XH ☎ 01451 830584
e-mail: info@horseandgroom.uk.com
dir: 1.5m S of Stow-on-the-Wold, just off A436

A 16th-century stone-built inn, the Horse &
Groom is located in a Cotswold conservation
village just a mile and a half from Stow-on-the-
Wold. It is immaculately kept, with pale polished
flagstone floors, beams, stripped stone walls and
log fires in the inglenook. In fine weather you can
enjoy the terrace and gardens, with grape vines
bounded by dry stone walls. A great selection
of cask ales is offered from local breweries and
the wine list is ever growing. Menus comprise
regional food sourced from as close to the kitchen
door as possible. Bread, for example, is made
daily from Cotswold Flour Millers flour. Dishes
might include pan-fried breast of Adlestrop
pheasant with thyme and garlic roasted sweet
potatoes and orange glazed chicory, or hand-cut,
finest 21-day aged Hereford beef steaks served
with a choice of sauces. Fish is featured on the
daily blackboard menu.

Open all wk noon-3 5.30-11 (Sun 6.30-10.30) Bar
Meals L served all wk 12-2 D served Mon-Sat 6.30-9,
Sun 7-9 Restaurant L served all wk 12-2 D served
Mon-Sat 6.30-9, Sun 7-9 ⊕ FREE HOUSE ◀ Wye
Valley Butty Bach, Wye Valley Best, Hereford Pale
Ale, Wickwar Bob Cotswold Premium Lager. ♥ 25
Facilities Children's menu Play area Garden Parking

WOODCHESTER

The Old Fleece ♥

Bath Rd, Rooksmoor GL5 5NB
☎ 01453 872582
e-mail: pheasantpluckers2003@yahoo.co.uk
dir: 2m S of Stroud on A46

Set amid beautiful countryside with miles of
footpaths to explore, this delightful coaching
inn was built in the 18th century from Cotswold
stone and has a traditional stone roof. From
the Old Fleece, you can walk to Rodborough,
Minchinhampton and Selsley Commons, or go
one step further and connect eventually with
the scenic Cotswold Way long distance trail. The
beautifully refurbished interior includes wooden
floors, wood panelling and exposed stone, and the
bar serves well kept Greene King Abbot Ale and
Otter Bitter. Predominantly French chefs offer a
comprehensive menu of British and continental
dishes, ranging from classics such as Old Spot
sausage and mash with onion gravy to the likes
of confit duck leg with hoi sin noodles, whole sea
bream with braised fennel, or pork loin steak with
apple and Calvados purée.

Open all day all wk 11-11 Closed: 25 Dec Bar
Meals L served all wk 11-2.45 D served all wk
5.30-10 Restaurant L served all wk 11-2.45 D
served all wk 5.30-10 ⊕ PHEASANT PLUCKERS
LTD ◀ Bass, Greene King Abbot Ale, Otter
Bitter. ♥ 12 Facilities Children's menu Dogs allowed
Garden Parking

MELLOR

The Oddfellows Arms ☙

73 Moor End Rd SK6 5PT ☎ 0161 449 7826
dir: *Telephone for details*

A friendly welcome can be expected in this c1650 building, which has had a liquor licence since 1805. It changed its name from 'The Angel Inn' in 1860 to accommodate the Oddfellows Society, a forerunner of the Trades Unions. There are always plenty of real ales to choose from. Recent change of hands.

Open all wk 4-late (Thu-Fri 12-late Sat 11-late Sun 11-6) Closed: 25-26 Dec, 31 Dec-1 Jan **Bar Meals** L served Thu-Fri 12-6, Sat-Sun 11-6 D served Thu-Fri 12-6, Sat-Sun 11-6 **Restaurant** L served Thu-Fri 12-2.30, Sun 12-5 booking required D served Wed-Sat 5.30-9 booking required ⊕ ENTERPRISE INNS PLC ◀ Adnams Southwold, Marston's Pedigree, Bitter, Fennicks Arizona, guest. ☙ 8 **Facilities** Children's menu Dogs allowed Garden Parking

STOCKPORT

The Arden Arms ☙

23 Millgate SK1 2LX ☎ 0161 480 2185
e-mail: steve@ardenarms.com
dir: *M60 junct 27 to town centre. Across mini-rdbt, at lights turn left. Pub on right of next rdbt behind Asda*

Last modernised in 1908, this Victorian coaching inn close to Stockport's historic market place ranks high among the country's timeless gems. Come to see the classic unspoilt layout, the original tiled floors and panelling, and order pint of Robinson's from the traditional curved bar, quaffing it by the coal fire in the tiny snug bar. Quality lunches include hot sandwiches, tempting ciabattas, gammon, egg and chips or grilled halloumi and vegetable kebabs, and banana and toffee pudding. There's a sheltered courtyard for summer drinking.

Open all wk noon-11.45 Closed: 25-26 Dec, 1 Jan **Bar Meals** L served Mon-Fri 12-2.30, Sat-Sun 12-4 Av main course £8.95 ⊕ ROBINSONS ◀ Unicorn Bitter, Hatters Mild, Robin Bitter, Double Hop, seasonal ales. ☙ 8 **Facilities** Children's menu Dogs allowed Garden **Notes** no credit cards

ANDOVER

Wyke Down Country Pub & Restaurant 🍷

Wyke Down, Picket Piece SP11 6LX
☎ 01264 352048 📄 01264 324661
e-mail: info@wykedown.co.uk
dir: *3m from Andover town centre/A303. Follow signs for Wyke Down Caravan Park*

Combining a pub/restaurant with a caravan park and golf driving range, this establishment is a diversified farm on the outskirts of Andover. It still raises beef cattle, but the pub started in a barn 25 years ago and the restaurant was built 11 years ago. Dishes range from lasagne, curry and Cajun chicken supreme on the bar menu to restaurant fare such as maple roasted pork chop, nut loaf, or steaks from the griddle.

Open all wk noon-3 6-11 Closed: 25 Dec-2 Jan
Bar Meals L served all wk 12-2 booking required
D served all wk 6-9 booking required Restaurant L served all wk 12-2 booking required D served all wk 6-9 booking required ⊕ FREE HOUSE ◀ Guinness, Timothy Taylor, real ale. 🍷 6 Facilities Children's menu Play area Garden Parking

BUCKLERS HARD

The Master Builders House Hotel ★★★ HL 🏵 🍷

SO42 7XB
☎ 01590 616253 📄 01590 616297
e-mail: enquiries@themasterbuilders.co.uk
dir: *From M27 junct 2 follow signs to Beaulieu. Left onto B3056. Left to Bucklers Hard. Hotel 2m on left*

Once home to master shipbuilder Henry Adams, this idyllic 18th-century inn is situated on the banks of the River Beaulieu, in the historic ship-building village of Bucklers Hard. Ducks, boats and river walks are all on the doorstep. Bar food includes grilled Lymington mackerel, tomato and red onion salad; Old Spot sausages, creamed potato and roast onions; and linguine with New Forest mushrooms, garlic and parsley, alongside a choice of real ales, particularly Ringwood, decent wines and Stowford Press cider.

Open all day all wk 11-11 (Sun 11-10.30) Bar Meals Av main course £9.50 food served all day
Restaurant L served Mon-Sat 12-2.30, Sun 12-3 booking required D served all wk 7-9.30 booking required Fixed menu price fr £15 Av 3 course à la carte fr £25 ⊕ HILLBROOKE HOTELS ◀ Ringwood Best, Ringwood Thumper ⚬ Stowford Press. 🍷 8
Facilities Children's menu Dogs allowed Garden Parking Rooms 25

CHALTON

The Red Lion ☂

PO8 0BG

☎ 023 9259 2246 📠 023 9259 6915

e-mail: redlionchalton@fullers.co.uk

dir: *Just off A3 between Horndean & Petersfield. Follow signs for Chalton*

Believed to be Hampshire's oldest pub, The Red Lion was built in 1147 as a workshop and residence for the craftsmen working on St Michael's church across the road. Constructed from wood, white daub and thatch, the ancient building blends effortlessly into the hills and trees of the South Downs, and original features inside include an inglenook fireplace. There are spectacular views from the large garden and modern dining room. The pub has a good reputation locally for the quality of its food. You can choose from the daily changing menu of freshly cooked dishes, which relies heavily on locally sourced produce, or the popular snack menu of traditional pub fare, all washed down with a pint of real ale or cider.

Open all day all wk 11.30-11 (Sun 11.45-10.30) **Bar Meals** food served all day **Restaurant** food served all day ⊕ FULLER, SMITH & TURNER PLC ◀ Fuller's, HSB, London Pride, Discovery, ESB, seasonal ales ♻ Heart of Hampshire, Boxing Dog, Sweet Russett. ☂ 20 **Facilities** Children's menu Family room Dogs allowed Garden Parking

CHARTER ALLEY

The White Hart Inn ☂

White Hart Ln RG26 5QA

☎ 01256 850048 📠 01256 850524

e-mail: enquiries@whitehartcharteralley.com

dir: *From M3 junct 6 take A339 towards Newbury. Turn right to Ramsdell. Right at church, then 1st left into White Hart Lane*

On the outskirts of the village overlooking open farmland and woods, this pub draws everyone from cyclists and walkers to real ale enthusiasts. Dating from 1818, it originally refreshed local woodsmen and coach drivers visiting the farrier next door. Today's more modern menu is likely to include confit of duck leg with orange and tarragon sauce; venison steak with red wine and redcurrant sauce; or vegetarian stir-fry. Look to the blackboard for specials and fish dishes.

Open all wk noon-2.30 7-11 (Sun 7-10.30) Closed: 25-26 Dec, 1 Jan **Bar Meals** L served all wk 12-2 D served Tue-Sat 7-9 Av main course £10 **Restaurant** L served Tue-Sun 12-2 booking required D served Tue-Sat 7-9 booking required ⊕ FREE HOUSE ◀ West Berkshire Mild, Palmers IPA, Triple FFF Alton Pride, Stonehenge Great Bustard, Loddon Ferryman's Gold. ☂ 7 **Facilities** Children's menu Family room Dogs allowed Garden Parking

CRAWLEY

The Fox and Hounds ♟

SO21 2PR

☎ 01962 776006 📠 01962 776006
e-mail: liamlewisairey@aol.com
dir: *A34 onto A272 then 1st right into Crawley*

Just north west of Winchester, at the heart of a peaceful Hampshire village, this mock Tudor traditional inn enjoys a burgeoning reputation for simple well-cooked food. Restored to former glories, it features beamed rooms warmed by log fires that create a welcoming, lived-in atmosphere. Typical dishes are roast beetroot salad with goats' cheese; smokey chicken with bacon leek and cream sauce; home-made beef lasagne; and sticky toffee pudding.

Open all wk 11-3 6-mdnt **Bar Meals** L served all wk 12-2 booking required **Restaurant** L served all wk 12-2 booking required D served all wk 6.30-9.30 booking required ⊕ ENTERPRISE INN 🍺 Wadworth 6X, Ringwood Best, Ringwood 49, Bombardier. ♟ 36 **Facilities** Children's menu Play area Garden Parking

EASTON

The Chestnut Horse ♟

SO21 1EG

☎ 01962 779257 📠 01962 779037
dir: *From M3 junct 9 take A33 towards Basingstoke, then B3047. Take 2nd right, then 1st left*

This 16th-century pub is located in the pretty village of Easton. Old tankards and teapots hang from the low-beamed ceilings in the two bar areas, where a large open fire is the central focus through the winter months. A good-value set price menu is offered Monday to Saturday lunchtime (12-2pm) or Monday to Thursday early evening (6-7.30pm). This might include fish and chips, local pheasant casserole or chilli con carne. Typical main menu dishes are baked trout fillet with chestnut and herb crust, or slow braised shoulder of lamb with butternut mash. A vegetarian alternative could be tagliatelle with Alresford watercress and gruyère cheese sauce.

Open all wk noon-3.30 5.30-11 (Sun eve closed winter) **Bar Meals** L served all wk 12-2.30 booking required D served Mon-Sat 6-9.30 booking required Av main course £12 **Restaurant** L served all wk 12-2 booking required D served Mon-Sat 6-9.30 booking required Fixed menu price fr £12 Av 3 course à la carte fr £24 ⊕ HALL & WOODHOUSE 🍺 Chestnut Horse Special, Badger First Gold, Tanglefoot Ö Stowford Press. ♟ 9 **Facilities** Children's menu Dogs allowed Garden Parking

EAST TYTHERLEY

The Star Inn
Tytherley ★★★★ INN ◉◉ ♈

SO51 0LW ☎ 01794 340225
e-mail: info@starinn.co.uk
dir: *5m N of Romsey off A3057, left for Dunbridge on B3084. Left for Awbridge & Kents Oak. Through Lockerley then 1m*

The 16th-century Star Inn stands overlooking the village cricket green in the smallest village in the Test Valley. You'll find Hidden Brewery beers and other guest ales behind the bar, plus an extensive international wine list. Dine where you like, in the bar, at dark-wood tables in the main dining room, or outside on the patio in summer. Lunchtime brings a variety of platters, sandwiches, and a good value two-course menu. The evening menu might offer braised belly pork with sage polenta and celeriac purée. There's a good choice at Sunday lunch, too, including traditional roasts. Children of well behaved parents are welcome.

Open 11-2.30 6-10 Closed: Sun eve & Mon (ex BH) **Bar Meals** L served Tue-Sun 12-2 booking required D served Tue-Fri 7-9 booking required Av main course £8.50 **Restaurant** L served Tue-Sun 12-2 booking required D served Tue-Sat 7-9 booking required Av 3 course à la carte fr £20 ⊕ FREE HOUSE ◄ Hidden Quest, Hidden Pint, guest ales ♂ Thatchers Gold. ♈ 8 **Facilities** Children's menu Dogs allowed Garden Parking **Rooms** 3

EVERSLEY

The Golden Pot ♈

Reading Rd RG27 0NB ☎ 0118 973 2104
e-mail: jcalder@goldenpot.co.uk
web: www.golden-pot.co.uk
dir: *Between Reading & Camberley on B3272 approx 0.25m from Eversley cricket ground*

Dating back to the 1700s, this well-established hostelry has recently converted to a free house. Expect three pumps rotating ales by Andwell Brewing Company, Loddon Brewery and Hogs Back among others. A warming fire connects the bar and restaurant, while the Snug and Vineyard are comfortable outside areas surrounded by colourful tubs and hanging baskets for summer relaxation. All food is home-made, offering traditional and modern choices, and prepared on the premises; children are not only welcome but also specially catered for.

Open all wk 11.30-3 5.30-10.30 Closed: 25-26 & 31 Dec, 1 Jan, (Sun eve) **Bar Meals** L served all wk 12-2.45 booking required D served Mon-Sat 6-9 booking required **Restaurant** L served all wk 12-2.45 booking required D served Mon-Sat 6-9 booking required ⊕ FREE HOUSE ◄ Andwell Brewery, Loddon Brewery, West Berkshire, Hogs Back Brewery, Shepherd Neame. ♈ 8 **Facilities** Children's menu Dogs allowed Garden Parking

FORDINGBRIDGE

The Augustus John 🍷

116 Station Rd SP6 1DG ☎ 01425 652098
e-mail: enquiries@augustusjohn.com
dir: *12m S of Salisbury on A338 towards Ringwood*

In keeping with its name, this pub and restaurant has a collection of paintings by Augustus John, who lived in the village. Set on the edge of the New Forest, it's a friendly, welcoming refuge offering a good selection of drinks including Ringwood Best Bitter and Wychwood cider. The extensive menu includes Thai food, fresh fish and hearty meals such as creamy garlic mushrooms followed by roast lamb with a red wine sauce.

Open all wk 10.30-3 5-11.30 (wknds open until 1.30am) Bar Meals Av main course £5 food served all day Restaurant Fixed menu price fr £8.95 Av 3 course à la carte fr £22 food served all day ⊕ MARSTONS ◄ Ringwood Best, Pedigree, Porter, Fortyniner Ŏ Wychwood. 🍷 8 Facilities Children's menu Dogs allowed Garden Parking

HANNINGTON

The Vine at Hannington 🍷

RG26 5TX
☎ 01635 298525 📄 01635 298027
e-mail: info@thevineathannington.co.uk
web: www.thevineathannington.co.uk
dir: *Hannington signed from A339 between Basingstoke & Newbury*

A traditional village pub high up on the beautiful Hampshire Downs. Visitors can be assured of friendly service and good home-made pub food. Seasonal menus of home-cooked, affordable dishes might suggest starting with local watercress and spinach soup with focaccia bread; or maybe a share of a generous plate of antipasti. Then follows a selection of mains; home-baked ham with egg and chips; free-range Hampshire pork loin with cider and apple sauce and stuffing; or spinach and Parmesan risotto. Turn your attention to the specials board for local venison pie with juniper, orange and honey; or grilled skate wing with black butter and capers; There are ploughman's and sandwiches, too.

Open 12-3 6-11 (Sat-Sun all day) Closed: 25 Dec, Sun eve & Mon in Winter Bar Meals L served Mon-Fri 12-2, Sat-Sun 12-2.30 D served all wk 6-9 Av main course £9 Restaurant L served Mon-Fri 12-2, Sat-Sun 12-2.30 D served all wk 6-9 Av 3 course à la carte fr £20 ◄ Black Sheep, Bombardier. 🍷 10 Facilities Children's menu Play area Family room Dogs allowed Garden Parking

HIGHCLERE

The Furze Bush Inn ★★★ INN 🍷

Hatt Common, East Woodhay RG20 0NQ
☎ 01635 253228 📠 01635 254883
e-mail: info@furzebushinn.co.uk
web: www.furzebushinn.co.uk
dir: *Please telephone for directions*

Handy for Highclere Castle, the M4, Newbury Races and hiking the Berkshire Downs, the Furze Bush lies tucked down lanes in a glorious rural location. Expect a peaceful night in one of the ten, well-appointed bedrooms, and a good range of pub food. In the bar, order favourites like chicken pie and ham, egg and chips, or book a restaurant table for game casserole, neck of lamb and rosemary sauce, and treacle tart and custard. There is a large front beer garden.

Open all day all wk **Bar Meals** L served Mon-Fri 12-2.30, Sat-Sun & BH all day D served Mon-Sat 6-10, Sun 6-9 Av main course £10 **Restaurant** L served Mon-Fri 12-2.30, Sat-Sun & BH 12-6 booking required D served Mon-Sat 6-10, Sun 6-9 booking required Fixed menu price fr £15 Av 3 course à la carte fr £22 ⊕ FREE HOUSE ◀ Flowers IPA, guest ale. 🍷 8 **Facilities** Children's menu Play area Dogs allowed Garden Parking **Rooms** 10

HURSLEY

The Dolphin Inn 🍷

SO21 2JY ☎ 01962 775209
e-mail: mandy@dolphininn.demon.co.uk
web: www.dolphinhursley.co.uk
dir: *Please telephone for directions*

Reputedly built from the timbers of an early HMS Dolphin, hence the pub name, the roadside village inn dates from the 16th century and was once a thriving coaching inn. Follow a stroll through nearby Farley Mount Country Park with a traditional pub lunch in the mature garden or in the beamed bars – ham, egg and chips, steak and Guinness pie, sausage and onion baguette, or a healthy tuna Niçoise. Look out for the local butcher's meat draw in Fridays nights.

Open all wk Mon-Thu 11-3 6-11 (Fri-Sat 11-11 Sun 12-10.30) **Bar Meals** L served Mon-Thu 12-2, Fri-Sat 12-2.30, Sun 12-8.30 booking required D served Mon-Thu 6-9, Fri-Sat 6.30-9.30, Sun 12-8.30 booking required Av main course £8 **Restaurant** Fixed menu price fr £15 ⊕ ENTERPRISE ◀ Ringwood, Summer Lightning, HBB, HSB ♻ Thatchers dry, Thatchers Premium. 🍷 23 **Facilities** Children's menu Play area Family room Dogs allowed Garden Parking

LINWOOD

The High Corner Inn ♥

BH24 3QY ☎ 01425 473973
e-mail: highcorner@wadworth.co.uk
dir: *From A338 (Ringwood to Salisbury road) follow brown tourist signs into forest. Pass Red Shoot Inn, after 1m turn down gravel track at Green High Corner Inn*

This much extended and modernised, early 18th-century inn is set in seven beautiful acres of woodland deep in the heart of the New Forest. A quiet hideaway in winter, mobbed in summer, it is a popular retreat for families with its numerous bar-free rooms, an outdoor adventure playground and miles of wildlife-rich forest and heathland walks and cycle trails. The beamy bars, replete with roaring winter log fires, and the lovely forest garden are very agreeable settings for sampling an extensive range of home-cooked meals and bar snacks; daily specials are shown on chalkboards and a carvery is available on Sunday. Leave room for a nursery-style pudding, perhaps a traditional crumble. Dogs and horses are welcome.

Open all wk 11-3 6-11 (3-6 winter) **Bar Meals** L served all wk 12-2.30 D served all wk 6-9 **Restaurant** L served all wk 12-2.30 D served all wk 6-9 ⊕ WADWORTH ◀ Wadworth 6X, Horizon, IPA, Red Shoot New Forest Gold, Toms Tipple Ŏ Westons, Thatchers Gold. ♥ 14 **Facilities** Children's menu Play area Dogs allowed Garden Parking

LYMINGTON

Mayflower Inn ♥

Kings Saltern Rd SO41 3QD
☎ 01590 672160   📄 01590 679180
e-mail: info@themayflower.uk.com
dir: *A337 towards New Milton, left at rdbt by White Hart, left to Rookes Ln, right at mini-rdbt, pub 0.75m*

A favourite with yachtsmen and dog walkers, this solidly built mock-Tudor inn overlooks the Lymington River, with glorious views to the Isle of Wight. There's a magnificent garden with glorious sun terraces, a purpose-built play area for children and an on-going summer barbecue in fine weather. Light bites and big bowl salads are backed up with heartier choices like traditional lamb and rosemary hotpot, pan-fried liver and bacon, and beer battered fish of the day.

Open all day all wk **Bar Meals** Av main course £8.50 food served all day **Restaurant** food served all day ⊕ ENTERPRISE INNS ◀ Ringwood Best, Fuller's London Pride, 6X, Goddards Fuggle Dee Dum. ♥ 8 **Facilities** Children's menu Play area Dogs allowed Garden Parking

NEW ALRESFORD

The Woolpack Inn ☼

Totford, Nr Northington SO24 9TJ
☎ 0845 293 8066 ▧ 0845 293 8055
e-mail: info@thewoolpackinn.co.uk
dir: *M3 south towards A27, take A339 to Alton and first right to B3046 Candovers & Alresford*

Approach this old drovers' inn at night and just as you prepare to descend a steep hill you'll see its welcoming lights down below. The inn changed hands in 2008 and the new owners have really smartened it up, creating a sense of calm modernity while still retaining a traditional feel. Its new seasonal menus offers, in the traditional bar area, bacon butty on farmhouse bread, and Heineken-battered fish and chips; and in the dining room, warm smoked trout and crispy bacon salad; pot-roast Candover Park partridge; and pan-roasted salmon with bacon, pea and potato broth.

Open 11.30am-3 6-close (Sat open all day) Closed: Sun eve in winter **Bar Meals** L served all wk 11.30-3 D served Mon-Sat 6-close Av main course £9.50 **Restaurant** L served all wk 11.30-3 D served Mon-Sat 6-close Av 3 course à la carte fr £20 ⊕ FREE HOUSE ◀ Palmers IPA, Palmers Copper, Moondance Triple FFF ♂ Thatchers Gold. ☼ 9 **Facilities** Children's menu Play area Dogs allowed Garden Parking

NORTH WALTHAM

The Fox ☼

RG25 2BE ☎ 01256 397288
e-mail: info@thefox.org
dir: *From M3 junct 7 take A30 towards Winchester. Village signed on right. Take 2nd signed road*

A peaceful village pub down a quiet country lane with splendid views across fields and farmland - an ideal stop off the M3. Built as three farm cottages in 1624, the Fox can offer families three large level gardens, one of which is a dedicated children's play area. The husband and wife team of Rob and Izzy MacKenzie split their responsibilities between bar and kitchen. Rob ensures that the beers are kept in top condition, while Izzy produces mouthwatering traditional dishes using seasonal produce; she prepares everything by hand from the mayonnaise upwards. A dedicated bar menu proffers the likes of ham, double egg and chips; and cottage pie. The monthly-changing restaurant choice may include Hampshire venison and slow roasted pork belly with grain mustard mash.

Open all day all wk 11-11 **Bar Meals** L served all wk 12-2.30 D served all wk 6-9.30 **Restaurant** L served all wk 12-2.30 booking required D served all wk 6-9.30 booking required ⊕ PUNCH TAVERNS ◀ Ringwood Best Bitter, Adnams Broadside, Brakspear, guest ale ♂ Aspall. ☼ 17 **Facilities** Children's menu Play area Dogs allowed Garden Parking

SILCHESTER

Calleva Arms ▼

Little London Rd, The Common RG7 2PH
☎ 0118 970 0305
dir: A340 from Basingstoke, signed Silchester. M4 junct 11, 20 mins signed Mortimer then Silchester

Standing opposite the village green, the pub is popular with walkers, cyclists, and visitors to the nearby Roman town of Calleva Atrebatum with the remains of its town walls and amphitheatre. A pleasant, airy conservatory added to the 19th-century building overlooks a large enclosed garden. Lunchtime favourites include steaks, bangers and mash and special salads. A typical dinner selection could start with Thai spiced crab cakes with mango salsa or Indian, nacho or antipasti sharing platters; followed by aromatic half duck with hoi sin sauce; and chef's fruit crumble served with custard.

Open all wk 11-3 5.30-11.30 (Sat 11-11.30 Sun noon-11) **Bar Meals** L served all week 12-2 D served all wk 6.30-9 **Restaurant** L served all wk 12-2 booking required D served all wk 6.30-9 booking required ⊕ FULLER, SMITH & TURNER ◀ London Pride, HSB, Guinness, Butser Bitter. ▼ 8 **Facilities** Children's menu Dogs allowed Garden Parking

UPPER FROYLE

The Hen & Chicken Inn ▼

GU34 4JH ☎ 01420 22115
e-mail: bookings@henandchicken.co.uk
dir: 2m from Alton, on A31 next to petrol station

Highwayman Dick Turpin is said to have hidden upstairs in this 18th-century coaching inn. Today it retains a traditional atmosphere thanks to large open fires, wood panelling and beams - but the post boxes above the inglenook remain empty. Food ranges from snacks to meals such as home-made linguine niçoise with a poached quail egg, followed by pan-fried calves' liver with bubble and squeak and red wine sauce; and then spotted dick with custard.

Open all wk 11.45-3 5.30-close (Sat-Sun all day) **Bar Meals** L served Mon-Sat 12-2.30, Sun 12-7 booking required D served Mon-Thu 6-9, Fri-Sat 6-9.30, Sun 12-7 booking required **Restaurant** L served Mon-Sat 12-2.30, Sun 12-7 booking required D served Mon-Thu 6-9, Fri-Sat 6-9.30, Sun 12-7 booking required ⊕ HALL & WOODHOUSE ◀ Badger Best, Tanglefoot, King, Barnes Sussex Ale ♂ Stowford Press. ▼ 8 **Facilities** Children's menu Play area Dogs allowed Garden Parking

WICKHAM

Greens Restaurant & Pub 🍷

The Square PO17 5JQ ☎ 01329 833197
e-mail: DuckworthGreens@aol.com
dir: *2m from M27, on corner of historic Wickham Square. 3m from Fareham*

The enduring popularity of Greens, on a corner of Wickham's picturesque square, is entirely down to the standards set by Frank and Carol Duckworth, who have run it for 25 years. Drinkers will find award-winning real ales from nearby Droxford, while front-of-house staff are trained in guest care ensure a warm and welcoming reception for diners. Modern European cooking may offer Rosary goats' cheese salad with walnut and raspberry dressing; braised beef with red wine and chorizo with basil mash; and spiced apricot bread and butter pudding.

Open 10-3 6-11 (Sun & BH noon-4) Closed: Sun eve & Mon **Bar Meals** L served Tue-Sat 12-2.30, Sun 12-3 booking required D served Tue-Sat 6.30-9.30 booking required **Restaurant** L served Tue-Sat 12-2.30, Sun 12-3 booking required D served Tue-Sat 6.30-9.30 booking required Fixed menu price fr £9.95 Av 3 course à la carte fr £20 FREE HOUSE Hopback Summer Lightning, Youngs Special, Guinness, Timothy Taylor, Local ales. 🍷 10 **Facilities** Children's menu Garden Parking

WINCHESTER

The Bell Inn 🍷

83 St Cross Rd SO23 9RE ☎ 01962 865284
e-mail: the_bellinn@btconnect.com
dir: *M3 junct 11, follow B rd into Winchester for approx 1m. Pub on right*

Edge of town local that's worth noting as it stands close to the 12th-century St Cross Hospital, with its fine Norman church, and glorious walks through the River Itchen water meadows to Winchester College and the city centre. Very much a community local, with Greene King ales and good-value food served in the main bar and the pine-furnished lounge, plus a warm welcome to families and dogs. Head for the sunny walled garden on warm summer days.

Open all day all wk 11-11 (Fri-Sat 11am-mdnt Sun noon-10.30) **Bar Meals** L served all wk 12-2 booking required D served all wk 6.30-9 booking required Av main course £8 GREENE KING IPA, 2 guest ales Stowford Press. 🍷 8 **Facilities** Children's menu Play area Dogs allowed Garden Parking

ASTON CREWS

The Penny Farthing Inn ♟

HR9 7LW

☎ 01989 750366   🖹 01989 750366

e-mail: info@pennyfarthinginn.co.uk

dir: *5m E of Ross-on-Wye*

This whitewashed 17th-century blacksmith's shop and coaching inn is located high above the River Wye valley. From its large, sloping garden you can take in views of the Malvern Hills, the Black Hills and the Forest of Dean. Inside are lots of nooks and crannies with oak beams, antiques, saddlery and cheerful log fires. At least two real ales and local cider are guaranteed to be on tap, and the wine list focuses on lesser known wineries to bring quality at a reasonable price. The same objective applies to the menu, which capitalises on the wealth of local vegetable and fruit growers' produce, and some of the best meat in the country. The lunchtime bar menu ranges from sandwiches, baguettes and jacket potatoes, to the pub's pie of the week, and chef's home-made curry. Main courses in the restaurant are likely to feature local lamb and renowned Hereford beef.

Open 12-3 6-11 Closed: Mon in winter **Bar Meals** food served all day **Restaurant** food served all day ◖ John Smith's, Black Sheep, Spitfire ♂ Westons Stowford Press. ♟ 7 **Facilities** Children's menu Dogs allowed Garden Parking

CANON PYON

The Nags Head Inn

HR4 8NY ☎ 01432 830252

dir: *Telephone for directions*

More than four hundred years old, with flagstone floors, open fires and exposed beams to prove it. A comprehensive menu might entice you into starting with slices of smoked salmon drizzled with brandy, lemon and cracked pepper, then to follow with medallions of lamb in a sticky Cumberland sauce, breast of Gressingham duck in a rich morello cherry sauce, or butterflied sea bass on sautéed strips of carrot and chopped coriander. Vegetarian options include stuffed peppers and tagliatelle. Curry nights and Sunday carvery. The large garden features a children's adventure playground.

Open all wk Mon-Thu 3-12.30 (Fri-Sun 3-mdnt) **Bar Meals** L served Mon-Fri 4-7, Sat-Sun 12-7 D served Mon- Fri 4-7, Sat-Sun 12-7 **Restaurant** L served Mon-Fri 4-7, Sat-Sun 12-7 D served Mon-Fri 4-7, Sat-Sun 12-7 ⊕ FREE HOUSE ◖ Fuller's London Pride, Boddingtons, Flowers, Nags Ale ♂ Stowford Press. **Facilities** Children's menu Play area Dogs allowed Garden Parking

HAMPTON BISHOP

The Bunch of Carrots ♟

HR1 4JR ☎ 01432 870237 📄 01432 870237
e-mail: bunchofcarrots@buccaneer.co.uk
dir: *From Hereford take A4103, A438, then B4224*

The name has nothing to do with crunchy orange vegetables - it comes from a rock formation in the River Wye, which runs alongside this friendly pub. Inside, expect real fires, old beams and flagstones. There is an extensive menu plus a daily specials board, a carvery, salad buffet, and simple bar snacks. Real ale aficionados should certainly sample the local organic beer, or enjoy a pint of Wye Valley Bitter or Black Bull, plus Westons real cider is available.

Open all wk **Bar Meals** L served Mon-Fri 12-2.30, Sat-Sun all day D served Mon-Fri 5.30-9, Sat-Sun all day **Restaurant** L served Mon-Fri 12-2.30, Sat-Sun all day booking required D served Mon-Fri 5.30-9, Sat-Sun all day booking required ⊕ FREE HOUSE ◀ Directors, Wye Valley Bitter, Black Bull Bitter, Organic Bitter ♂ Westons Stowford Press. ♟ 11 **Facilities** Children's menu Play area Dogs allowed Garden Parking

MADLEY

The Comet Inn ♟

Stoney St HR2 9NJ ☎ 01981 250600
e-mail: thecometinn-madley@hotmail.co.uk
dir: *6m from Hereford on B4352*

Originally three cottages, this black and white 19th-century inn occupies a prominent corner position and is set in two and a half acres. Inside it retains many original features and a roaring open fire. Expect simple, hearty pub food ranging from baguettes and jacket potatoes to comforting options such as steak and ale pie, shank of lamb, grilled gammon, chicken curry, cod in crispy batter, mushroom stroganoff, and a variety of steaks.

Open all wk 12-3 6-11 (Fri-Sun all day) **Bar Meals** Av main course £4.95 food served all day **Restaurant** Fixed menu price fr £9.95 food served all day ⊕ FREE HOUSE ◀ Wye Valley Bitter ♂ Stowford Press. ♟ 6 **Facilities** Children's menu Play area Garden Parking

ORLETON

The Boot Inn

SY8 4HN ☎ 01568 780228 🖷 01568 780228
e-mail: traceytheboot65@live.co.uk
web: www.thebootinnorleton.co.uk
dir: *Follow A49 S from Ludlow (approx 7m) to B4362 (Woofferton), 1.5m off B4362 turn left. Inn in village centre*

A black and white half timbered village inn, The Boot dates from the 16th century, and in winter a blazing fire in the inglenook warms the bar. You will be welcomed with excellent service, a good quality English menu with locally sourced produce and a fine range of cask ales. The wine list has been chosen to compliment the menu and to suit all pockets. Recent change of ownership.

Open all wk 12-3 5-11 (Sat-Sun noon-11) **Bar Meals** L served all wk 12-3 D served all wk 6-9 Av main course £10 **Restaurant** L served all wk 12-3 D served all wk 6-9 ⊕ VILLAGE GREEN INNS LTD ◀ Hobsons Best, Local Real Ales, Woods, Wye Valley ♂ Stowford Press. **Facilities** Children's menu Play area Dogs allowed Garden Parking

ST OWENS CROSS

The New Inn ♟

HR2 8LQ ☎ 01989 730274 🖷 01989 730557
e-mail: info@newinn.biz
web: www.newinn.biz
dir: *Off A4137 W of Ross-on-Wye*

This delightful 16th-century inn has been totally refurbished, preserving characterful features such as exposed beams and woodwork, creating a cosy and traditional backdrop for a drink, a quick snack or a leisurely meal. The spacious beer garden overlooks rolling Herefordshire countryside, and family-friendly outdoor games include giant versions of Jenga and Connect Four. The ever-changing menus reveal a keen sense of the seasons and a commitment to sourcing excellent local ingredients. Creamy garlic mushrooms on toasted baguette could be followed by steak, ale and mushroom pie made with Herefordshire beef; or shank of local lamb with red wine sauce and champ. An irresistible list of traditional puddings takes in fruit crumble with granola topping and home-made ice cream.

Open all day all wk 11-11 **Bar Meals** L served all wk from 12 D served all wk from 12 Av main course £8.75 food served all day **Restaurant** L served all wk from 12 D served all wk from 12 Av 3 course à la carte fr £20 food served all day ⊕ MARSTONS ♟ 8 **Facilities** Children's menu Play area Dogs allowed Garden Parking

WALFORD

The Mill Race ▼

HR9 5QS ☎ 01989 562891
e-mail: enquiries@millrace.info
dir: *From Ross-on-Wye take B4234 to Walford. Pub 3m on right after village hall*

There's a great mix of old and new in this comfortable, contemporary village pub. In winter there's a roaring fire, while in summer the patio doors are flung open into the external dining area, from where Goodrich Castle is visible across the fields. The pub has its own 1000-acre farm, rearing free-range cattle, rare-breed pigs, poultry and game. Dishes on the menu change weekly, and might feature Madgetts Farm chicken breast with potato rösti, chestnut mushrooms and sage sauce; or oxtail faggots with crushed root vegetables and red wine sauce. Afterwards, try apple and cinnamon crumble or the farmhouse cheese selection. The wine list includes a Welsh Seyval Blanc.

Open all wk 11-3 5-11 (Sat-Sun all day) **Bar Meals** L served Mon-Fri 12-2, Sat-Sun 12-2.30 booking required D served Mon-Sat 6-9.30, Sun 6-9 booking required Av main course £8 **Restaurant** L served Mon-Fri 12-2, Sat-Sun 12-2.30 booking required D served Mon-Sat 6-9.30, Sun 6-9 booking required Fixed menu price fr £8 Av 3 course à la carte fr £23 ⊕ FREE HOUSE ◀ Wye Valley Bitter, Guest Ales, Guinness Ŏ Westons, Stowfords Press, Roaring Meg. ▼ 9 **Facilities** Children's menu Garden Parking

WELLINGTON

The Wellington ▼

HR4 8AT ☎ 01432 830367
e-mail: thewellington@hotmail.com
dir: *Off A49 into village centre. Pub 0.25m on left*

Owners Ross and Philippa Williams came from London to create one of Herefordshire's finest gastro-pubs. They've done well, with Ross quickly becoming an award-winning champion of food prepared from local, seasonal produce. Start with Parma ham and porcini mushroom lasagne, followed by slow-roasted belly and pan-fried tenderloin of Welsh white pork with cider sauce and mustard mash, and then lemon semifreddo with home-made orange shortbread. Sunday lunch could include roast leg of local venison.

Open 12-3 6-11 Closed: Mon L, Sun eve in winter **Bar Meals** L served Tue-Sun 12-2 D served all wk 7-9 Av main course £8.50 **Restaurant** L served Tue-Sun 12-2 D served all wk 7-9 Av 3 course à la carte fr £25 ⊕ FREE HOUSE ◀ Hobsons, Wye Valley Butty Bach, Wye Valley HPA, Guest ales Ŏ Westons Scrumpy. ▼ 8 **Facilities** Children's menu Play area Dogs allowed Garden Parking

WHITNEY-ON-WYE

Rhydspence Inn ★★★★ INN

HR3 6EU ☎ 01497 831262 📠 01497 831751
e-mail: info@rhydspence-inn.co.uk
dir: *N side of A438, 1m W of Whitney-on-Wye*

This charming inn dates from 1380 and was extended in the 17th and 20th centuries. It was most likely built to provide comfort for travellers and pilgrims from Abbey Cwmhir to Hereford Cathedral, but these days the pub is rather more elegant, with a cosy bar and spacious dining room giving way to stunning views over the Wye Valley. Food options range from deep-fried cod in lemon batter and French fries or braised shank of lamb from the bar bites and brasserie selection, to main menu dishes such as peppered venison with fricassee of mushrooms and port and redcurrant reduction or pan-fried sea bass with tempura courgettes and lemon aïoli. There is also a good choice of steaks from the grill. The friendly ghost of a former landlady is said to frequent the inn, though only when young children are staying.

Open all wk 11-2.30 7-11 **Bar Meals** L served all wk 11-2.30 D served all wk 7-9 Av main course £9 **Restaurant** L served all wk 11-2 booking required D served all wk 7-9 booking required Av 3 course à la carte fr £25 ⊕ FREE HOUSE ◀ Robinsons Best, Interbrew Bass. **Facilities** Children's menu Family room Garden Parking **Rooms** 7

WOOLHOPE

The Crown Inn ♟

HR1 4QP ☎ 01432 860468 📠 01432 860770
e-mail: menu@crowninnwoolhope.co.uk
dir: *B4224 to Mordiford, left after Moon Inn. Pub in village centre*

Every cider and perry producer in Herefordshire is represented at this real, old fashioned free house, and over 100 types of real ale are served over the course of the year. Good quality local ingredients — wet and dry — are to the fore, with lunchtime baguettes and pub favourites such as chilli, Hereford beef burger, or cider braised ham with chunky chips. There is also an outdoor bar with a heated smoking area and beautiful views.

Open all wk 12-2.30 6.30-11 (Sat-Sun all day) **Bar Meals** L served all wk 12-2 D served all wk 6.30-9 Av main course £10 **Restaurant** L served all wk 12-2 D served all wk 6.30-9 Fixed menu price fr £18 Av 3 course à la carte fr £18 ⊕ FREE HOUSE ◀ Wye Valley Best, Black Sheep, guest ales Ŏ Westons Stowford Press. ♟ 6 **Facilities** Children's menu Garden Parking

ALDBURY

The Valiant Trooper 🍷

Trooper Rd HP23 5RW
☎ 01442 851203 📠 01442 851071
e-mail: info@thevalianttrooper.co.uk
dir: *A41 at Tring junct, follow rail station signs 0.5m, at village green turn right, 200yds on left*

This country pub and restaurant is set in a pretty village at the foot of the Chiltern Hills. It was originally a group of 17th-century cottages, then The Royal Oak. It became The Trooper Alehouse in 1803, allegedly because the Duke of Wellington discussed tactics here with his troops. The large beer garden now has a wooden adventure trail, and children are handsomely catered for with their own healthy home-cooked menu. Dogs are also welcome in the bar or garden. The emphasis is on quality local produce in a menu of British classics. Snacks take in tempting sandwiches, cured meat or seafood platters, and savouries such as Welsh rarebit on toast. Typical main courses are pie of the day, or marinated chicken breast with white wine, garlic and spinach creamed tagliatelle.

Open all day all wk 11.30am-11pm (Sun noon-10.30) **Bar Meals** Av main course £9.50 food served all day **Restaurant** Fixed menu price fr £13.50 Av 3 course à la carte fr £19 food served all day FREE HOUSE Fuller's London Pride, Tring Jack O'Legs, 2 Guest ales. 🍷 8 **Facilities** Children's menu Play area Family room Dogs allowed Garden Parking

ASHWELL

The Three Tuns 🍷

High St SG7 5NL
☎ 01462 742107 📠 01462 743662
e-mail: claire@tuns.co.uk
dir: *Telephone for directions*

The building, dating from 1806, replaces an earlier one first recorded as a public house in 1700. Original features survive in the two bars and large dining room, probably once a smokehouse, judging by the rows of old hanging hooks. Traditional pub food and an à la carte menu are on offer. The menu might offer steak and kidney pie; Spanish pork casserole and a selection of steaks with interesting sauces.

Open all day all wk 11am-11.30pm (Fri-Sat 11am-12.30am) **Bar Meals** L served Mon-Fri 12-2.30, Sat-Sun all day booking required D served Mon-Fri 6.30-9.30, Sat-Sun all day booking required Av main course £18 **Restaurant** L served Mon-Fri 12-2.30, Sat-Sun all day booking required D served Mon-Fri 6.30-9.30, Sat-Sun all day booking required Av 3 course à la carte fr £20 GREENE KING Greene King IPA, Abbot, Guest. 🍷 12 **Facilities** Children's menu Play area Family room Dogs allowed Garden Parking

BARLEY

The Fox & Hounds 🍷

High St SG8 8HU
☎ 01763 848459 📠 01763 849080
e-mail: info@foxandhoundsbarley.co.uk
dir: *A505 onto B1368 at Flint Cross, pub 4m*

Set in a pretty village, this former 17th-century hunting lodge is notable for its pub sign which extends across the lane. It has real fires, a warm welcome and an attractive garden. A typical menu includes wild mushroom risotto, beef burger with chunky-cut chips, Irish stew, and beer-battered fish and chips. Opening in 2009, the Saffron Deli and Farm Shop.

Open 10-3 6-late (Sat 10am-late, Sun 10-6) Closed: Mon **Bar Meals** L served Tue-Fri 12-3, Sat 12-late, Sun 12-5.30 booking required D served Tue-Sun 6-10 booking required Av main course £8.95 food served all day **Restaurant** L served Tue-Fri 12-3, Sat 12-4, Sun 12-5 booking required D served Tue-Sun 6-10 booking required Av 3 course à la carte fr £20 food served all day ⊕ SAFFRON LEISURE ◀ Adnams Best, Flowers IPA, Woodforde's Wherry. 🍷 12 **Facilities** Children's menu Play area Garden Parking

BUNTINGFORD

The Sword Inn Hand ★★★★ INN 🍷

Westmill SG9 9LQ ☎ 01763 271356
e-mail: welcome@theswordinnhand.co.uk
dir: *Off A10 1.5m S of Buntingford*

Midway between London and Cambridge in the lovely award-winning village of Westmill, and welcoming travellers since the 14th century - you can't miss the oak beams, flag floor and open fireplace. It styles itself a 'real English', family-run pub offering a large selection of snacks, specials, beers and wines. Fresh produce is delivered daily to create herb-crushed rack of lamb, sea bass fillet with stir-fry vegetables, escalope of veal with melted brie or Chef's cod and chips. There are four ground floor bedrooms available.

Open all wk 12-3 5-11 (Sun Sep-Apr 12-7, May-Aug 12-10) **Bar Meals** L served Mon-Sat 12-2.30, Sun 12-4 D served Mon-Sat 6.30-9.30 **Restaurant** L served Mon-Sat 12-2.30, Sun 12-4 D served Mon-Sat 6.30-9.30 ⊕ FREE HOUSE ◀ Greene King IPA, Young's Bitter, Timothy Taylor Landlord, Guest ales 🍏 Aspalls. 🍷 8 **Facilities** Children's menu Play area Dogs allowed Garden Parking **Rooms** 4

HEXTON

The Raven ♈

SG5 3JB ☎ 01582 881209 📄 01582 881610
e-mail: jack@ravenathexton.f9.co.uk
dir: *5m W of Hitchin. 5m N of Luton, just outside Barton-le-Clay*

This neat 1920s pub is named after Ravensburgh Castle in the neighbouring hills. It has comfortable bars and a large garden with a terrace and play area. Snacks include ploughman's and salad platters, plus tortilla wraps, filled baguettes and jacket potatoes. The main menu offers lots of steak options, and dishes like smoky American chicken, whole rack of barbecue ribs, Thai red vegetable curry and an all-day breakfast.

Open all wk **Bar Meals** L served 12-2.15 (Fri-Sun all day) D served 6-9 (Fri-Sun all day) Av main course £9 **Restaurant** L served 12-2.15 (Fri-Sun all day) D served 6-9 (Fri-Sun all day) Av 3 course à la carte fr £15 ⊕ ENTERPRISE INNS ◀ Greene King, Old Speckled Hen, Fuller's London Pride, Greene King IPA. ♈ 24 **Facilities** Children's menu Play area Garden Parking

HUNSDON

The Fox and Hounds ♈

2 High St SG12 8NH
☎ 01279 843999 📄 01279 841092
e-mail: info@foxandhounds-hunsdon.co.uk
web: www.foxandhounds-hunsdon.co.uk
dir: *From A414 between Ware & Harlow take B180 in Stanstead Abbotts N to Hunsdon*

Nestled in a sleepy village in the heart of the Hertfordshire countryside, this pub has a warm, welcoming atmosphere and a large pretty garden, with a heated covered terrace. Expect serious cooking that combines classics with modern touches. Lunch could begin with mussels, cider, leeks and cream; followed by calves' liver persillade and duck fat potato cake. For dinner, perhaps try rabbit rillettes, pickles and toast, followed by Black Angus côte de boeuf, fat chips and sauce bearnaise. Roast black figs, honey and mascarpone is an elegant way to round matters off.

Open noon-4 6-11 Closed: Sun, Mon eve **Bar Meals** L served Tue-Sun 12-3 D served Tue-Sat 6.30-9.30 Av main course £15 **Restaurant** L served Sun 12-3 booking required D served Fri-Sat 7-9.30 booking required Fixed menu price fr £12.50 Av 3 course à la carte fr £26 ⊕ FREE HOUSE ◀ Adnams Bitter, Adnams Broadside, Guinness ♂ Aspall. ♈ 10 **Facilities** Children's menu Play area Dogs allowed Garden Parking

LITTLE HADHAM

The Nags Head ♀

The Ford SG11 2AX
☎ 01279 771555 ▤ 01279 771555
e-mail: paul.arkell@virgin.net
dir: M11 junct 8 take A120 towards Puckeridge & A10. Left at lights in Little Hadham. Pub 1m on right

Formerly a coaching inn, this 16th-century pub has also been a brewery, a bakery and Home Guard arsenal in its time. The 1960s folk-rock group Fairport Convention once performed in concert opposite and the pub ran dry! Open brickwork and an old bakery oven are among the features at this village inn. An extensive menu offers everything from braised lamb joint and roast spiced duck breast to pasta carbonara and mixed grill. Plenty of starters available and more than 20 fish choices.

Open all wk **Bar Meals** L served Mon-Sat 12-2, Sun 12-3 D served Mon-Sat 6-9, Sun 7-9 Av main course £10 **Restaurant** L served Mon-Sat 12-2, Sun 12-3 booking required D served Mon-Sat 6-9, Sun 7-9 booking required ⊕ GREENE KING ◖ Greene King Abbot Ale, IPA, Old Speckled Hen & Ruddles County Ale, Marstons Pedigree. ♀ 6 **Facilities** Children's menu Garden

ROYSTON

The Cabinet Free House and Restaurant ♀

High St, Reed SG8 8AH ☎ 01763 848366
e-mail: thecabinet@btconnect.com
dir: 2m S of Royston, just off A10

The Cabinet is a 16th-century country inn and restaurant located in the little village of Reed. The menu is an eclectic mix, based on personal taste and sound cooking techniques and prepared from the best local produce, offering an interesting variety of dishes including traditional favourites. Lunchtime offerings range from soup of the day or macaroni cheese, to toad-in-the-hole with scallion mash. Evening suppers are equally appealing: start with bouillabaisse of red mullet; continue with daube of venison with dumplings, roasted beetroot and mustard mash and round off with chocolate torte with walnut meringue. Mind the resident ghost - an old gentleman in a dark coat.

Open 12-3 6-11 (Sat-Sun 12-11) Closed: 1 Jan, Mon L **Bar Meals** L served Tue-Sun 12-3 D served Tue-Sat 6-9 Av main course £10 **Restaurant** L served Tue-Sun 12-3 booking required D served Tue-Sat 6-9 booking required Fixed menu price fr £10-25 Av 3 course à la carte fr £25 ⊕ FREE HOUSE ◖ Woodforde's Wherry, Adnams, Old Speckled Hen, Nelson's Revenge, Timothy Taylor, Augustinian ♂ Aspall. ♀ 12 **Facilities** Children's menu Family room Dogs allowed Garden Parking

ST ALBANS

Rose & Crown ♥

10 Saint Michael St AL3 4SG
☎ 01727 851903　📠 01727 761775
e-mail: ruth.courtney@ntlworld.com
dir: *Telephone for details*

Traditional 16th-century pub situated in a beautiful part of St Michael's 'village', opposite the entrance to Verulanium Park and the Roman Museum. It has a classic beamed bar with a huge inglenook, open fire in winter and a lovely walled garden. The pub offers a distinctive range of American deli-style sandwiches, which are served with potato salad, kettle crisps and pickled cucumber. There is traditional folk music on Thursday nights, live music on Monday nights.

Open all day all wk 11.30-3 5.30-11 (Sat 11.30-11.30) Bar Meals L served Mon-Sat 12-2.30, Sun 12-5 D served Mon-Sat 6-9 ⊕ PUNCH TAVERNS ◼ Adnams Bitter, Tetley Bitter, Fuller's London Pride, Courage Directors, guest ales. ♥ 20 Facilities Children's menu Dogs allowed Garden Parking

CANTERBURY

The Chapter Arms ♥

New Town St, Chartham Hatch CT4 7LT
☎ 01227 738340
e-mail: david.durell@vmicombox.co.uk
dir: *3m from Canterbury. Off A28 in Chartham Hatch or A2 at Upper Harbledown*

Situated on the North Downs Way, this charming and picturesque free house is set in over an acre of gardens overlooking apple orchards and oast houses. It was once three cottages owned by Canterbury Cathedral's Dean and Chapter - hence the name. Any day's menu might offer Kentish lamb crusted with garlic and thyme, Thai salmon fishcakes, or steak and kidney pie. Live Sixties music and jazz evenings are popular. Suitable for marquee weddings.

Open all wk Closed: 25 Dec eve Bar Meals L served all wk 12-2.30 D served Mon-Sat 6.30-9 booking required Av main course £8.95 Restaurant L served all wk 12-2.30 D served Mon-Sat 6.30-9 booking required Av 3 course à la carte fr £25 ⊕ FREE HOUSE ◼ Shepherd Neame Master Brew, Adnams, Harveys, Youngs, Wells Bombardier, guest ales. ♥ 10 Facilities Children's menu Play area Dogs allowed Garden Parking

FAVERSHAM

Shipwright's Arms ♥

Hollowshore ME13 7TU ☎ 01795 590088
dir: *A2 through Ospringe then right at rdbt. Right at T-junct then left opposite Davington School, follow signs*

Step back in time to this remote pub on the Swale marshes which is well over 300 years old, and once a favourite with sailors and fishermen waiting to dock in Faversham. The pub still draws its water from a well. Examine the maritime artefacts in the many nooks and crannies, while downing a Kent-brewed cask ale. Home cooked food includes locally caught fish in season, and English pies and puddings during the winter, where four open fires keep things cosy.

Open Closed: Mon (Oct-Mar) **Bar Meals** L served Tue-Sat 11-2.30, Sun 12-2.30 D served Tue-Sat 7-9 **Restaurant** L served Tue-Sat 11-2.30, Sun 12-2.30 D served Tue-Sat 7-9 ⊕ FREE HOUSE ◀ Local ales. ♥ 6 **Facilities** Children's menu Family room Dogs allowed Garden Parking

FOLKESTONE

The Lighthouse Inn ♥

Old Dover Rd, Capel le Ferne CT18 7HT
☎ 01303 223300 📄 01303 842270
e-mail: james@thelighthouseinn.net
dir: *M20 junct 13 follow signs for Capel le Ferne*

There are sweeping Channel views from this pub on the edge of Dover's famous White Cliffs. The Lighthouse began as an ale house in 1840, later becoming, successively, a billiard hall, convalescent home, psychiatric hospital and country club while, more recently still, Channel Tunnel builders headquartered here. Expect decent home-made food along the lines of traditional prawn cocktail followed by local sausages with mash and onion jus, Channel fisherman's pie or classic ham, egg and chips.

Open all day all wk 11-11 **Bar Meals** Av main course £12.50 food served all day **Restaurant** Fixed menu price fr £14 Av 3 course à la carte fr £25 food served all day ⊕ FREE HOUSE ◀ IPA, 6X, Adnams. ♥ 14 **Facilities** Children's menu Play area Family room Dogs allowed Garden Parking

GOUDHURST

The Star & Eagle ★★★★ INN ⬤

High St TN17 1AL
☎ 01580 211512 📄 01580 212444
e-mail: starandeagle@btconnect.com
dir: *Just off A21 towards Hastings. Take A262 into Goudhurst. Pub at top of hill next to church*

A commanding position at 400 feet above sea level gives the 14th-century Star & Eagle outstanding views of the orchards and hop fields that helped earn Kent the accolade 'Garden of England'. It's a place to unwind and enjoy fine traditional and continental food, prepared under the guidance of Spanish chef/proprietor Enrique Martinez. A typical bar meal might be field mushrooms stuffed with bacon and stilton; and cod, salmon and smoked haddock fish pie. From the restaurant menu might come soupe de poisson laced with brandy and cream; and Scottish rope mussels with chilli. Follow with pot-roast shoulder of lamb baked Spanish style; or sautéed calves' livers. Comfortable bedrooms are available.

Open all wk 11-11 (Sun 12-3 6.30-10.30) **Bar Meals** L served all wk 12-2.30 D served all wk 7-9.30 Av main course £15 **Restaurant** L served all wk 12-2.30 D served all wk 7-9.30 Fixed menu price fr £24 A la carte fr £30 ⊕ FREE HOUSE ◀ Adnams Bitter, Harvey's, Grasshopper. ⬤ 24 **Facilities** Children's menu Family room Garden Parking **Rooms** 10

HAWKHURST

The Great House ⬤

Gills Green TN18 5EJ
☎ 01580 753119 📄 01622 851881
e-mail: enquiries@thegreathouse.net
dir: *Just off A229 between Cranbrook & Hawkhurst*

The Great House is a wonderfully atmospheric 16th-century free house with a warm and comfortable ambience. The food is fresh and seasonal, and all meat is sourced from a local organic farm. Dishes from the bar menu might include Park Farm Cumberland sausages or mash, liver and bacon. Alongside the deli board selection (cheese, fish, antipasti, charcuterie), there are starters of grilled goats' cheese with sesame crust and sweet chilli dressing, or Nicoise-style fish soup with potato aioli, which may be followed by roast breast of Norfolk chicken with haricot beans and bacon ragout. Imaginative desserts might take in Kentish apple and cinnamon crumble. Part of the pub has been transformed into a deli/farmers' market.

Open all wk noon-11 **Bar Meals** L served Mon-Fri 12-3, Sat 12-10, Sun 12-8 D served Mon-Fri 6.30-9.30, Sat 12-10, Sun 12-8 Av main course £11 **Restaurant** L served Mon-Fri 12-3, Sat 12-10, Sun 12-8 D served Mon-Fri 6.30-9.30, Sat 12-10, Sun 12-8 Fixed menu price fr £11 Av 3 course à la carte fr £22 ⊕ FREE HOUSE ◀ Harvey's, Guinness, Youngs. ⬤ 13 **Facilities** Children's menu Garden Parking

HODSOLL STREET

The Green Man

TN15 7LE ☎ 01732 823575
e-mail: the.greenman@btinternet.com
dir: *On North Downs between Brands Hatch & Gravesend on A227*

Set in the picturesque village of Hodsoll Street on the North Downs, this 300-year-old, family-run pub is loved for its decent food and real ales. Food is prepared to order using fresh local produce, and includes a wide variety of fish (especially on Wednesday, which is fish night). Curry takes centre stage on Thursday nights, while Tuesday night is steak and rib night. Live music features every second Thursday of each month.

Open all wk **Bar Meals** L served Mon-Fri 12-2, Sat-Sun 12-3 D served Mon-Sat 6.30-9.30, Sun 6.30-9 **Restaurant** L served Mon-Fri 12-2, Sat-Sun 12-3 D served Mon-Sat 6.30-9.30, Sun 6.30-9 ⊕ HAYWOOD PUB COMPANY LTD ◁ Timothy Taylor Landlord, Harvey's, Old Speckled Hen, guest ale. **Facilities** Children's menu Play area Dogs allowed Garden Parking

IDEN GREEN

The Peacock ▼

Goudhurst Rd TN17 2PB ☎ 01580 211233
dir: *A21 from Tunbridge Wells to Hastings, onto A262, pub 1.5m past Goudhurst*

A Grade II listed building dating from the 17th century with low beams, an inglenook fireplace, old oak doors, real ales on tap, and a wide range of traditional pub food. A large enclosed garden with fruit trees and picnic tables on one side of the building is popular in summer, and there's also a patio.

Open all wk 12-11 (Sun 12-6) **Bar Meals** L served Mon-Fri & Sun 12-2.30, Sat all day D served Mon-Fri 6-8.45, Sat all day **Restaurant** L served Mon-Fri & Sun 12-2.30, Sat all day D served Mon-Fri 6-8.45, Sat all day ⊕ SHEPHERD NEAME ◁ Shepherd Neame Master Brew, Spitfire, seasonal ales. ▼ 12 **Facilities** Children's menu Family room Dogs allowed Garden Parking

IVY HATCH

The Plough at Ivy Hatch ♥

High Cross Rd TN15 0NL ☎ 01732 810100
e-mail: theploughpubco@tiscali.co.uk
dir: *Off A25 between Borough Green & Sevenoaks,*
follow signs to Ightham Mote

Set deep in Kent countryside, the 17th-century
Plough is the perfect spot for a lingering lunch or
supper. Now the last bastion of a once-thriving
community, it fulfils an integral part of village
life. Plans to establish a kitchen garden within
the grounds will complement the locally sourced
produce that's already used, including a wide
selection of seafood from the south coast.
Starters might include lentil and lovage soup;
to follow, tackle a Sussex rib-eye steak with
caramelised banana shallots and peppercorn
sauce. Desserts include a range of ice creams;
lemon tart with mascarpone; and crème brûlée.
There's a terrace and garden ideal for alfresco
dining. If you go on one of the many good walks
in the area, don't worry about how muddy your
boots are when you squelch to the pub.

Open all wk noon-3 6-11 (Sat noon-11 Sun 10-6) **Bar
Meals** L served Mon-Sat 12-2.45, Sun 12-6 D served
Mon-Sat 6-9.30 Av main course £10 **Restaurant** L
served Mon-Sat 12-2.45, Sun 12-6 D served Mon-Sat
6-9.30 Fixed menu price fr £15 Av 3 course à la carte
fr £19.50 ⊕ FREE HOUSE ◀ Harveys Best, Seasonal
ales, Westerham Finchcocks ♂ Stowford Press. ♥ 8
Facilities Children's menu Garden Parking

PENSHURST

The Spotted Dog ♥

Smarts Hill TN11 8EE
☎ 01892 870253 ▤ 01892 870107
e-mail: info@spotteddogpub.co.uk
dir: *Off B2188 between Penshurst & Fordcombe*

Deep in the Kent countryside, this 16th-century
white weather-boarded free house enjoys fine
views over the Weald from the rear terrace. The
rambling interior with its tiled and oak floors,
low beams and three open fireplaces creates
a welcoming atmosphere for both locals and
visitors alike. But don't expect fast food or a
huge menu, because everything here is freshly
prepared to order, using traceable local produce
wherever possible. Starters like rare roasted
venison salad with red wine vinaigrette set
the stage for main course choices that might
include calves' liver and bacon with creamy
mash, vegetables and rich gravy; or grilled
whole sea bass, lemon hollandaise sauce, new
potatoes and vegetables. **Open** all wk noon-3
6-11 (Sun noon-10.30) **Bar Meals** L served Mon-Sat
12-2.30 D served Mon-Sat 6-9 **Restaurant** L served
Mon-Sat 12-2.30, Sun 12-5 D served Mon-Fri 6-9,
Sat 6-9.30 ⊕ FREE HOUSE ◀ Sharp's Doom Bar,
Larkins Traditional, guest ale ♂ Chiddingstone. ♥ 20
Facilities Children's menu Dogs allowed Garden
Parking

PLUCKLEY

The Dering Arms ☻

Station Rd TN27 0RR
☎ 01233 840371 📠 01233 840498
e-mail: jim@deringarms.com
web: www.deringarms.com
dir: *M20 junct 8, A20 to Ashford. Right onto B2077 at Charing to Pluckley*

The Dering Arms has two traditional bars with mounted stags' heads and fishing rods, roaring fires in winter, an intimate restaurant, and a family room with a baby grand piano (there to be played). The extensive daily menus offers starters of Sussex mackerel smokies and grilled Irish oysters with chorizo, while main course options might be confit of duck with bubble and squeak potato cake and wild mushroom sauce; or pan-fried tuna steak with garlic and lemon butter. Do check the blackboards for specials, as well. Desserts range from oranges in caramel with Grand Marnier, to prunes marinated in Cointreau.

Open 11.30-3.30 6-11 Closed: 26-29 Dec, Sun eve & Mon **Bar Meals** L served Tue-Sun 12-2 booking required D served Tue-Sat 7-9.30 booking required Av main course £17 **Restaurant** L served Tue-Sun 12-2 booking required D served Tue-Sat 7-9.30 booking required Av 3 course à la carte fr £32 ⊕ FREE HOUSE ◀ Goacher's Dering Ale, Maidstone Dark, Gold Star, Old Ale. ☻ 7 **Facilities** Children's menu Family room Dogs allowed Garden Parking

PLUCKLEY

The Mundy Bois ☻

Mundy Bois TN27 0ST
☎ 01233 840048 📠 01233 840193
e-mail: helen@mundybois.com
dir: *From A20 at Charing exit towards Pluckley. Right into Pinnock at bottom of Pluckley Hill. Next right into Mundy Bois Rd. 1m left*

An ale house since 1780 and formerly named the Rose and Crown, this creeper-clad pub is on the outskirts of Pluckley, considered to be the most haunted place in England. A blackboard menu features frequently changing dishes created from local produce where possible, and a nearby farm specializing in rare breeds – rare breed Welsh pork chops on mustard mash with caramelised apples and cider sauce. A patio dining area allows alfresco eating, and the garden has an adventure playground.

Open all wk **Bar Meals** L served all wk 12-2 D served all wk 6.30-9 **Restaurant** L served all wk 12-2 D served all wk 6.30-9 ⊕ FREE HOUSE ◀ Master Brew, Youngs. ☻ 8 **Facilities** Children's menu Play area Dogs allowed Garden Parking

103

ST MARGARET'S AT CLIFFE

The Coastguard

St Margaret's Bay CT15 6DY
☎ 01304 853176
e-mail: thecoastguard@talk21.com
dir: *2m off A258 between Dover & Deal, follow St Margaret's at Cliffe signs. Through village towards sea*

The Coastguard is set in one of the most delightful spots on the Kentish coast, with its breathtaking white cliffs and beach walks. The pub stands only a stone's throw from the water's edge and has spectacular views out to sea. It is renowned for its food and hospitality, and everything is freshly made on the premises, including the breads and sauces, using local produce whenever possible. The menu changes daily, even during service, depending on the weather and what is available, and features award-winning fish dishes, beef from a local farm and 'garden of Kent' fresh salad. The cheeseboard is highly regarded and has attracted many accolades.

Open all day all wk 11-11 (Sun 11-10.30) **Bar Meals** L served all wk 12.30-2.45 D served all wk 6.30-8.45 food served all day **Restaurant** L served all wk 12.30-2.45 D served all wk 6.30-8.45 ⊕ FREE HOUSE ◀ Gadds of Ramsgate, Hop Daemon, Adnams, Caledonian, Isle of Arran. **Facilities** Children's menu Play area Dogs allowed Garden Parking

SELLING

The Rose and Crown

Perry Wood ME13 9RY ☎ 01227 752214
e-mail: perrywoodrose@btinternet.co.uk
dir: *From A28 right at Badgers Hill, left at end. 1st left signed Perry Wood. Pub at top*

Set amidst 150 acres of woodland in the middle of an Area of Outstanding Natural Beauty, this 16th-century pub's beamed interior is decorated with hop garlands, corn dollies, horse brasses and brass cask taps. The perfumed summer garden includes a children's play area and bat and trap pitch. Expect a choice of four real ales including a guest, and a menu high in comfort factor. The ploughman's is served with huffkin, a bread made with eggs, milk and ground paragon wheat - a little like brioche but less sweet. A game menu is available in season.

Open all wk noon-3 6.30-11 Closed: 25-26 Dec eve, 1 Jan eve, Mon eve **Bar Meals** L served all wk 12-2 D served Tue-Sun 7-9 **Restaurant** L served all wk 12-2 D served Tue-Sun 7-9 ⊕ FREE HOUSE ◀ Adnams Southwold, Harvey's Sussex Best Bitter, guest ale. **Facilities** Children's menu Play area Dogs allowed Garden Parking

SPELDHURST

George & Dragon ♥

Speldhurst Hill TN3 0NN
☎ 01892 863125 🖹 01892 863216
e-mail: julian@speldhurst.com
dir: *Telephone for directions*

Built around 1500, the George and Dragon is a venerable timber-clad village hostelry. At the beginning of the 17th century the curative powers of the village's iron-rich waters were discovered, which put nearby Tunbridge Wells on the map. Today's customers enjoy a modern gastro-pub, where refreshments include a range of local organic fruit juices. Start with parsnip and coriander soup with parsnip crisps and follow with Ashdown Forest venison stew, sautéed potatoes and wilted greens; roast guinea fowl with chilli and tarragon butter; or fillet of wild sea bass with brown shrimp and caper butter. Food can be served in the two gardens - one a modern layout with bay trees and herbs, the other a Mediterranean garden with 200-year-old olive tree.

Open all wk **Bar Meals** L served all wk 12-2.45 D served Mon-Sat 7-9.45 Av main course £9 **Restaurant** L served Sat-Sun 12-3 booking required D served Fri-Sun 7-10 booking required Av 3 course à la carte fr £25 ⊕ FREE HOUSE ◀ Harvey's Best, Sussex Pale, Larkins, Porter. ♥ 10 **Facilities** Children's menu Family room Dogs allowed Garden Parking

TUNBRIDGE WELLS (ROYAL)

The Beacon ★★★★ INN ♥

Tea Garden Ln, Rusthall TN3 9JH
☎ 01892 524252 🖹 01892 534288
e-mail: beaconhotel@btopenworld.com
web: www.the-beacon.co.uk
dir: *From Tunbridge Wells take A264 towards East Grinstead. Pub 1m on left*

Set amid seventeen acres of grounds, the Beacon oozes with country house charm; the bar, with its moulded plaster ceiling, bookshelves and stained glass windows is a wonderful place to relax. Enjoy a drink on the terrace with amazing views in summer or by the fire in the bar on cooler days. The menus take full advantage of seasonal local produce; start with pork and apricot terrine with grape and apple chutney; main course dishes include smoked halibut ragout with poached egg, and seared rib-eye steak with caramelised onion mash and sauteed green vegetables.

Open all day all wk Mon-Sat 11-11 (Sun 12-10.30) **Bar Meals** L served Mon-Thu 12-2.30, Fri-Sun 12-9.30 D served Mon-Thu 6.30-9.30, Fri-Sun 12-9.30 Av main course £9.50 **Restaurant** L served Mon-Thu 12-2.30, Fri-Sun 12-9.30 D served Mon-Thu 6.30-9.30, Fri-Sun 12-9.30 Av 3 course à la carte fr £22 ⊕ FREE HOUSE ◀ Harveys Best, Timothy Taylor Landlord, Larkins Traditional ♂ Stowford Press Draught Cider, Westons Organic Bottled Pear Cider. ♥ 12 **Facilities** Children's menu Play area Garden Parking **Rooms** 3

WESTERHAM

The Fox & Hounds 🍷

Toys Hill TN16 1QG ☎ 01732 750328
e-mail: hickmott1@hotmail.com
dir: *Telephone for directions*

High up on Kent's Greensand Ridge, in an Area of Outstanding Natural Beauty, this late 18th-century ale house adjoins a large National Trust estate incorporating an old water tower now protected as a home for hibernating bats. The pub has a traditionally styled restaurant, where starters include smoked salmon and crab roulade, and deep-fried brie with cranberry sauce, while among the mains are fillet of pork stuffed with dates and apricots on horseradish mash, leg of lamb on bubble and squeak with rosemary jus, and daily specials. A children's menu is available.

Open 10-3 6-11 (Sat-Sun 10am-11pm) Closed: 25 Dec, Mon eve **Bar Meals** L served Mon-Sat 12-2, Sun 12-3 D served Tue-Sat 6-9 Av main course £11 **Restaurant** L served Mon-Sat 12-2, Sun 12-3 D served Tue-Sat 6-9 Av 3 course à la carte fr £20 ⊕ GREENE KING ◀ Greene King IPA, Abbot Ale, Ruddles County. 🍷 9 **Facilities** Children's menu Dogs allowed Garden Parking

WHITSTABLE

The Sportsman 🌼🌼 🍷

Faversham Rd CT5 4BP ☎ 01227 273370
e-mail: contact@thesportsmanseasalter.co.uk
dir: *3.5m W of Whitstable, on the coast road between Whitstable and Faversham*

Reached via a winding lane across open marshland from Whitstable, and tucked beneath the sea wall, the Sportsman may seem an unlikely place to find such good food. The rustic yet comfortable interior, with its wooden floors, stripped pine furniture and interesting collection of prints has a warm and welcoming feel. The daily menu is based on local produce from farms, boats and game dealers. Fish dishes might include seared Thornback ray with cockles, sherry vinegar and brown butter. Starters also feature lots of seafood, typically rock oysters and hot chorizo. Amongst the mains is Monkshill Farm pork belly and apple sauce. There is also a tasting menu available for a maximum of 6 people. Food is not served on Sunday evenings or Mondays

Open all wk noon-3 6-11 Closed: 25 Dec **Bar Meals** Av main course £16 **Restaurant** L served Tue-Sun 12-2 booking required D served Tue-Sat 7-9 booking required Av 3 course à la carte fr £30 ⊕ SHEPHERD NEAME ◀ Shepherd Neame Late Red, Master Brew, Porter, Early Bird, Goldings, Whitstable Bay. 🍷 8 **Facilities** Children's menu Family room Dogs allowed Garden Parking

BILSBORROW

Owd Nell's Tavern ☂

Guy's Thatched Hamlet, Canal Side PR3 0RS
☎ 01995 640010 📄 01995 640141
e-mail: info@guysthatchedhamlet.com
dir: *M6 junct 32 N on A6. In approx 5m follow brown tourist signs to Guy's Thatched Hamlet*

The Wilkinson family has owned and run Guy's Thatched Hamlet beside the Lancaster Canal for nearly 30 years, of which this tavern forms a part. Flagstone floors, fireplaces and low ceilings create an authentic ambience. Excellent real ales are supplemented by a lovingly assembled collection of wheat beers, fruit beers and pilsners. All-day fare is typified by home-made steamed chicken, leek and mushroom pudding; famous steak and kidney pudding; spinach and cheese cannelloni; and bacon, brie and cranberry panini. Children's menus are available. There is a cider festival at the end of July.

Open all wk 7am-2am Closed: 25 Dec **Bar Meals** Av main course £7.50 food served all day **Restaurant** L served Mon-Sat 12-2.30, Sun 12-10.30 D served Mon-Sat 5.30-10.30, Sun 12-10.30 Fixed menu price fr £7.95 Av 3 course à la carte fr £17 ⊕ FREE HOUSE ◀ Boddingtons Bitter, Jennings Bitter, Copper Dragon, Black Sheep, Owd Nells Canalside Bitter, Moorhouses Bitter, Pendle Witch Ŏ Thatchers Heritage, Cheddar Valley. ☂ 40 **Facilities** Children's menu Play area Family room Dogs allowed Garden Parking

CLITHEROE

The Shireburn Arms ★★★ HL ☂

Whalley Rd, Hurst Green BB7 9QJ
☎ 01254 826518 📄 01254 826208
e-mail: sales@shireburnarmshotel.com
dir: *Telephone for directions*

A privately run, 17th-century inn with super views, in the heart of the Ribble Valley. 'Lord of the Rings' author J R R Tolkien used to drink here when visiting his son at Stonyhurst College nearby, and the pub has become and home of the 'Tolkien Trail'. Using the finest local produce from around Lancashire, the menu ranges from sandwiches and salads to roasted Goosnargh duck with black cherry jus; wild sea trout on crushed peas; and mushroom, cranberry and brie Wellington. A conservatory links the restaurant with the patio and gardens.

Open all day all wk **Bar Meals** Av main course £8.50 food served all day **Restaurant** L served Mon-Fri 12-2, Sun 12-6 D served all wk 6-9 Fixed menu price fr £10.95 Av 3 course à la carte fr £20 ⊕ FREE HOUSE ◀ Theakstons Best Bitter, guest ales. ☂ 10 **Facilities** Children's menu Play area Family room Dogs allowed Garden Parking **Rooms** 22

FENCE

Ye Old Sparrowhawk Inn ☂

Wheatley Lane Rd BB12 9QG
☎ 01282 603034 📠 01282 603035
e-mail: mail@yeoldsparrowhawk.co.uk
web: www.yeoldsparrowhawk.co.uk
dir: *M65 junct 13, A6068, at rdbt take 1st exit
0.25m. Turn right onto Carr Hall Rd, at top turn left
0.25m, pub on right*

Sipping a pint outside the half-timbered
Sparrowhawk on a summer's evening is one of
life's great pleasures. The pub stands at the
gateway to Pendle Forest, famous for its witches,
but here you'll find friendly service and stylish
surroundings. The classically trained chefs work
with locally sourced fresh ingredients to create
menus that include stilton-glazed Pendle pork
chop with Lyonnaise sauté potatoes and Mr
Mellin's traditional sausages with mash and
onion gravy.

Open all wk **Bar Meals** L served Mon-Sat 12-2.30,
Sun 12-8 booking required D served Mon-Sat
5.30-9.30, Sun 12-8 booking required Av main
course £10.50 **Restaurant** L served Mon-Sat
12-2.30, Sun 12-8 booking required D served
Mon-Sat 5.30-9.30, Sun 12-8 booking required
Fixed menu price fr £9 ◀ Thwaites Cask, Draught
Bass, Moorhouse Blonde Witch, Black Sheep
Best ☼ Addlestones. ☂ 13 **Facilities** Children's menu
Dogs allowed Garden Parking

PARBOLD

The Eagle & Child ☂

Maltkiln Ln, Bispham Green L40 3SG
☎ 01257 462297 📠 01257 464718
dir: *3m from M6 junct 27. Over Parbold Hill, follow
signs for Bispham Green on right*

This pub maintains its traditional atmosphere
and offers five regularly changing guest ales,
real ciders and a beer festival every May. All food
is made on the premises with ingredients from
local suppliers. The bar menu is extensive with
the likes of crayfish and lemon risotto; chargrilled
sweet cured gammon; and steak and real ale
pie. The carte menu might include pan-fried
Gressingham duck strips with orange and brandy
sauce. There's a deli shop in the barn next door.

Open all wk **Bar Meals** L served all wk 12-2
booking required D served Sun-Thu 5.30-8.30, Fri-
Sat 5.30-9 booking required Av main course £12
Restaurant L served all wk 12-2 booking required D
served Sun-Thu 5.30-8.30, Fri-Sat 5.30-9 booking
required ⊕ FREE HOUSE ◀ Moorhouse Black Cat
Mild, Thwaites Bitter, Southport Golden Sands, guest
ales. ☂ 6 **Facilities** Children's menu Family room
Dogs allowed Garden Parking

TUNSTALL

The Lunesdale Arms ♥

LA6 2QN ☎ 015242 74203 📄 015242 74229
e-mail: info@thelunesdale.co.uk
*dir: M6 junct 36. A65 Kirkby Lonsdale. A638
Lancaster. Pub 2m on right*

Set in a small village in the beautiful Lune Valley,
The Lunesdale Arms has quite a reputation for
its food, wines and fine regional beers. Presided
over by an ever-popular landlady, the pub is
bright, cheery and welcoming. The food is freshly
prepared, with bread baked on the premises.
Most of the meat is supplied by local farms,
and there is always roast lamb, beef or pork for
Sunday lunch. Both lunch and evening menus
are likely to change on a daily basis according
to the seasonality of ingredients and new ideas.
Dishes range from Lancashire cheese rarebit with
smoked Cumbrian ham to roasted fillet of salmon
on a bed of Puy lentils with roasted tomatoes,
peppers and balsamic vinegar, or steak,
Guinness and mushroom pie with chips.

Open Closed: 25-26 Dec, Mon (ex BH) **Bar Meals** L
served Tue-Fri 12-2, Sat-Sun 12-2.30 booking
required D served Tue-Sun 6-9 booking required Av
main course £10.75 **Restaurant** L served Tue-Fri
12-2, Sat-Sun 12-2.30 booking required D served
Tue-Sun 6-9 booking required Av 3 course à la carte
fr £20 ⊕ FREE HOUSE ◀ Black Sheep, Dent Aviator,
Guinness. ♥ 8 **Facilities** Children's menu Family
room Dogs allowed Garden Parking

WHALLEY

The Three Fishes ◎ ♥

Mitton Rd, Mitton BB7 9PQ
☎ 01254 826888 📄 01254 826026
e-mail: enquiries@thethreefishes.com
*dir: M6 junct 31, A59 to Clitheroe. Follow signs for
Whalley, take B6246 for 2m*

Mitton lies in a wedge of land between the
Rivers Hodder and Ribble, and The Three Fishes
has been a public house for some 400 years,
supposedly named after the fishes in the coat
of arms of the last abbot of Whalley Abbey. The
21st-century interior very much respects the
past and retains its most attractive features,
including the big open fires. The strength of the
menu of regional and British classics comes
from using best quality local produce. A generous
selection includes braised shin of Ribble Valley
beef; toad in the hole with Forager's Cumberland
sausage; and breast of devilled Goosnargh
chicken. Salads, lunchtime sandwiches and light
meals are also available, while children have
their own, quite grown-up, menu.

Open all day all wk Closed: 25 Dec **Bar Meals** L
served Mon-Sat 12-2, Sun 12-10.30 D served
Mon-Fri 6-9, Sat 5.30-9, Sun 12-10.30 Av main
course £10.95 food served all day ⊕ FREE
HOUSE ◀ Thwaites Traditional, Thwaites
Bomber, Bowland Brewery Hen Harrier. ♥ 13
Facilities Children's menu Dogs allowed Garden
Parking

BELTON

The Queen's Head ★★★★ RR 🎖

2 Long St LE12 9TP
☎ 01530 222359 📠 01530 224860
e-mail: enquiries@thequeenshead.org
web: www.thequeenshead.org
dir: *On B5324 between Coalville & Loughborough*

This village centre pub has all-round appeal, whether you want to settle into a leather sofa in the contemporary bar, enjoy the food in the restaurant, garden or terrace, or stay overnight in a smartly designed bedroom. A Lite Bites/ Classics menu incorporates club sandwiches; burger and fries; risotto of the day; and sausage and mash. The modern British set menu offers starters of grilled red mullet with houmous and cucumber spaghetti; and carpaccio of beef, tarragon cream and rocket, with mains including fillet or rump of beef with smoked mash and cauliflower cheese; sweet potato curry with jasmine rice and home-made naan bread; and assiette of rabbit with beetroot purée.

Open all day all wk Closed: 25-26 Dec **Bar Meals** L served all wk 12-2.30, Sat all day D served Mon-Fri 7-9.30, Sat all day Av main course £11 **Restaurant** L served all wk 12-2.30, Sun 12-4 D served Mon-Sat 7-9 Fixed menu price fr £13 Av 3 course à la carte fr £25 ⊕ FREE HOUSE ◀ Worthington, Pedigree, Queens Special ♂ Merrydown. 🎖 14 **Facilities** Children's menu Play area Dogs allowed Garden Parking **Rooms** 6

EVINGTON

The Cedars 🎖

Main St LE5 6DN ☎ 0116 273 0482
e-mail: cedars@king-henrys-taverns.co.uk
dir: *From London Road out of Leicester turn left at lights, follow road to Evington. Pub located in centre of Evington village*

King Henry's Taverns, the owners, like to say that you get two for the price of one here – and you can. The Bar Restaurant serves the group's usual range of competitively priced, freshly prepared steaks, fish and seafood, rumpburgers, traditional favourites, and international and vegetarian dishes. Take the Titanic Challenge – a 48oz (uncooked) rump steak, too big to be cooked 'well done'. Panoramic windows in the main eating area overlook a fountain and pond, and the gardens are a great place for alfresco dining. Friday nights here are devoted to karaoke – you have been warned!

Open all day all wk noon-11 **Bar Meals** Av main course £3 food served all day **Restaurant** food served all day ⊕ KING HENRY'S TAVERNS ◀ Guinness, IPA, Marstons Pedigree. 🎖 15 **Facilities** Children's menu Play area Family room Garden Parking

GRIMSTON

The Black Horse

3 Main St LE14 3BZ ☎ 01664 812358
e-mail: wymeswold@supanet.com
dir: *Telephone for directions*

A traditional 16th-century coaching inn
displaying much cricketing memorabilia in a
quiet village with views over the Vale of Belvoir.
Overlooking the village green, there are plenty
of opportunities for country walks, or perhaps
a game of pétanque on the pub's floodlit pitch.
Good home-cooked meals with daily specials,
including lots of game. Fish choices and specials
include monkfish, lemon sole, whole grilled
plaice, and Arctic char. There is an alfresco
eating area for warmer weather.

Open all wk 12-3 6-11 (Sun 12-6) Bar Meals L
served Mon-Sat 12-2, Sun 12-3 booking required D
served Mon-Sat 6-9 booking required Restaurant L
served Mon-Sat 6-9 booking required D served Mon-
Sat 6-9 booking required ⊕ FREE HOUSE ◀ Adnams,
Marston's Pedigree, St Austell Tribute, Belvoir Mild,
guest ales Ŏ Thatchers Gold. Facilities Children's
menu Dogs allowed Garden

LOUGHBOROUGH

The Falcon Inn ★★★ INN

64 Main St, Long Whatton LE12 5DG
☎ 01509 842416 📄 01509 646802
e-mail: enquiries@thefalconinnlongwhatton.com

Just ten minutes' drive from East Midlands
airport and the M1, this traditional country inn
offers great food, stylish en suite accommodation
in a converted stable and school house at the
rear of the pub, and stunning award-winning
flower displays in the outdoor areas in summer.
Food choices range from classic pub favourites
like filled jacket potatoes; roast rack of lamb;
and steak and ale pie to more exotic dishes
including a full Lebanese mezzeh that reflects
the traditions of Lebanese-born proprietor Jad
Otaki. Look out for the special events throughout
the year.

Open all day all wk Bar Meals L served all wk
12-2 D served all wk 6.30-9 Av main course £9.50
Restaurant L served all wk 12-2 D served all wk
6.30-9 booking required Av 3 course à la carte fr
£18 ⊕ EVERARDS ◀ Tiger Best Bitter, Everards
Original, guest ale. Facilities Children's menu
Family room Garden Parking Rooms 11

LUTTERWORTH

Man at Arms 🍷

The Green, Bitteswell LE17 4SB
☎ 01455 552540
e-mail: man@king-henrys-taverns.co.uk
dir: *Take Ullesthorpe road out of Lutterworth, turn left at small white cottage. Pub on left after college on village green*

This was the first pub bought by the King Henry's Taverns group, named after a bequest left by Henry VIII to the nearby village of Bitteswell to provide a 'man at arms' at times of war. Henry was indeed a big eater and, yes, some pretty sizeable meals are available here, but there are healthy options too. A change of decor and style is promised, modelled on sister pub The Ragley Boat Stop in Barrow-upon-Trent.

Open all day all wk noon-11 **Bar Meals** Av main course £3 food served all day **Restaurant** food served all day KING HENRY'S TAVERNS Greene King IPA, Marstons Pedigree, Guinness. 🍷 15 **Facilities** Children's menu Play area Family room Garden Parking

NETHER BROUGHTON

The Red House 🍷

23 Main St LE14 3HB
☎ 01664 822429 📠 01664 823805
e-mail: bernie@mulberrypubco.com
dir: *M1 junct 21A take A46. Right onto A606. Or take A606 from Nottingham.*

The Red House is a fine mixture of a 300-year-old village pub with log fires in winter and light contemporary design. The lounge bar opens into an airy restaurant, and a conservatory area overlooks the outdoor bar, terrace and courtyard grill. Immaculate gardens include a small play area and a permanent marquee for weddings, parties and corporate functions. Dishes range from locally sourced pork pie, or sausages of the week in the bar, to diver-caught scallops, or braised lamb shank in the restaurant. An ideal spot for walking, fishing and bird-watching.

Open all day all wk **Bar Meals** Av main course £10 food served all day **Restaurant** Av 3 course à la carte fr £25.30 food served all day MULBERRY PUB CO LTD Guinness, Red House Special, Greene King IPA. 🍷 13 **Facilities** Children's menu Play area Dogs allowed Garden Parking

OLD DALBY

The Crown Inn ☙

Debdale Hill LE14 3LF ☎ 01664 823134
e-mail: oldcrown@castlerockbrewery.co.uk
dir: *A46 turn for Willoughby/Broughton. Right into Nottingham Ln, left to Old Dalby*

A classic creeper-covered, country pub dating from 1509, set in extensive gardens and orchards, with small rooms, all with open fires. The new owners have returned the pub to its former glory - traditional with a contemporary feel. They place a strong emphasis on fresh seasonal produce: if the food doesn't all come from Leicestershire, the county's suppliers are nonetheless wholeheartedly supported. Expect dishes like pan-fried sea bass with lemon and crayfish risotto, or oven roasted rack and braised shoulder of lamb with minted pea purée. There's a good choice of real ales to help wash down a meal, or to enjoy without food: Castle Rock Hemlock and Harvest Pale are among the selection.

Open all wk noon-close Closed: Mon L **Bar Meals** L served Tue-Fri 12-2, Sat-Sun 12-3 booking required D served Tue-Sat 6-9 booking required Av main course £8 **Restaurant** L served Tue-Sun 12-2 booking required D served Tue-Sun 6-9 booking required Av 3 course à la carte fr £25 ⊕ FREE HOUSE ◀ Castle Rock Hemlock, Beaver, Harvest Pale, 3 Guest Ales ♻ Stowford Press. ☙ 10 **Facilities** Children's menu Family room Dogs allowed Garden Parking

SOMERBY

Stilton Cheese Inn ☙

High St LE14 2QB ☎ 01664 454394
dir: *From A606 between Melton Mowbray & Oakham follow signs to Pickwell & Somerby. Enter village, 1st right to centre, pub on left*

This attractive 17th-century inn enjoys a good reputation for its food, beer, wine and malt whiskies. Built from mellow local sandstone, it stands in the centre of the village surrounded by beautiful countryside. An interesting range of food from the regularly-changing specials board includes smoked salmon and mascarpone roulade; Rutland Water trout with prawn and tarragon butter; liver, bacon, onion gravy with bubble and squeak; and ginger and walnut treacle tart.

Open all wk 12-3 6-11 (Sun 7-11) **Bar Meals** L served all wk 12-2 D served Mon-Sat 6-9, Sun 7-9 Av main course £9 **Restaurant** L served all wk 12-2 D served Mon-Sat 6-9, Sun 7-9 ⊕ FREE HOUSE ◀ Grainstore Ten Fifty, Brewster's Hophead, Belvoir Star, Tetley's Cask, Marston's Pedigree. ☙ 15 **Facilities** Children's menu Family room Garden Parking

WELHAM

The Old Red Lion ♚

Main St LE16 7UJ ☎ 01858 565253
e-mail: redlion@king-henrys-taverns.co.uk

This old country pub is part of the King Henry's Taverns group. It was once a coaching inn, and the small area opposite the main bar was originally the archway where the coaches would swing in to offload their weary passengers. In winter the leather chesterfields around the log fires create a cosy feel, while in summer take an evening stroll along one of the many footpaths and bridleways. The menu goes in for traditional pub grub, burgers, curries, and vegetarian dishes. For those with a larger appetite it offers the Mary Rose Special, a 16oz T-bone steak.

Open all day all wk noon-11 Bar Meals Av main course £3 food served all day Restaurant food served all day ⊕ KING HENRY'S TAVERNS ◀ Greene King IPA, Marstons Pedigree, Guinness. ♚ 15 Facilities Children's menu Play area Family room Parking

WOODHOUSE EAVES

The Wheatsheaf Inn ★★★ INN ♚

Brand Hill LE12 8SS
☎ 01509 890320 📄 01509 890571
e-mail: richard@wheatsheafinn.net
dir: M1 junct 22, follow Quorn signs

Around the turn of the 19th century, when local quarrymen wanted somewhere to drink, they built themselves the Wheatsheaf. It's what locals call a Dim's Inn, a succession of pubs run by three generations of the Dimblebee family. Bistro-style menus include chargrilled prime steaks and popular Wheatsheaf burgers. Fresh fish is a feature of the daily chalkboard - maybe linguine with prawns and salmon in creamy saffron sauce. An additional dining room is now available called The Mess. Three modern en suite bedrooms are available.

Open Closed: Sun eve in winter Bar Meals L served Mon-Fri 12-2, Sat 12-2.30, Sun 12-3.30 D served All wk 6.30-9.15 Restaurant L served Mon-Fri 12-2, Sat 12-2.30, Sun 12-3.30 D served All wk 6.30-9.15 ⊕ FREE HOUSE ◀ Greene King Abbot Ale, Draught Burton Ale, Timothy Taylor Landlord, Adnams Broadside, Tetley Smooth, guest ale. ♚ 14 Facilities Children's menu Dogs allowed Garden Parking Rooms 3

ALLINGTON

The Welby Arms ★★★★ INN ♛

The Green NG32 2EA

☎ 01400 281361 📄 01400 281361

dir: *From Grantham take either A1 N, or A52 W. Allington 1.5m*

A creeper-covered inn overlooking the village green, the Welby Arms has a traditional country pub aspect. It is popular with travellers on the A1 as it also provides overnight accommodation. An excellent choice of real ales is offered alongside home-cooked food. Bar snacks take in home-made beef burgers, baguettes and chilli, and there is a full restaurant menu. Specials include steak and kidney pudding or monkfish wrapped in Parma ham with king prawns.

Open all wk 12-3 6-11 (Sun 12-10.30) Bar Meals L served Mon-Sat 12-2 D served Mon-Sun 6-9 Av main course £4.95 Restaurant L served Mon-Sun 12-2 booking required D served Mon-Sat 6-9, Sun 6-8.30 booking required Av 3 course à la carte fr £19.95 ⊕ FREE HOUSE ◀ John Smith's, Interbrew Bass, Timothy Taylor Landlord, Jennings Cumberland Ale, Badger Tanglefoot, Adnams Broadside. ♛ 22 Facilities Children's menu Garden Parking Rooms 3

FROGNALL

The Goat ♛

155 Spalding Rd PE6 8SA ☎ 01778 347629

e-mail: graysdebstokes@btconnect.com

dir: *A1 to Peterborough, A15 to Market Deeping, old A16 to Spalding, pub approx 1.5m from A15 & A16 junct*

Families are welcome at this cosy, friendly country free house, which has an open fire, large beer garden and plenty to amuse the children. Main courses include beef stroganoff; pork in sweet and sour sauce; leek and mushroom pie; warm bacon and stilton salad; and home-made prawn curry. Beer is taken seriously, with five different guest ales each week and regular beer festivals throughout the year.

Open all wk 11.30-3 6-11.30 (Sun noon-11) Closed: 25 Dec, 1 Jan Bar Meals L served Mon-Sat 12-2 booking required D served Mon-Sat 6.30-9.30, Sun 12-9 booking required Av main course £9 Restaurant L served Mon-Sat 12-2, Sun 12-9 booking required D served Mon-Sat 6.30-9.30, Sun 12-9 booking required Fixed menu price fr £15.95 Av 3 course à la carte fr £18 ⊕ FREE HOUSE ◀ Guest ales: Elgoods, Batemans, Abbeydale, Nethergate, Hopshackle ♖ Westons Old Rosie, Broadoak Moonshine, Thatchers Cheddar valley. ♛ 16 Facilities Children's menu Play area Family room Garden Parking

LINCOLN

The Victoria ☻

6 Union Rd LN1 3BJ ☎ 01522 541000
e-mail: jonathanjpc@aol.com
dir: *From city outskirts follow signs for Cathedral Quarter. Pub 2 mins' walk from all major up-hill car parks*

Situated right next to the Westgate entrance of the Castle and within a stone's throw of Lincoln Cathedral, a long-standing drinkers' pub with a range of real ales, including six changing guest beers, ciders and perries, as well as two beer festivals a year. As well as the fantastic views of the castle, the pub also offers splendid meals made from exclusively home-prepared food including hot baguettes and filled bacon rolls, Saturday breakfast and Sunday lunches. House specials include sausage and mash, various pies, chilli con carne and home-made lasagne.

Open all day all wk 11-mdnt (Fri-Sat 11-1am)
Bar Meals L served all wk 12-2.30 Av main course £4.50 ⊕ JPC ◀ Timothy Taylor Landlord, Batemans XB, Castle Rock Harvest Pale, guest ales Ŏ Westons. ☻ 10 **Facilities** Children's menu Play area Dogs allowed Garden Parking

SOUTH WITHAM

Blue Cow Inn & Brewery

High St NG33 5QB
☎ 01572 768432 📄 01572 768432
e-mail: enquiries@bluecowinn.co.uk
dir: *Between Stamford & Grantham on A1*

Just in Lincolnshire, with the Rutland border a few hundred yards away, this once-derelict, 13th-century inn stands close to the source of the River Witham. Part-timbered outside, the interior has a wealth of beamed ceilings and walls, stone floors and open log fires when the easterly winds whip across The Fens from Siberia. Simon Crathorn brews his own beers. The inn has a patio beer garden for warm evenings.

Open all day all wk 11-11 **Bar Meals** Av main course £8.50 food served all day **Restaurant** food served all day ⊕ FREE HOUSE **Facilities** Children's menu Family room Dogs allowed Garden Parking

WOODHALL SPA

Village Limits Country Pub, Restaurant & Motel ☻

Stixwould Rd LN10 6UJ

☎ 01526 353312 📄 01526 352203

e-mail: info@villagelimits.co.uk

dir: *At rdbt on main street follow Petwood Hotel signs. Motel 500yds past Petwood Hotel*

The pub and restaurant are situated in the original part of the building, so expect bare beams and old world charm. Typical meals, championing the ingredients of many local Lincolnshire suppliers, include fillet steak with wild mushrooms; chargrilled rainbow trout; and gammon steak. There's a good choice of real ales to wash it all down

Open Closed: Mon & Sun eve **Bar Meals** L served Tue-Sat 11.30-2 booking required D served Tue-Sat 6.30-9 booking required Av main course £10 **Restaurant** L served Tue-Sun 11.30-2 booking required D served Tue-Sat 6.30-9 booking required Av 3 course à la carte fr £19 ⊕ FREE HOUSE ◀ Batemans XB, Tetley's Smooth Flow, Highwood Tom Wood's Best, Fulstow IPA, Dixon's Major Bitter. ☻ 8 **Facilities** Children's menu Garden Parking

N1

The Barnsbury ☻

209-211 Liverpool Rd, Islington N1 1LX

☎ 020 7607 5519 📄 020 7607 3256

e-mail: info@thebarnsbury.co.uk

dir: *Please telephone for directions*

This 'free house and dining room' in the heart of Islington is a welcome addition to the London scene. It's a gastro-pub where both the food and the prices are well conceived – and its walled garden makes it a secluded and sought-after summer oasis for alfresco relaxation. The food is cooked from daily supplies of fresh ingredients which have been bought direct from the market, itemised in refreshingly concise terms on the menu. Weekday lunches range from oysters to mushroom tagliatelle or lamb shank shepherd's pie. The dinner choice is also a no-nonsense selection of the day's produce: grilled sardines, caponata and basil oil could be your starter. Pork fillet with sweet potato purée and caramelised apples gives a flavour of the half dozen main course options. Pear and cranberry crumble with clotted cream rounds things off nicely.

Open all day all wk noon-11 (Sun noon-10.30) Closed: 25-26 Dec, 1 Jan **Bar Meals** L served Mon-Fri 12-3 Av main course £8 **Restaurant** L served Sat-Sun 12-4 D served all wk 6.30-10 Av 3 course à la carte fr £26 ⊕ FREE HOUSE ◀ Gravesend Shrimpers, 2 guest ales ♂ Thatchers Gold. ☻ 12 **Facilities** Children's menu Dogs allowed Garden

N19

The Landseer ♥

37 Landseer Rd N19 4JU ☎ 020 7263 4658
e-mail: info@thelandseer.wanadoo.co.uk
dir: *Nearest tube stations: Archway & Tufnell Park*

Sunday roasts are a speciality at this unpretentious gastro-pub. Well-kept beers and a range of ciders are supported by 14 wines served by the glass. This is an ideal spot to relax with the weekend papers, or while away an evening with one of the pub's extensive library of board games. Weekend lunches and daily evening meals are served from separate bar and restaurant menus. Recent change of ownership.

Open all day all wk noon-mdnt (Mon-Tue & Sun noon-11) Closed: 25 Dec **Bar Meals** Av main course £11 food served all day **Restaurant** food served all day ⊕ FREE HOUSE ◀ Timothy Taylor Landlord, Abbot Ale, Adnams ♂ Brothers Pear Cider, Aspall. ♥ 14 **Facilities** Children's menu Play area Dogs allowed

NW1

The Engineer ♥

65 Gloucester Av, Primrose Hill NW1 8JH
☎ 020 7722 0950 🖷 020 7483 0592
e-mail: info@the-engineer.com
dir: *Telephone for directions*

Situated in a residential part of Primrose Hill close to Camden Market, this unassuming corner street pub is worth seeking out. Built by Isambard Kingdom Brunel in 1841, it attracts a discerning dining crowd for imaginative and well-prepared food and a friendly, laid-back atmosphere. Inside it is fashionably rustic, with a spacious bar area, sturdy wooden tables with candles, simple decor and changing art exhibitions in the restaurant area. A walled, paved and heated garden to the rear is extremely popular in fine weather. The regularly-changing menu features an eclectic mix of inspired home-made dishes and uses organic or free-range meats.

Open all day all wk 9am-11pm (Sun & BH 9am-10.30pm) **Bar Meals** Av main course £15.50 food served all day **Restaurant** L served Mon-Fri 12-3, Sat-Sun 12.30-4 booking required D served Mon-Sat 7-11, Sun & BH 7-10.30 booking required Fixed menu price fr £30 Av 3 course à la carte fr £30 ◀ Erdinger, Bombardier, Amstel. ♥ 10 **Facilities** Children's menu Family room Dogs allowed Garden

SW7

The Anglesea Arms ⬤

15 Selwood Ter, South Kensington SW7 3QG

☎ 020 7373 7960

e-mail: enquiries@angleseaarms.com

dir: *Telephone for directions*

Feeling like a country pub in the middle of South Kensington, the interior has barely changed since 1827, though the dining area has been tastefully updated with panelled walls and leather-clad chairs, plus there's a heated and covered terrace. The Great Train Robbery was said to have been plotted here. Lunch and dinner menus place an emphasis on quality ingredients, fresh preparation and cosmopolitan flavours. From the daily changing menu expect perhaps a charcuterie plate with celeriac remoulade and capers; chicken and vegetable pie; lightly battered whiting and home-made chips; and apple and blackberry crumble with custard. Sunday lunches are popular, booking is advisable.

Open all wk Closed: 25-26 Dec **Bar Meals** L served Mon-Fri 12-3, Sat-Sun 12-5 D served Mon-Fri 6.30-10, Sat 6-10, Sun 6-9.30 Av main course £12 **Restaurant** L served Sat-Sun 12-5 booking required D served Mon-Fri 6.30-10, Sat 6-10, Sun 6-9.30 Av 3 course à la carte fr £19 ⊕ FREE HOUSE ◀ Fuller's London Pride, Adnams Bitter, Broadside, Brakspear, Hogs Back Tea. ⬤ 21 **Facilities** Children's menu Dogs allowed Garden

SW13

The Bull's Head ⬤

373 Lonsdale Rd, Barnes SW13 9PY

☎ 020 8876 5241 ▤ 020 8876 1546

e-mail: jazz@thebullshead.com

dir: *Telephone for directions*

Facing the Thames and established in 1684, the Bull's Head has become a major venue for mainstream modern jazz and blues. Nightly concerts draw music lovers from far and wide, helped in no small measure by some fine cask-conditioned ales, over 200 wines, and more than 80 malt whiskies. Traditional home-cooked meals are served in the bar, with dishes ranging from haddock and crab to a variety of roasts and pies. Popular home-made puddings. An important and intrinsic feature of the pub is the Thai menu, available throughout the pub in the evening.

Open all day all wk noon-mdnt Closed: 25 Dec **Bar Meals** L served all wk 12-4 Av main course £8 food served all day **Restaurant** D served all wk 6-11 Av 3 course à la carte fr £12 ⊕ YOUNG & CO BREWERY PLC ◀ Young's Special, Bitter, Winter Warmer, St Georges, Ramrod, Guinness. ⬤ 32 **Facilities** Children's menu Family room Dogs allowed Garden

W4

The Devonshire ⚜🍷

126 Devonshire Rd, Chiswick W4 2JJ
☎ 020 7592 7962 📄 020 7592 1603
e-mail: reservations@gordonramsay.com
dir: 150yds off Chiswick High Rd. 100yds from
Hogarth rdbt & A4

A laid back and unpretentious gastro-pub
located in a leafy district of Chiswick. Expect
high ceilings, large windows, original fireplaces
and the restoration of its unique wood panelling
and façade as well as an attractive landscaped
garden to the rear of the pub. A typical three
courses might comprise swede and honey soup
with pressed ham hock; followed by Gloucester
pork sausages with champ and red onion gravy;
and cranberry and Clementine shortcake to
finish. Children are made to feel welcome with a
secure garden to play in, plus books, crayons and
games to keep them entertained.

Open all day 12-11 (Wed-Thu 6-12, Sun 12-10.30)
Closed: Mon-Tue **Bar Meals** L served Fri-Sun booking
required D served Wed-Sun booking required Av main
course £12 food served all day **Restaurant** L served
Fri 12-3, Sat 12-4, Sun 12-10.30 booking required
D served Fri 6-10.30, Sat 5-10.30, Sun 12-10.30
booking required ⊕ GORDON RAMSAY HOLDINGS
LTD ◀ London Pride, Guinness, Caledonian
Deuchars IPA, San Miguel, Kronenberg. 🍷 12
Facilities Children's menu Dogs allowed Garden

BARNSTON

Fox and Hounds 🍷

Barnston Rd CH61 1BW
☎ 0151 648 7685 📄 0151 648 0872
e-mail: ralphleech@hotmail.com
dir: M53 junct 4 take A5137 to Heswell. Right to
Barnston on B5138. Pub on A551

The pub, located in a conservation area,
was built in 1911 on the site of an alehouse
and barn. Its Edwardian character has been
preserved in the pitch pine woodwork and leaded
windows. Incredible collections of 1920s/1930s
memorabilia include ashtrays, horse brasses,
police helmets and empty whisky cases. Real ales
and 12 wines by the glass are served alongside
a range of bar snacks such as toasted ciabattas,
jacket potatoes, sandwiches and meat or seafood
platters. Daily specials and desserts are posted
on the chalkboard.

Open all wk 11-11 (Sun noon-10.30) **Bar Meals** L
served Mon-Sat 12-2, Sun 12-2.30 booking required
Av main course £6.50 ⊕ FREE HOUSE ◀ Websters
Yorkshire Bitter, Theakston's Best & Old Peculier, 3
guest ales. 🍷 12 **Facilities** Children's menu Family
room Dogs allowed Garden Parking

HIGHTOWN

The Pheasant Inn 🍷

20 Moss Ln L38 3RA ☎ 0151 929 2106
dir: *Off the A565, on the B5193*

An original brick in the restaurant wall is dated 1719, when the pub was known as the 'Ten Billets Inn'; the present name was adopted in 1952. By the 19th century a small on-site brewery was producing just 2½ barrels a week, but today you'll find Timothy Taylor Landlord alongside Aspall's cider. The menu starts with jacket potatoes and sandwiches with interesting fillings, and typical hot dishes include baked salmon fishcakes with capers, smoked salmon and lemon chive crème fraîche; corned beef hash with free-range eggs; and daily fish special.

Open all day all wk noon-11pm (Sun noon-10.30pm) **Bar Meals** Av main course £9.50 food served all day **Restaurant** Fixed menu price fr £9.95 Av 3 course à la carte fr £20 food served all day MITCHELLS & BUTLERS Timothy Taylor Landlord Aspall Draught & Organic. 🍷 6 **Facilities** Children's menu Dogs allowed Garden Parking

BINHAM

Chequers Inn

Front St NR21 0AL ☎ 01328 830297
e-mail: steve@binhamchequers.co.uk
dir: *On B1388 between Wells-next-the-Sea & Walsingham*

The Chequers is home to the Front Street Brewery, but even though they brew their own beer they still have regular Norfolk/East Anglian guest ales, and a large selection of bottled beers. The pub has been owned by a village charity since the early 1640s, and was originally a trade hall. Many stones from the nearby priory were used in its construction. The daily changing menu offers dishes such as Norfolk duck pâté, fresh lobster thermidor and plum crumble.

Open all wk 11.30-2.30 6-11 (Fri-Sat 11.30-2.30 6-11.30 Sun noon-2.30 7-11) **Bar Meals** L served all wk 12-2 D served all wk 6-9 FREE HOUSE Binham Cheer 3.9%, Callums Ale 4.3%, Unity Strong 5%, Seasonal specials, micro brewery on site. **Facilities** Children's menu Garden Parking

BLAKENEY

The Kings Arms ▼

Westgate St NR25 7NQ

☎ 01263 740341 📄 01263 740391

e-mail: kingsarmsnorfolk@btconnect.com

dir: *From Holt or Fakenham take A148, then B1156 for 6m to Blakeney*

This Grade II listed free house is located on the beautiful north Norfolk coast, close to the famous salt marshes. Owners Marjorie and Howard Davies settled here after long and successful showbiz careers and their son Nic, now handles the day-to-day running of the pub. The Kings Arms is an ideal centre for walking, or perhaps a ferry trip to the nearby seal colony and world-famous bird sanctuaries. Locally-caught fish and seasonal seafood feature on the menu – crab in summer and mussels in winter - together with local game, home-made lasagne and steaks.

Open all day all wk 11-11 Closed: 25 Dec eve **Bar Meals** Av main course £6 ⊕ FREE HOUSE 🍺 Greene King Old Speckled Hen, Woodforde's Wherry Best Bitter, Marston's Pedigree, Adnams Best Bitter. ☘ 12 **Facilities** Children's menu Play area Family room Dogs allowed Garden Parking

BLAKENEY

White Horse Hotel ▼

4 High St NR25 7AL

☎ 01263 740574 📄 01263 741303

e-mail: info@blakeneywhitehorse.co.uk

dir: *From A148 (Cromer to King's Lynn road) onto A149 signed to Blakeney*

A short stroll from Blakeney quayside stands the 17th-century White Horse, formerly a coaching inn, built of traditional brick-and-flint. Inside, the bar, dining room and airy conservatory are tastefully decorated in creams and darkwood with soft lamplight, and the informal bar is adorned with local artwork. As befits its seaside location, fish dominates the constantly evolving menu, with lobster, crab and mussels sourced from local fishermen. It also delves into the rich larder of local produce available along the coast, including meat and game from nearby Holkham Estate, and soft fruit, salads and vegetables from small farms and suppliers, and both bread and puddings are made on the premises.

Open all wk 10.30am-11pm Closed: 25 Dec **Bar Meals** L served all wk 12-2.15 D served Thu-Sun 6-9, Fri-Sat 6-9.30 ⊕ FREE HOUSE 🍺 Adnams Bitter, Woodforde's Wherry, Adnams Broadside, Yetmans ○ Aspalls. ☘ 12 **Facilities** Children's menu Family room Garden Parking

BRANCASTER STAITHE

The White Horse ★★★ HL ◎◎ ⬤

PE31 8BY

☎ 01485 210262 📄 01485 210930
e-mail: reception@whitehorsebrancaster.co.uk
dir: A149 (coast road), midway between Hunstanton
& Wells-next-the-Sea

A popular gastro-pub gloriously situated in
an Area of Outstanding Natural Beauty, with
panoramic views from its conservatory restaurant
and sun-deck over tidal creeks and marshes
to Scolt Head Island. Scrubbed pine tables and
high-backed settles help to create a welcoming
atmosphere for diners ready for food based
on fresh local produce. The extensive, daily-
changing restaurant menus and specials offer
cockles, mussels and oysters, in season; slow-
roasted belly of Norfolk pork with caramelised
root vegetables and apple compote; confit duck
leg with mixed beans and chorizo; pan-fried fillet
of sea bass with pancetta, broad beans, peas
and baby leeks. Tastefully furnished en suite
bedrooms look out over the water.

Open all day all wk 9am-11pm (Sun 9am-10.30pm)
Bar Meals Av main course £7 food served all day
Restaurant L served all wk 12-2 booking required D
served all wk 6.30-9 booking required Av 3 course
à la carte fr £25 ⊕ FREE HOUSE ◀ Adnams Best
Bitter, Fuller's London Pride, Woodforde's Wherry,
guest Ŏ Aspall. ♗ 17 Facilities Children's menu
Dogs allowed Garden Parking Rooms 15

EATON

The Red Lion ⬤

50 Eaton St NR4 7LD

☎ 01603 454787 📄 01603 456939
e-mail: redlioneaton@hotmail.co.uk
dir: Off A11, 2m S of Norwich city centre

This heavily-beamed 17th-century coaching
inn has bags of character, thanks to its Dutch
gables, panelled walls and inglenook fireplaces.
The covered terrace enables customers to enjoy
one of the real ales or sample the extensive
wine list outside during the summer months.
The extensive lunch menu offers everything
from steak and kidney suet pudding to grilled
red snapper fillets with mango and sweet chilli
salsa; or Swannington baked gammon with a
Cumberland sauce.

Open all day all wk Bar Meals L served all wk
12-2.15 booking required D served all wk 6.30-9
booking required Restaurant L served all wk 12-2.15
booking required D served all wk 6.30-9 booking
required ⊕ ENTERPRISE INNS ◀ Old Speckled Hen,
Courage Directors, Greene King IPA, Adnams Bitter,
Woodforde's Wherry, Fuller's London Pride. ♗ 10
Facilities Children's menu Garden Parking

GREAT RYBURGH

The Blue Boar Inn

NR21 0DX ☎ 01328 829212
dir: *Off A1067 4m S of Fakenham*

Dating back to 1683, this whitewashed free house stands opposite the round towered Saxon church of St Andrew. A large magnolia tree ushers you into the rambling old building with its beams and inglenook fireplace. Adnams ales are offered at the bar, whilst local produce features strongly on the extensive chalkboard menu. Typical dishes include breast of Norfolk chicken with prawn thermidor; Ryburgh lamb cutlets with mustard mash; and steamed Brancaster mussels when in season. Recent change of Landlord.

Open 11.30-2.30 6.30-11.30 Closed: Tue Bar Meals L served Wed-Mon 11.30-2.30 D served Wed-Mon 6.30-10.30 Av main course £10 Restaurant L served Wed-Mon 11.30-2.30 D served Wed-Mon 6.30-10.30 ⊕ FREE HOUSE ◀ Adnams Bitter, Bass, Murphy's. Facilities Children's menu Play area Family room Garden Parking

HAPPISBURGH

The Hill House ♥

NR12 0PW
☎ 01692 650004 ▤ 01692 650004
dir: *5m from Stalham, 8m from North Walsham*

Expect to be corrected if you pronounce Happisburgh the way it's spelt - it's Haze-borough. Once the favourite haunt of the creator of Sherlock Holmes, Sir Arthur Conan Doyle, this Grade II listed, 16th-century coaching inn offers good value bar food including sandwiches, jacket potatoes, a range of ploughman's and local crab and fish dishes in season. The restaurant menu includes a wide selection of fish and seafood, steaks and other meat dishes, as well as a vegetarian selection. Look out for the Solstice Beer Festival in June for the chance to sample a wide range of real ales, ciders and perries.

Open all wk noon-11.30 (Mon-Wed noon-3 7-11.30 low season) Bar Meals L served all wk 12-2.30 D served Mon-Sat 7-9.30, Sun 7-9 booking required Restaurant L served all wk 12-2.30 D served Mon-Sat 7-9.30, Sun 7-9 booking required ⊕ FREE HOUSE ◀ Shepherd Neame Spitfire, Buffy's, Woodforde's Wherry, Adnams Bitter, House Bitter ⌀ Aspall, Westons Stowford Press. ♥ 10 Facilities Children's menu Play area Dogs allowed Garden Parking

HEVINGHAM

Marsham Arms
Freehouse ⌂ ★★★★ INN ♥

Holt Rd NR10 5NP ☎ 01603 754268
e-mail: nigelbradley@marshamarms.co.uk
web: www.marshamarms.co.uk
dir: *On B1149 N of Norwich airport, 2m through Horsford towards Holt*

Built as a roadside hostel for poor farm labourers by Victorian philanthropist and landowner Robert Marsham. Some original features remain, including the large open fireplace, and there's a spacious garden with paved patio and a dedicated family room. A good range of fresh fish dishes includes cod, haddock, sea bass, herrings and crab. Specialities such as beef stew with dumplings and beer battered haddock are backed by a daily blackboard. There are vegetarian and gluten-free dishes too. Look out for the monthly jazz nights and wine tasting evenings.

Open all wk Bar Meals L served all wk 12-2.30 D served all wk 6-9.30 Restaurant L served all wk 12-2.30 D served all wk 6-9.30 ⊕ FREE HOUSE ◀ Adnams Best, Woodforde's Wherry Best Bitter, Mauldens, Worthington, Broadside ♂ Aspall. ♥ 6 Facilities Children's menu Play area Family room Dogs allowed Garden Parking Rooms 11

HORSEY

Nelson Head

The Street NR29 4AD ☎ 01493 393378
dir: *On B1159 (coast road) between West Somerton & Sea Palling*

Located on a National Trust estate, which embraces nearby Horsey Mere, this 17th-century inn will, to many, epitomise the perfect country pub. It enjoys the tranquillity of a particularly unspoilt part of the Norfolk coast - indeed, the Broads are ½ mile away and glorious beaches only a mile - and the sheltered gardens look out towards the dunes and water meadows. Haddock and chips, cottage pie, and a selection of vegetarian choices are among the dishes available. Local beers are Woodforde's Wherry and Nelson's Revenge.

Open all day all wk 11-11 Bar Meals L served all wk 12-2.30 D served all wk 6-8.30 Restaurant L served all wk 12-2.30 D served all wk 6-8.30 ⊕ FREE HOUSE ◀ Woodforde's Wherry, Nelson's Revenge. Facilities Children's menu Play area Family room Dogs allowed Garden Parking

ITTERINGHAM

Walpole Arms ◎ ▼

NR11 7AR

☎ 01263 587258 📠 01263 587074
e-mail: goodfood@thewalpolearms.co.uk
web: www.thewalpolearms.co.uk
dir: *From Aylsham towards Blickling. After Blickling Hall take 1st right to Itteringham*

The Walpole Arms has been a pub since 1836, and the kitchen team uses the best seasonal and local produce to create thoroughly modern dishes. Both restaurant and bar offer a daily changing three-course carte; children are welcome and have their own menu to choose from. Typical starters include escabèche of red mullet with pine nuts, sultanas and butter beans; main course choices might include home-made Catalonian pork sausage with black-eyed beans and spring cabbage. Extensive gardens to the front and rear of the vine-covered terrace encourage relaxation on summer days.

Open all wk noon-3 6-11 (Sun noon-5) Closed: 25 Dec **Bar Meals** L served all wk 12-2 D served all wk 6-9.30 Av main course £11.12 **Restaurant** L served Thu-Sun 12-2 D served Thu-Sun 6-9.30 Av 3 course à la carte fr £25.50 ⊕ NOBLE ROT ASSOCIATES LTD ◀ Adnams Broadside & Bitter, Woodforde's Wherry Best Bitter, Walpole. ▼ 12 **Facilities** Children's menu Play area Dogs allowed Garden Parking

LARLING

Angel Inn ▼

NR16 2QU

☎ 01953 717963 📠 01953 718561
dir: *5m from Attleborough, 8m from Thetford. 1m from station*

Three generations of the Stammers family have been running this 17th-century free house for more than 80 years. There's a homely, local feel to the heavily-beamed public bar, whilst the lounge bar has a cosy log fire and a collection of over 100 water jugs. The cooking is underpinned by local ingredients wherever possible, and the light bites menu supplements sandwiches and jacket potatoes with ham, eggs and chips; and sausages in French bread. Main menu options start with home-made pâté; and deep-fried Camembert; moving on to choices like lamb chops with mint sauce; grilled local trout; and pork in peppered cream sauce. The pub also offers camping in Angel meadow just across the road, and an annual beer festival in August.

Open all day all wk 10am-mdnt **Bar Meals** L served Sun-Thu 12-9.30, Fri-Sat 12-10 D served Sun-Thu 12-9.30, Fri-Sat 12-10 Av main course £9.95 food served all day **Restaurant** L served Sun-Thu 12-9.30, Fri-Sat 12-10 D served Sun-Thu 12-9.30, Fri-Sat 12-10 food served all day ⊕ FREE HOUSE ◀ Adnams Bitter, Wolf Bitter, Caledonian Deuchars IPA, Timothy Taylor Landlord, Mauldons Ŏ Aspall. ▼ 10 **Facilities** Children's menu Play area Garden Parking

STOW BARDOLPH

The Hare Arms ♀

PE34 3HT

☎ 01366 382229   🖷 01366 385522

e-mail: trishmc@harearms222.wanadoo.co.uk

dir: *From King's Lynn take A10 to Downham Market. After 9m village signed on left*

Trish and David McManus have been licensees at this attractive ivy-clad pub for over 30 years. The pub was built during the Napoleonic wars and takes its name from the surrounding estate, ancestral home of the Hare family since 1553. The L-shaped bar and adjoining conservatory are packed with decades-worth of fascinating bygones. An extensive menu of regular pub food is supplemented by daily specials, including the award-winning steak and peppercorn pie, and fish dishes like whole sea bream with lemon and lime butter. The restaurant offers an à la carte menu Monday to Saturday evening.

Open all wk 11-2.30 6-11 (Sun noon-10.30) Closed: 25-26 Dec **Bar Meals** L served Mon-Sat 12-2, Sun 12-10 D served Mon-Sat 6.30-10, Sun 12-10 Av main course £10 **Restaurant** D served Mon-Sat 7-9 booking required Av 3 course à la carte fr £27 ⊕ GREENE KING ◀ Greene King Abbot Ale, IPA & Old Speckled Hen, guest ale. ♀ 7 **Facilities** Children's menu Play area Family room Garden Parking

SWANTON MORLEY

Darbys Freehouse

1&2 Elsing Rd NR20 4NY

☎ 01362 637647   🖷 01362 637928

e-mail: louisedarby@hotmail.co.uk

dir: *From A47 (Norwich to King's Lynn) take B1147 to Dereham*

Built in the 1700s as a large country house, then divided into cottages in the late 19th century. In 1987, after the village's last traditional pub closed, it was converted into the pub you see today, while retaining its old beams and inglenooks. Traditional pub food includes steak and mushroom pudding, braised lamb shank, chargrilled pork loin, scampi, beer-battered haddock, steaks, curries and a vegetarian selection. Children have their own menu and a play area.

Open all wk 11.30-3 6-11 (Sat 11.30-11, Sun 12-10.30). Food served all day Sat-Sun ⊕ FREE HOUSE ◀ Woodforde's Wherry, Adnams Broadside & Best, 2 guest ales. **Facilities** Children's menu Play area Family room Dogs allowed Garden Parking

THORNHAM

Lifeboat Inn ★★ HL 🌀 ♇

Ship Ln PE36 6LT
☎ 01485 512236 📠 01485 512323
e-mail: reception@lifeboatinn.co.uk
dir: *A149 from Hunstanton for approx 6m. 1st left after Thornham sign*

The Lifeboat is a 16th-century inn overlooking Thornham Harbour and the salt marshes. Despite being extended, its original character has been retained. Inside, the warm glow of paraffin lamps enhances the welcoming atmosphere, while the adjoining conservatory is renowned for its ancient vine and adjacent walled patio garden. The best available fish and game feature on the frequently changing menus, in the form of salmon and dill fishcakes with a sun dried tomato and pesto sauce, or Brancaster mussels steamed in Chardonnay with lemon grass, ginger and cream. For a satisfying main course, try lightly bread-crumbed lamb cutlets with ratatouille and a minted garlic gravy, or local partridge casserole with Guinness and mushrooms. Nearby is Thornham Beach, Blakeney, Cley, Sandringham and Nelson's birthplace at Burnham Thorpe.

Open all wk Bar Meals food served all day ⊕ FREE HOUSE ◀ Adnams, Woodforde's Wherry, Greene King IPA & Abbot Ale, guest ales. ♇ 10 Facilities Children's menu Play area Family room Dogs allowed Garden Parking Rooms 13

WARHAM ALL SAINTS

Three Horseshoes

NR23 1NL ☎ 01328 710547
dir: *From Wells A149 to Cromer, then right onto B1105 to Warham*

This gem of a pub first opened its doors in 1725. Inside you'll find a gas-lit main bar, stone floors, scrubbed wooden tables and a grandfather clock ticking in the corner. Real ales are served directly from the cask through a hole in the bar wall, and the largely original interior includes a curious green and red dial in the ceiling - a rare example of Norfolk twister, an ancient pub game. Vintage posters, clay pipes, photographs and memorabilia adorn the walls, while down a step are old one-arm bandits. The pub is well known for its home cooking, with local game and shellfish; steak, kidney and Wherry bitter pie; Norfolk chicken and leek suet pudding; and woodman's pie (mushrooms and nuts in red wine sauce). Home-made puddings, such as spotted dick and syrup sponge, are listed over the fire in the main bar.

Open all wk Bar Meals L served all wk 12-1.45 D served all wk 6-8.30 Av main course £7.80 ⊕ FREE HOUSE ◀ Greene King IPA, Woodforde's Wherry. Facilities Children's menu Family room Dogs allowed Garden Parking Notes no credit cards

WELLS-NEXT-THE-SEA

The Crown 🏵 🍷

The Buttlands NR23 1EX
☎ 01328 710209 📄 01328 711432
e-mail: reception@thecrownhotelwells.co.uk
dir: *10m from Fakenham on B1105*

Striking contemporary decor and furnishings blend effortlessly with the old-world charm of this 17th-century former coaching inn. The hotel overlooks a tree-lined green near the heart of the town, and has been refurbished to create a traditional atmosphere of uncluttered comfort. Lunchtime sandwiches might include smoked salmon, cream cheese and cucumber, whilst main course dishes such as seared liver and bacon with roast root vegetables, or butternut squash, Parmesan and sage risotto are also available in the evening. Meanwhile, dinner in the restaurant might begin with seared pigeon breast, mushroom and crouton salad, before a main course of baked salmon with tiger prawn, tomato and lemongrass brochette. Meals are also served in the new, warm and cheerful Orangery or outside with its great views.

Open all wk **Bar Meals** L served all wk 12-2.30 D served all wk 6.30-9.30 **Restaurant** D served all wk 7-9 booking required Av 3 course à la carte fr £34.95 🌐 FREE HOUSE 🍺 Adnams Bitter, Woodforde's Wherry, guest ale 🍏 Aspall. 🍷 14 **Facilities** Children's menu Dogs allowed Garden Parking

WINTERTON-ON-SEA

Fishermans Return 🍷

The Lane NR29 4BN ☎ 01493 393305
e-mail: fishermansreturn@yahoo.co.uk
web: www.fishermans-return.com
dir: *8m N of Great Yarmouth on B1159*

Long beaches and National Trust land are within 300 metres of this 350-year-old brick and flint pub – and it's dog-friendly too, making it an ideal spot to finish a walk. Behind the bar are Woodforde's Wherry and Adnams, with seasonal guests from Mauldons and Blackfriars. Menus include popular favourites, from toasted sandwiches to cottage pie. But look to the daily changing blackboard for fish and seafood specials, when freshly caught sea bass and mackerel may be on offer.

Open all wk **Bar Meals** L served all wk 12-2.30 D served all wk 6-9 Av main course £8 **Restaurant** L served all wk 12-2.30 D served all wk 6-9 🌐 FREE HOUSE 🍺 Woodforde's Wherry, Adnams Bitter & Broadside, John Smith's 🍏 Westons Stowford Press, Old Rosie Scrumpy. 🍷 10 **Facilities** Children's menu Play area Family room Dogs allowed Garden Parking

BULWICK

The Queen's Head ♥

Main St NN17 3DY ☎ 01780 450272
e-mail: queenshead-bulwick@tiscali.co.uk
dir: *Just off A43, between Corby & Stamford*

Parts of this quintessential English free house date back to 1400. Overlooking the village church, the pub is a warren of small rooms with exposed wooden beams, four open fireplaces and flagstone floors. Relax by the fire or on the patio with a pint of Spitfire or local Rockingham Ale, and some hearty pub food. Lunchtime brings great sandwich choices and interesting snacks such as baked goat's cheese with garlic and roasted peppers. The evening menu might include slow-cooked Cornish lamb with root vegetables, pearl barley and herb suet dumpling; celeriac and porcini mushroom risotto with sage and gorgonzola; or pan-fried Scottish salmon with Portland crab and potato chowder. Typical desserts include warm apple and caramel tart with clotted cream.

Open Closed: Mon **Bar Meals** L served Tue-Sun 12-2.30 booking required D served Tue-Sat 6-9.30 booking required **Restaurant** L served Tue-Sun 12-2.30 booking required D served Tue-Sat 6-9.30 booking required Fixed menu price fr £12.50 ⊕ FREE HOUSE ◀ Shepherd Neame, Spitfire, Elland, Rockingham Ales, Newby Wyke, Guest Ales. ♥ 9 **Facilities** Children's menu Dogs allowed Garden Parking

FARTHINGSTONE

The Kings Arms

Main St NN12 8EZ
☎ 01327 361604 ▤ 01327 361604
e-mail: paul@kingsarms.fsbusiness.co.uk
dir: *M1 junct 16, A45 towards Daventry. At Weedon take A5 towards Towcester. Right signed Farthingstone*

Tucked away in perfect walking country near Canons Ashby (a National Trust property), this 18th-century Grade II listed inn is every inch the traditional country pub - albeit it a highly distinctive one. On fine days many come for the beautiful garden; in colder weather they warm themselves by the real fires, but there is always a warm welcome. The pub has a retail business specialising in Cornish fish, which is reflected on the short menu, available at weekend lunchtimes. British cheese and Loch Fyne fish platters are also available.

Open 7-11.30 (Sat-Sun 12-3.30 7-11.30) Closed: Mon **Bar Meals** L served Sat-Sun 12-2 Av main course £8.75 ⊕ FREE HOUSE ◀ Thwaites Original, Adnams, Brakspear Bitter, Young's Bitter, Hoggleys Northamptonshire Bitter ♂ Westons Old Rosie Scrumpy. **Facilities** Children's menu Family room Dogs allowed Garden Parking **Notes** no credit cards

SIBBERTOFT

The Red Lion ♥

43 Welland Rise LE16 9UD ☎ 01858 880011
e-mail: andrew@redlionwinepub.co.uk
dir: *From Market Harborough take A4304, through Lubenham, left through Marston Trussell to Sibbertoft*

Wine is the special passion of owner Andrew Banks at this friendly 300-year-old free house. Over 200 bins are included on the ever-growing wine list, with many varieties available by the glass. The pub offers an appealing blend of contemporary and classic decor, with oak beams, leather upholstery and a smartly turned-out dining room. In fine weather, meals are served in the quiet garden, which is a favourite with local walkers and cyclists; there's also an outdoor play area for children. The same monthly-changing menu is served throughout, and features local and seasonal produce wherever possible. Regular themed evenings include a weekly curry night.

Open 12-2 6.30-11 Closed: Mon & Tue lunch, Sun eve **Bar Meals** L served Wed-Sun 12-2 booking required D served Mon-Sat 6.30-9.30 booking required Av main course £10 **Restaurant** L served Wed-Sun 12-2 booking required D served Mon-Sat 6.30-9.30 booking required Fixed menu price fr £14.95 Av 3 course à la carte fr £19 ⊕ FREE HOUSE ◀ Adnams, Timothy Taylor Landlord, Black Sheep. ♥ 20 **Facilities** Children's menu Play area Garden Parking

STOKE BRUERNE

The Boat Inn

NN12 7SB
☎ 01604 862428 📄 01604 864314
e-mail: info@boatinn.co.uk
web: www.boatinn.co.uk
dir: *In village centre, just off A508 or A5*

Just across the lock from a popular canal museum, this waterside free house has been run by the same family since 1877. Beneath its thatched roof you'll find cosy bars, open fires and flagstone floors, as well as a traditional skittle alley. Boat trips on the pub's narrowboat can be arranged. Home-made soups, sandwiches, jackets, salads and baguettes support more substantial meals such as pan-fried sea bream, supreme of chicken or Gressingham duck breast with apricot and bacon stuffing.

Open all day all wk 9.30am-11pm (Sun 9.30am-10.30pm) **Bar Meals** L served all wk 9.30-2.30 (all day Mar-Oct) D served all wk 6-9 (all day Mar-Oct) Av main course £8 **Restaurant** L served Tue-Sun 12-2 booking required D served all wk 7-9 booking required Fixed menu price fr £10 Av 3 course à la carte fr £15 ⊕ FREE HOUSE ◀ Banks Bitter, Marstons Pedigree, Frog Island Best, Marstons Old Empire, Wychwood Hobgoblin ♂ Thatcher's Traditional. **Facilities** Children's menu Dogs allowed Garden Parking

WOODNEWTON

The White Swan ▼

22 Main St PE8 5EB ☎ 01780 470944
dir: *5m off A605/A47*

The pub, which dates from the 1600s, is a stone-built, Grade II listed building set in the middle of an idyllic English village. It has recently been re-opened following major refurbishment and has wasted no time in establishing a reputation for its good modern British food, beers and wines. Entertainment is provided in the form of traditional pub games, such as dominoes and shove ha'penny, and speciality evenings are held throughout the year, including game suppers and wine dinners.

Open 11-2.30 6-11 (Sat 11-3 6-11, Sun 12-5)
Closed: Sun eve, Mon **Bar Meals** L served
Tue-Sat 12-2, Sun 12-2.30 D served Tue-Thu
6-9, Fri-Sat 6-9.30 Av main course £8.50
Restaurant Fixed menu price fr £12 Av 3 course
à la carte fr £23 ⊕ FREE HOUSE ◀ Adnams,
Timothy Taylor Landlord, Bass, Guinness, Greene
King IPA, Woodforde's Wherry ♂ Aspall. ▼ 10
Facilities Children's menu Garden Parking

BELFORD

Blue Bell Hotel ★★★ HL

Market Place NE70 7NE
☎ 01668 213543   📄 01668 213787
e-mail: enquiries@bluebellhotel.com
dir: *Off A1, 15m N of Alnwick , 15m S of Berwick-upon-Tweed*

A touch of old-world charm with modern day comforts permeate this 17th-century coaching inn on the A1 London to Edinburgh route, and there are spectacular views across the hotel gardens to Belford church. The innovative menu takes its cue from the best of country kitchens, and choices from the restaurant menu might include mussels in Lindisfarne mead broth; Eyemouth fish pie; slow roasted lamb Henry with creamed potatoes and vegetables; or tempura vegetables with rice and sweet chilli dip.

Open all day all wk 11am-mdnt **Bar Meals** L served
all wk 12-3 D served all wk 5-9 Av main course £8.95
Restaurant L served Sun 12-3 booking required
D served all wk 6-9 booking required Fixed menu
price fr £21 Av 3 course à la carte fr £40 ⊕ FREE
HOUSE ◀ Calders, Tetleys Smooth, Black Sheep,
Timothy Taylor Landlord. **Facilities** Children's menu
Play area Family room Garden Parking **Rooms** 28

BLANCHLAND

The Lord Crewe Arms

DH8 9SP ☎ 01434 675251 📄 01434 675337
e-mail: lord@crewearms.freeserve.co.uk
dir: *10m S of Hexham via B6306*

Built in the 12th century, once the private
chapel of the abbot of Blanchland Abbey, and a
significant location in the first Jacobite Rebellion
in 1715, this is one of England's oldest inns.
Antique furniture, blazing log fires and flagstone
floors make for an atmospheric setting. Wide-
ranging, good-value bar and restaurant menus
with specials offer salads, savoury bean hot
pot, and game pie. Watch out, there are lots of
ghosts, and often filming crews too!

Open all day all wk 11-11 (Sun 12-10.30) **Bar
Meals** L served all wk 12-2 D served all wk 7-9
Av main course £7 **Restaurant** D served all wk
7-9.15 booking required Av 3 course à la carte
fr £21 ⊕ FREE HOUSE ◀ Black Sheep, John
Smiths, Guinness, Boddingtons Ŏ Thatchers.
Facilities Children's menu Play area Family room
Dogs allowed Garden Parking

CARTERWAY HEADS

The Manor House Inn ♥

DH8 9LX ☎ 01207 255268
dir: *A69 W from Newcastle, left onto A68 then S for
8m. Inn on right*

A very traditional free house enjoying spectacular
views across open moorland and the Derwent
Reservoir from its elevated position high on
the A68. Built circa 1760, the completely
refurbished inn is an ideal centre for exploring
Northumberland's rolling hills and beautiful
beaches. The cosy stone-walled bar, with its log
fires, low-beamed ceiling and massive timber
support, serves five well-kept real ales all year.
The bar and lounge are ideal for a snack, while
the restaurant is divided into two dining areas,
the larger of which welcomes families with
children. The focus on fresh local produce is
typified by dishes such as smoked kippers with
crisp side salad; slow-braised oxtail on a bed of
black pudding mash; and supreme of chicken
breast with sautéed leeks and Northumbrian
nettle cheese sauce.

Open all day all wk 11-11 (Sun 12-10.30) **Bar
Meals** food served all day **Restaurant** food served
all day ⊕ FREE HOUSE ◀ Theakstons Best, Mordue
Workie Ticket, Greene King Ruddles County, Courage
Directors, Wells Bombardier Ŏ Westons Old Rosie
Scrumpy. ♥ 12 **Facilities** Children's menu Dogs
allowed Garden Parking

FALSTONE

The Blackcock Inn ★★★ INN

NE48 1AA ☎ 01434 240200
e-mail: thebcinn@yahoo.co.uk
dir: *From Hexham take A6079, then B6320 to Bellingham, follow brown signs to Kielder & Falstone*

Stone walls, log fires and original beams reflect the 17th-century origins of this traditional family-run free house. An ideal base for walking, boating and fishing, it sits close to Kielder Water and is handy for the Rievers cycle route. The food draws on excellent local produce, with options ranging from light lunchtime snacks through to full evening meals in the intimate Chatto's restaurant: perhaps Japanese-style king prawns followed by lamb shank in red wine and rosemary.

Open Closed: Tue in low season **Bar Meals** L served Wed-Sun 12-2 booking required Av main course £8.80 **Restaurant** L served Wed-Sun 12-2 booking required D served Wed-Mon 7-8.30 booking required Av 3 course à la carte fr £15.85 ⊕ FREE HOUSE ◀ John Smiths, Worthington, guest ale Ŏ Westons. **Facilities** Children's menu Play area Family room Dogs allowed Garden Parking **Rooms** 6

FALSTONE

The Pheasant Inn ★★★★ INN

Stannersburn NE48 1DD
☎ 01434 240382 ▤ 01434 240382
e-mail: enquiries@thepheasantinn.com
dir: *A69, B6079, B6320, follow signs for Kielder Water*

This sprawling stone-walled building in the north Tyne Valley dates back to 1624. It was originally a large farmstead, but for over 250 years one room was always used as a locals' bar. The rustic atmosphere remains intact - around the walls old photos record local people engaged in long-abandoned professions. The cooking is fresh, generous and tasty, producing wholesome traditionally English fare. Meals may be taken alfresco in the pretty grassed courtyard with a stream running through, or in the oak-beamed restaurant. The bar menu changes daily according to season, but classic dishes like steak and kidney pie, home-made soups, ploughman's and sandwiches are always available.

Open 12-3 6.30-11 Closed: 25-26 Dec, Mon-Tue (Nov-Mar) **Bar Meals** L served Mon-Sat 12-2.30 **Restaurant** L served Mon-Sat 12-2.30 booking required D served Mon-Sat 6.30-8.30 booking required ⊕ FREE HOUSE ◀ Timothy Taylor Landlord, Wylam Gold, Wylam Rocket. **Facilities** Children's menu Play area Family room Dogs allowed Garden Parking **Rooms** 8

HEXHAM

Miners Arms Inn

Main St, Acomb NE46 4PW ☎ 01434 603909
e-mail: info@theminersacomb.com
dir: *17m W of Newcastle on A69. 2m W of Hexham*

Close to Hadrian's Wall in peaceful surroundings, this welcoming village pub with open hearth fire dates from 1746. Pride is taken in the range and quality of the ales and in the good home-cooked food. Sunday lunches are especially popular, when North Acomb beef or lamb roasts are accompanied by home-made Yorkshire puddings, roast potatoes and a selection of vegetables. There is a pleasant beer garden and families are welcome.

Open all wk **Bar Meals** L served Sat 12-2.30 booking required D served Thu-Sat 5-8.30 booking required **Restaurant** L served Sun 12-2.30 booking required D served Thu-Sat 5-8.30 booking required ⊕ FREE HOUSE ◀ Black Sheep, Wylam Bitter, Pilsner Urquell, Mordue, Yates Bitter ♂ Wylam Perry's Farmhouse Cider. **Facilities** Children's menu Dogs allowed Garden

LONGFRAMLINGTON

The Anglers Arms

Weldon Bridge NE65 8AX
☎ 01665 570271 & 570655
e-mail: johnyoung@anglersarms.fsnet.co.uk
dir: *From N, 9m S of Alnwick right Weldon Bridge sign. From S, A1 to by-pass Morpeth, left onto A697 for Wooler & Coldstream. 7m, left to Weldon Bridge*

This former coaching inn has commanded the picturesque Weldon Bridge over the River Coquet since the 1760s. The interior is full of nice little touches, antiques and quaint bric-a-brac; the walls are full of pictures and fishing memorabilia, and open log fires are a welcoming treat on winter days. A range of popular bar meals include home-made steak and ale pie; grilled salmon fillet with sweet chilli sauce; and vegetable stew with home-made dumplings. Outside, there's plenty of space for alfresco summer dining in the carefully-tended half-acre of garden, which also includes a children's play park. But for more style and a different set of options, the pub's own Pullman railway carriage provides an unusual restaurant experience.

Open all day all wk 11-11 (Sun 12-11) **Bar Meals** Av main course £8 food served all day **Restaurant** Fixed menu price fr £20 Av 3 course à la carte fr £30 food served all day ⊕ FREE HOUSE ◀ Timothy Taylor Landlord, Old Speckled Hen, Abbot Ale, Theakstons Best Bitter. **Facilities** Children's menu Play area Family room Garden Parking

NEWTON-ON-THE-MOOR

The Cook and Barker Inn ★★★★ INN ♥

NE65 9JY

☎ 01665 575234 📠 01665 575887

dir: *0.5m from A1 S of Alnwick*

From its elevated position in the picturesque village of Newton-on-the-Moor, this traditional country inn commands outstanding views of the Cheviot Hills and the Northumbrian coast. Food can be served in the restaurant, bar, snug or lounge. The tempting bar lunch menu and mouthwatering à la carte evening menu are backed by daily specials on the blackboard, all served wherever the customer chooses to sit; a gourmet seven-course fixed-price menu is also available. Appetisers are along the lines of warm toasted muffin with black pudding, king scallop and fresh green pea purée; follow with noisettes of pork pan-fried with wild forest mushrooms deglazed with Madeira wine and set on a pillow of roasted vegetables.

Open all wk **Bar Meals** Av main course £8.95 food served all day **Restaurant** L served all wk 12-2 booking required D served all wk 7-9 booking required Fixed menu price fr £25 Av 3 course à la carte fr £35 ⊕ FREE HOUSE ◀ Timothy Taylor Landlord, Theakstons Best Bitter, Fuller's London Pride, Batemans XXXB, Black Sheep. ♥ 12 **Facilities** Children's menu Family room Garden Parking **Rooms** 18

BLIDWORTH

Fox & Hounds ♥

Blidworth Bottoms NG21 0NW

☎ 01623 792383

e-mail: info@foxandhounds-pub.com

dir: *Right off B6020 between Ravenshead & Blidworth*

A traditional country pub, extensively refurbished a few years ago to create attractive surroundings in which to eat and drink. It was probably built as a farmhouse in the 19th century, when Blidworth Bottoms was a thriving community, with shops and a post office. A reputation for good pub food comes from dishes such as steak and ale pie; Mediterranean chicken; blackened salmon in Cajun spices; home-made vegetarian cottage pie; and hot chilli con carne.

Open all day all wk 11.30am-11.30pm (Fri-Sat 11.30am-mdnt) **Bar Meals** L served Mon-Wed 11.30-8.30, Thu-Sun 11.30-9 D served Mon-Wed 11.30-8.30, Thu-Sun 11.30-9 food served all day ⊕ GREENE KING ◀ H&H Cask Bitter, Old Speckled Hen, Olde Trip H&H, seasonal guest ales. ♥ 9 **Facilities** Children's menu Play area Dogs allowed Garden Parking

CAUNTON

Caunton Beck ☻

NG23 6AB

☎ 01636 636793   📠 01636 636828
e-mail: email@cauntonbeck.com
dir: *6m NW of Newark on A616 to Sheffield*

This civilised village pub opens daily for breakfast and carries on serving food until around midnight, just like its sister establishment, the Wig & Mitre in Lincoln. It is built around a beautifully restored 16th-century cottage with herb gardens and a colourful rose arbour. The main menu changes with the seasons and is served throughout. To start you might choose soup of the day or twice-baked Caunton Beck soufflé with portobello mushroom and Roquefort cheese. Mains include locally sourced rib-eye of beef with a choice of sauces, or whole roast sea bass stuffed with piri piri, coriander and lime. Dishes are accompanied with a wine suggestion. Vegetarian and gluten-free options are clearly marked. A sandwich and light meal menu is also available, with tea, coffees and home-made fudge on offer.

Open all day all wk 8am-mdnt **Bar Meals** Av main course £16.10 food served all day **Restaurant** Fixed menu price fr £11 Av 3 course à la carte fr £22.20 food served all day ⊕ FREE HOUSE ◀ Batemans Valiant, Marston's Pedigree, Tom Woods Best Bitter. ♚ 34 **Facilities** Children's menu Dogs allowed Garden Parking

ELKESLEY

Robin Hood Inn ☻

High St DN22 8AJ ☎ 01777 838259
e-mail: a1robinhood@aol.com
dir: *5m SE of Worksop off A1 towards Newark-on-Trent*

Parts of this unassuming village inn date back to the 14th century. Ceilings and floors are deep red, while the green walls are adorned with pictures of food. The comprehensive choice is served in both the bar and restaurant, and includes a fixed price menu, carte and daily specials board. Beef bourguignon; grilled rump or fillet steak; pan-fried Normandy style chicken breast; or sausages, onions and mustard mash will satisfy the heartiest of appetites.

Open 11.30-2.30 6-11 Closed: Sun eve & Mon lunch **Bar Meals** L served Tue-Sun 12-2 D served Mon-Sat 6-8 Av main course £9 **Restaurant** L served Tue-Sun 12-2 D served Mon-Sat 6-9 Fixed menu price fr £12.50 Av 3 course à la carte fr £15 ⊕ ENTERPRISE INNS ◀ John Smiths Extra Smooth, Black Sheep Best Bitter, guest ale. ♚ 6 **Facilities** Children's menu Play area Garden Parking

137

HARBY

Bottle & Glass ☕

High St NG23 7EB

☎ 01522 703438 ▤ 01522 703436
e-mail: email@bottleandglassharby.com
dir: S of A57 (Lincoln to Markham Moor road)

Situated in a charming village a few miles west of Lincoln, the pub's original beams and flagstone floors date back many years. Queen Eleanor reputedly died here in 1290. Proprietor Michael Hope aims to create the reassuringly civilised ambience of a music-free meeting house, reading room, watering hole and restaurant. Young's Bitter rubs shoulders with Farmer's Blonde and Black Sheep, while seasonal dishes of twice-baked cheese soufflé with roasted red onions may be followed by roast fillet of pollack with Puy lentils. There are wine suggestions with each dish.

Open all day all wk 12-12 **Bar Meals** Av main course £14.25 food served all day **Restaurant** Fixed menu price fr £12.50 Av 3 course à la carte fr £20.40 food served all day ⊕ FREE HOUSE ◀ Young's Bitter, Farmers Blonde, Black Sheep. ☕ 34 **Facilities** Children's menu Dogs allowed Garden Parking

KIMBERLEY

The Nelson & Railway Inn

12 Station Rd NG16 2NR

☎ 0115 938 2177 ▤ 0115 938 2179
dir: 1m N of M1 junct 26

The landlord of more than 30 years gives this 17th-century pub its distinctive personality. Next door is the Hardy & Hanson brewery that supplies many of the beers, but the two nearby railway stations that once made it a railway inn are now sadly derelict. A hearty menu of pub favourites includes soup, ploughman's, and hot rolls, as well as grills and hot dishes like home-made steak and kidney pie; gammon steak; and mushroom stroganoff.

Open all day all wk 11am-mdnt **Bar Meals** L served all wk 12-2.30 D served all wk 5.30-9 Av main course £5.50 **Restaurant** L served all wk 12-2.30 D served all wk 5.30-9 ⊕ HARDY & HANSONS PLC ◀ Hardys, Hansons Best Bitter, Cool & Dark, Olde Trip, Morlands, Ruddles. **Facilities** Children's menu Family room Dogs allowed Garden Parking

LAXTON

The Dovecote Inn ♟

Moorhouse Rd NG22 0SX ☎ 01777 871586
e-mail: dovecote-inn@btconnect.com
dir: *Exit A1 at Tuxford through Egmanton to Laxton*

Like most of the village of Laxton, this family-run, 18th-century pub is Crown Estate property belonging to the Royal Family. Outside is a delightful beer garden with views of the church. The interior includes a bar and three cosy wining and dining rooms. Here the seasonal, home-cooked dishes could include wild Alaskan salmon, slow-roast belly pork with apple and onion compote, chicken breast and bacon, or 28-day matured steak. The village still practises the Medieval strip field farming method – there is a visitor centre in the pub car park.

Open all wk 11.30-3 6.30-11 (Sun 12-10.30) **Bar Meals** Av main course £9 **Restaurant** L served Mon-Sat 12-2, Sun 12.30-6 D served Mon-Sat 6.30-9.30 booking required Av 3 course à la carte fr £18 ⊕ FREE HOUSE ◀ Mansfield Smooth, John Smith's Smooth, Black Sheep, Greene King Old Speckled Hen, Adnams. ♟ 10 **Facilities** Children's menu Dogs allowed Garden Parking

MORTON

The Full Moon Inn ♟

Main St NG25 0UT
☎ 01636 830251   📄 01636 830554
e-mail: info@thefullmoonmorton.co.uk
dir: *Newark A617 to Mansfield. Past Kelham, turn left to Rolleston & follow signs to Morton*

Recently transformed into a light, comfortable and contemporary space, with exposed beams and brickwork, and reclaimed panels and furniture. The kitchen's emphasis is on farm-fresh food sourced mostly locally, with a set menu running alongside the pub menu at lunchtime and in the evenings. There's plenty on offer, from sandwiches, baguettes, pastas, burgers and omelettes to Gonalston Farm Shop bangers with mash, red cabbage and gravy. On Friday and Saturday nights the set menu is replaced with a specials board. There's plenty here to keep children occupied too, with a designated indoor play area, an outdoor castle and a sand pit, while dogs are also welcome.

Open all wk fr 10.30am **Bar Meals** L served all wk 12-2.30 booking required D served all wk 6-9.30 booking required Av main course £10 **Restaurant** L served all wk 12-2.30 booking required D served all wk 6-9.30 booking required Fixed menu price fr £16 Av 3 course à la carte fr £22 ⊕ FREE HOUSE ◀ Bombardier, Dover Beck, Moonshine, guest ales. ♟ 8 **Facilities** Children's menu Play area Family room Dogs allowed Garden Parking

TUXFORD

The Mussel & Crab ♟

NG22 0PJ

☎ 01777 870491   📄 01777 872302
e-mail: musselandcrab1@hotmail.com
dir: *From Ollerton/Tuxford junct of A1 & A57. N on B1164 to Sibthorpe Hill. Pub 800yds on right*

Beautifully fresh fish and seafood dominate the menu at this quirky pub with a multitude of rooms, all decked out in inimitable style. The piazza room is styled as an Italian courtyard, with murals by artist Tony Cooke; the beamed restaurant is big on rustic charm; and the gents' toilets is brightened with a tank of fish! Countless blackboards offer ever-changing dishes such as crab chowder; and monkfish in a red wine and mushroom sauce, plus some fish you have never tasted.

Open all wk **Bar Meals** L served all wk 11-2.30 booking required D served Mon-Sat 6-10, Sun 6-9 booking required Av main course £10 **Restaurant** L served all wk 11-2.30 booking required D served Mon-Sat 6-10, Sun 6-9 booking required Av 3 course à la carte fr £28 ⊕ FREE HOUSE ◼ Tetley Smooth, Tetley Cask, Guinness. ♟ 16 **Facilities** Children's menu Family room Dogs allowed Garden Parking

BAMPTON

The Romany

Bridge St OX18 2HA

☎ 01993 850237   📄 01993 852133
e-mail: romany@barbox.net
dir: *Telephone for details*

A shop until 20 years ago, The Romany is housed in an 18th-century building of Cotswold stone with a beamed bar, log fires and intimate dining room. The choice of food ranges from bar snacks and bar meals to a full carte restaurant menu, with home-made specials like hotpot, Somerset pork, or steak and ale pie. There is a good range of vegetarian choices. Regional singers provide live entertainment a couple of times a month.

Open all wk **Bar Meals** L served all wk 12-2.30 D served all wk 6-9.30 Av main course £10 **Restaurant** L served all wk 12-2.30 D served all wk 6-9.30 ⊕ PUNCH ◼ Archers Village, Fuller's London Pride, Brakspears, guest ales ♻ Westons Stowford Press. **Facilities** Children's menu Play area Dogs allowed Garden Parking

BANBURY

The Wykham Arms ☝

Temple Mill Rd, Sibford Gower OX15 5RX
☎ 01295 788808
e-mail: info@wykhamarms.co.uk
dir: *Between Banbury & Shipston-on-Stour off B4035. 20m S of Stratford-upon-Avon*

A charming 18th-century thatched inn built of mellow stone with lovely countryside views, where drinkers and diners congregate in intimate beamed rooms. Along with well kept real ales and a good wine list, the bar menu, also available in the terrace and garden, offers great sandwiches like sirloin steak or Wykham club. Restaurant main courses may include Caesar salad with roasted maize-fed chicken or Salcombe crab and mango salad.

Open 12-2.30 6-11 Closed: Mon **Bar Meals** L served Tue-Sat 12-2.30 D served Tue-Sat 7-9.30 Av main course £15 **Restaurant** L served Tue-Sun 12-2.30 D served Tue-Sat 7-9.30 Av 3 course à la carte fr £26.50 ⊕ FREE HOUSE ◀ Hook Norton Best, Guinness, St Austell Tribute, Adnams Broadside, London Pride. ☝ 17 **Facilities** Children's menu Family room Dogs allowed Garden Parking

BLOXHAM

The Elephant & Castle

OX15 4LZ ☎ 0845 873 7358
e-mail: elephant.bloxham@btinternet.com
dir: *M40 junct 11, pub just off A361, in village centre. 11m from Banbury*

The arch of this family-run 15th-century Cotswold-stone coaching inn used to straddle the former Banbury to Chipping Norton turnpike. At night the gates of the pub were closed, and no traffic could get over the toll bridge. Locals play Aunt Sally or shove-ha'penny in the big wood-floored bar, whilst the two-roomed lounge boasts a bar-billiards table and a large inglenook fireplace. The menu offers a range of sandwiches and crusty filled baguettes, plus pub favourites like roast chicken breast with stuffing, crispy battered cod and lasagne verdi.

Open all wk 10-3 5-12 (Fri 10-3 5-2am, Sat 10am-2am, Sun 10am-mdnt) **Bar Meals** L served Mon-Sat 12-2 Av main course £5 **Restaurant** L served Mon-Sat 12-2 ⊕ HOOK NORTON BREWERY ◀ Hook Norton Best Bitter, Hook Norton seasonal ales, guest ales ⚬ Westons Old Rosie Scrumpy. **Facilities** Children's menu Play area Family room Dogs allowed Garden Parking

BURCOT

The Chequers ♀

OX14 3DP

☎ 01865 407771 🖷 01865 407771
e-mail: enquiries@thechequers-burcot.co.uk
dir: *On A415 (Dorchester to Abingdon road) between Clifton Hampden & Dorchester on Thames*

Once a staging post for barges on the Thames, this 400-year-old thatched and timber framed pub now combines the best of old and new. On winter days the blazing fire surrounded by sofas is the favoured spot, especially for toasting marshmallows; in summer, the enclosed beer garden takes precedence. The food is serious, pubby home cooking: think pan-fried field mushrooms in garlic and herb butter on toast to start; then beer battered haddock with hand cut chips; or slow roasted lamb shank with mint and redcurrant gravy.

Open all day all wk 12-11 (Sun 12-4) **Bar Meals** L served all wk 12-3 D served Mon-Sat 6.30-9.30 Av main course £13 **Restaurant** L served all wk 12-3 booking required D served Mon-Sat 6.30-9.30 booking required Av 3 course à la carte fr £23 ⊕ FREE HOUSE ◀ Hook Norton Bitter, Ridgway, Young's, guest ales Ȯ Westons Stowford Press. ♀ 21 **Facilities** Children's menu Garden Parking .

CHALGROVE

The Red Lion Inn ♀

The High St OX44 7SS ☎ 01865 890625
e-mail: raymondsexton@btinternet.com
web: www.redlionchalgrove.co.uk
dir: *B480 from Oxford ring road, through Stadhampton, left then right at mini-rdbt. At Chalgrove Airfield right into village*

Rather unusually, the cruck-framed 15th-century Red Lion is one of only two pubs in the country owned by its local parish church. From a 'menu that tries to please everyone' come starters such as salad of spicy merguez sausage, potatoes and shallots topped with a crispy poached egg; and pan-fried pigeon breasts with wild rice and a port wine jus. Main dishes may include pork loin chops grilled and served on a rich goats' cheese and sage cream. Sandwiches and side orders are also available at lunchtime.

Open all wk 11.30-3 6-mdnt (Sat 11.30-3 6-1am Sat 11.30am-1am Sun 11.30am-mdnt in summer) **Bar Meals** L served Mon-Sat 12-2, Sun 12-3 D served Mon-Sat 6-9 Av main course £11.50 **Restaurant** L served Mon-Sat 12-2, Sun 12-3 D served Mon-Sat 6-9 Fixed menu price fr £6.50 Av 3 course à la carte fr £21 ⊕ FREE HOUSE ◀ Fuller's London Pride, Adnams Best, Timothy Taylor Landlord, Boddingtons, guest ale Ȯ Aspalls, Westons Stowford Press. ♀ 8 **Facilities** Children's menu Play area Dogs allowed Garden

CUMNOR

Bear & Ragged Staff ♥

28 Appleton Rd OX2 9QH
☎ 01865 862329 ▤ 01865 862048
e-mail: enquiries@bearandraggedstaff.com
dir: A420 from Oxford, right onto B4017 signposted
Cumnor

The Bear & Ragged Staff reopened early in 2009.
A recently renovated restaurant is backed up by
a first class kitchen, while the front part of the
building, dating back to the 16th century, is a
three-section pub. The food is best described as
hearty, country-style cooking, and casseroles,
stews and pub classics, such as bangers and
mash, will always be found on the menus. Lunch
might offer a platter of charcuterie, or Greek
meze to share; or ale, mushroom and beef pies.
There's just that little bit more sophistication
in the evening, with confit duck leg with wild
mushroom and braised chicory; and sea bass
fillet with wilted mache lettuce, Japanese udon
noodles and lime leaf and celery white bean
broth. As for dessert, Chef says 'Don't forget to
try the chocolate fondant'.

Open all day all wk 11-11 **Bar Meals** L served all wk
12-3 D served all wk 6.30-10 Av main course £8.50
Restaurant L served all wk 12-3 D served all wk
6.30-10 Fixed menu price fr £10.50 Av 3 course à la
carte fr £24 ⊕ GREENE KING ◀ IPA, Old Speckled
Hen, Abbot Ale, guest ales. ♥ 6 **Facilities** Children's
menu Play area Dogs allowed Garden Parking

FARINGDON

The Trout at Tadpole Bridge ♥

Buckland Marsh SN7 8RF ☎ 01367 870382
e-mail: info@troutinn.co.uk
dir: Halfway between Oxford & Swindon on A420 take
road signed Bampton, pub approx 2m

Sitting peacefully on the River Thames twenty
minutes from Oxford is this historic free house.
A destination in its own right, it offers log fires,
cask ales, riverside walks, berthing for six boats
and a kitchen that makes expert use of local
ingredients. Having run several fine-dining
restaurants, owners Gareth and Helen wanted
somewhere to raise their family, so the need
for games, toys, space and a decent children's
menu is understood. From a sample menu come
smoked eel salad with Noilly Prat jelly and shallot
purée; pithivier of ceps, leeks and red onion
marmalade with red pepper sauce; steamed beef
and ale pudding; and blue brie and sun-blushed
tomato strudel.

Open 11.30-3 6-11 Closed: 25-26 Dec, Sun eve
(1 Nov-30 Apr) **Bar Meals** L served all wk 12-2
booking required D served all wk 7-9 booking
required Av main course £14 **Restaurant** L served
all wk 12-2 booking required D served all wk
7-9 booking required Av 3 course à la carte fr
£30 ⊕ FREE HOUSE ◀ Ramsbury Bitter, Youngs PA
Bitter Ö Stowford Press. ♥ 10 **Facilities** Children's
menu Dogs allowed Garden Parking

FYFIELD

The White Hart ♥

Main Rd OX13 5LW ☎ 01865 390585
e-mail: info@whitehart-fyfield.com
web: www.whitehart-fyfield.com
dir: *6m S of Oxford just off A420 (Oxford to Swindon road)*

Like so many pubs, the White Hart has quite a history. The interior is breathtaking, with an arch-braced roof; the main restaurant is a grand hall of a place with soaring eaves, beams and flagstone floors. The owners are passionate about freshness, using seasonal produce of the highest quality from mostly local suppliers with meats sourced from trusted farms and estates. Menus change frequently to offer salmon fillet with beetroot risotto and horseradish foam; slow-roasted belly of Kelmscott pork with celeriac purée, crackling and cider jus; and home-made ice creams and sorbets.

Open noon-3 5.30-11 (Sat noon-11 Sun noon-10.30) Closed: Mon ex BH **Bar Meals** L served Tue-Sat 12-2.30, Sun 12-4 booking required D served Tue-Sat 7-9.30 booking required Av main course £15 **Restaurant** L served Tue-Sat 12-2.30, Sun 12-4 booking required D served Tue-Sat 7-9.30 booking required Fixed menu price fr £15 Av 3 course à la carte fr £28 ⊕ FREE HOUSE ◄ Hooky Bitter, Doom Bar, Hullabaloo, guest Ales ♂ Thatchers Cheddar Valley. ♥ 14 **Facilities** Children's menu Play area Garden Parking

HAILEY

Bird in Hand ★★★★ INN ♥

Whiteoak Green OX29 9XP
☎ 01993 868321 📄 01993 868702
e-mail: welcome@birdinhandinn.co.uk
dir: *From Witney N onto B4022 through Hailey to Whiteoak Green for 5m. At Charlbury S onto B4022 for 5m*

Set in the Oxfordshire countryside just outside the village of Hailey, this classic Cotswold stone inn is Grade II listed and dates from the 16th century. The beamed interior has huge inglenook fireplaces, with log fires in winter. Food ranges from traditional rarebit on toast topped with a poached egg, to marinated Cotswold game casserole; or home-made faggots with onion gravy and mashed potato.

Open all wk noon-11.30 **Bar Meals** L served Mon-Sat 12-2.30, Sun 12-3 D served Mon-Sat 6.30-9.30, Sun 6-9 ⊕ Free House ◄ Ramsbury ♂ Stowford Press. ♥ 14 **Facilities** Children's menu Dogs allowed Garden Parking **Rooms** 16

HENLEY-ON-THAMES

WhiteHartNettlebed ★★★★ GA 🏵 ☕

High St, Nettlebed RG9 5DD
☎ 01491 641245 📠 01491 649018
e-mail: info@whitehartnettlebed.com
dir: *On A4130 between Henley-on-Thames &
Wallingford*

During the 17th and 18th centuries the area
was plagued by highwaymen, but these days
the beautifully restored property is favoured by
a stylish crowd who appreciate the chic bar and
restaurant. A typical three-course meal selection
could comprise sweet potato and gruyère
tartlet with rocket; spinach, feta and cumin
spanakopita with babaganouche; and lemon and
thyme pannacotta with red wine poached pear.
Continental flavours are equally abundant on
the Sunday lunch menu: grilled sardines with
romesco sauce; confit of duck leg with butter
beans in tomato sauce; and chocolate pot and
red wine with Chantilly cream.

Open all day all wk 11am-11pm (Sun 11am-6pm)
Bar Meals L served Mon-Sat 12-2.30, Sun 12-3
booking required D served Mon-Sat 6-9.30 booking
required **Restaurant** L served Mon-Sat 12-2.30, Sun
12-3 booking required D served Mon-Sat 6-9.30
booking required ⊕ BRAKSPEAR ◀ Brakspear,
Guinness. ☕ 12 **Facilities** Children's menu Play area
Family room Garden Parking **Rooms** 12

MILTON

The Black Boy Inn ☕

OX15 4HH
☎ 01295 722111 📠 01295 722978
e-mail: info@blackboyinn.com
web: www.blackboyinn.com
dir: *From Banbury take A4260 to Adderbury. After
Adderbury turn right signed Bloxham. Onto Milton
Road to Milton. Pub on right*

A gorgeous 16th-century building, where recent
refurbishment has created a charming interior
that's entirely in keeping with the 400 year-old
building. Outside, the patio and a lovely half-
acre garden offer plenty of seating and space
for children to run around. The modern British
food is based on fresh, seasonal ingredients;
pub classics include the likes of cottage pie
with wholegrain mustard mash, while the main
menu offers pea and ham hock soup, followed
by Cornish cannon of lamb with gratin potato
and roasted butternut squash. Leave space for
Yorkshire rhubarb with vanilla pannacotta is
typical.

Open all wk 12-3 5.30-11.30 (Sat-Sun 12-11.30)
Bar Meals L served all wk 12-2.30 D served Mon-
Thu 6.30-9, Fri-Sat 6.30-9.30 booking required
Restaurant L served all wk 12-2.30 D served
Mon-Thu 6.30-9, Fri-Sat 6.30-9.30 booking
required ◀ Adnams, Abbot Ale, rotating guest
ales. ☕ 8 **Facilities** Children's menu Play area Dogs
allowed Garden Parking

OXFORD

The Anchor ♥

2 Hayfield Rd, Walton Manor OX2 6TT
☎ 01865 510282
dir: *A34 (Oxford ring road N), exit Peartree rdbt, 1.5m then right at Polstead Rd, follow road to bottom, pub on right*

This 1937 Art Deco-styled pub is particularly popular with North Oxford's well-heeled locals, firmly on the map for its well-kept ales, carefully chosen wines and good quality seasonal British food. Lunchtime specials include roast monkfish with courgettes, peas, bacon and spinach, while the main menu offers belly pork with black pudding and greens; and smoked haddock fishcakes with ginger lime mayo. Bar snacks and sandwiches are also available.

Open all day all wk noon-11 Closed: Xmas **Bar Meals** L served all wk 12-2.30 D served all wk 6-9.30 Av main course £11 **Restaurant** L served all wk 12-2.30 booking required D served all wk 6-9.30 booking required Av 3 course à la carte fr £23 ⊕ WADWORTH ◀ Wadworth 6X, Henrys IPA, Bishops Tipple Ō Westons Stowford Press. ♥ 11 **Facilities** Children's menu Dogs allowed Garden Parking

STADHAMPTON

The Crazy Bear ★★★★★ GA ◎◎ ♥

Bear Ln OX44 7UR
☎ 01865 890714 📄 01865 400481
e-mail: enquiries@crazybear-stadhampton.co.uk
dir: *M40 junct 7, A329. In 4m left after petrol station, left into Bear Lane*

The 16th-century Crazy Bear combines ancient features into a modern, distinctive interior, which combines contemporary and art deco influences. There are two restaurants, one serving Thai food, and the other modern British, as well as some stylish bedrooms and a wonderful garden with a waterfall and statues. For breakfast/brunch choose duck eggs Benedict or farm-smoked haddock kedgeree; at lunch order a roast Angus beef and horseradish sandwich; or look to the main menu for seared scallops with a shallot and herb butter, or Old Spot ham hock terrine, followed by seared sea bass with shellfish bisque, or chicken and mushroom pie. Leave room for spiced plum crumble tart with clotted cream.

Open all day all wk 7am-mdnt **Bar Meals** Av main course £14 food served all day **Restaurant** Fixed menu price fr £10 food served all day ⊕ FREE HOUSE ◀ Old Speckled Hen, IPA, Timothy Taylor Landlord Ō Aspall, Stowford Press. ♥ 20 **Facilities** Children's menu Garden Parking Rooms 17

EMPINGHAM

The White Horse Inn ★★★ INN ♟

Main St LE15 8PS
☎ 01780 460221 📄 01780 460521
e-mail: info@whitehorserutland.co.uk
dir: *From A1 take A606 signed Oakham & Rutland Water. From Oakham take A606 to Stamford*

An ideal place to recharge your batteries following a walk or cycle around Rutland Water, this former 17th-century courthouse has lost none of its period charm. The open fire, beamed bar and friendly staff are a recipe for total relaxation. The home-made food starts with sandwiches, home-made soup and baguettes and runs to hearty meals such as cheese and ale soup followed by Elizabethan pork casserole, or local trout fillets with a herb butter. Bedrooms are available.

Open all day all wk Closed: 25 Dec **Bar Meals** L served Mon-Thu 12-2.15, Fri-Sun 12-9 D served Mon-Thu 6.30-9, Fri-Sun 12-9 Av main course £9.50 **Restaurant** L served Mon-Thu 12-2.15, Fri Sun 12-9 D served Mon-Thu 6.30-9, Sun 12-9 Av 3 course à la carte fr £19 ⊕ ENTERPRISE INNS ◀ John Smith's, Adnams Best Bitter, Oakham Ales JHB & Bishops Farewell, Timothy Taylor Landlord. ♟ 9 **Facilities** Children's menu Dogs allowed Garden Parking **Rooms** 13

LYDDINGTON

Old White Hart ♟

51 Main St LE15 9LR
☎ 01572 821703 📄 01572 821978
e-mail: mail@oldwhitehart.co.uk
dir: *From A6003 between Uppingham & Corby take B672. Pub on main street opp village green*

Set amongst the sandstone cottages of rural Lyddington, this 17th-century free house close to Rutland Water has retained its original beamed ceilings, stone walls and open fires, and is surrounded by well-stocked gardens. Greene King and Timothy Taylor are amongst the beers on offer, along with interesting, freshly prepared food. The menu might include home cured gravadlax with horseradish dressing; and roast local pheasant breast with buttered mash. Fish and vegetarian choices plus daily specials and early bird menu also available.

Open all wk 12-3 6.30-11 (Sun 12-3 7-10.30) Closed: 25 Dec, 26 Dec eve **Bar Meals** L served Mon-Fri 12-2, Sat-Sun 12-2.30 booking required D served all wk 6.30-9, (Sun in summer 7-9) booking required Av main course £12.95 **Restaurant** L served Mon-Fri 12-2, Sat-Sun 12-2.30 booking required D served all wk 6.30-9 (Sun in summer 7-9) booking required Fixed menu price fr £10.95 Av 3 course à la carte fr £25 ⊕ FREE HOUSE ◀ Greene King IPA & Abbot Ale, Timothy Taylor Landlord, Fuller's London Pride, Timothy Taylor Golden Best. ♟ 8 **Facilities** Children's menu Play area Garden Parking

STRETTON

Ram Jam Inn

The Great North Rd LE15 7QX
☎ 01780 410776 📠 01780 410361
dir: On A1 N'bound carriageway past B668, through service station into car park

The inn was originally a humble ale house called the Winchelsea Arms, and belonged to the Earl of that title who lived nearby. It is thought that its current name stems from a home-brew invented by a resident publican during the 18th century, when the pub sign advertised 'Fine Ram Jam'. Sadly no recipe survives, so its ingredients remain a mystery. Today's informal café-bar and bistro, with a patio overlooking orchard and paddock, welcomes visitors with its comprehensive daily-changing menu.

Open all day all wk 7.30am-10pm (Sun 8.30am-6pm) Closed: 25 Dec **Bar Meals** Av main course £9 food served all day **Restaurant** Av 3 course à la carte fr £15 food served all day ⊕ FREE HOUSE ◀ John Smith's Smooth, Fuller's London Pride. **Facilities** Children's menu Play area Garden Parking

ADMASTON

The Pheasant Inn at Admaston

TF5 0AD ☎ 01952 251989
e-mail: info@thepheasantadmaston.co.uk
web: www.thepheasantadmaston.co.uk
dir: M54 junct 6 follow A5223 towards Whitchurch then follow B5063 towards Shawbirch & Admaston. Pub is on left of main rd

Once owned by the Great Western Railway, this lovely old country pub dates from the 19th century. Stylish interior décor and a real fire add character to the dining areas, whilst the large enclosed garden is ideal for families. Using the best of local produce, expect pan-seared lamb's liver with crispy bacon and home-grown sage and red wine gravy; roast sea bass with prawn and cucumber butter; and broccoli, leek and field mushroom pie. There is also a very good 'Little People's' menu.

Open all day all wk **Bar Meals** L served Mon-Sat 12-2, Sun 12-3 D served Mon-Sat 6-9 Av main course £9 ◀ Shropshire Gold, Greene King IPA, Shropshire Lad, Guinness. **Facilities** Children's menu Play area Dogs allowed Garden Parking

BRIDGNORTH

Halfway House Inn ★★★ INN ▼

Cleobury Rd, Eardington WV16 5LS
☎ 01746 762670   🖷 01746 768063
e-mail: info@halfwayhouseinn.co.uk
dir: *M5 junct 6, A449 towards Kidderminster. Follow ring road to right. At next rdbt take A442 N towards Bridgnorth. 12m, take A458 towards Shrewsbury. Follow brown tourist signs to pub*

An original Elizabethan wall mural is a fascinating feature of this former coaching inn, but the Halfway House owes its current name to a visit in 1823 by Princess Victoria and her entourage. (She was halfway between Shrewsbury and Worcester.) The pub is renowned for its locally sourced, home-cooked food, at least three local real ales, 40 malts, and around 100 wines. Dishes range from bar snacks to braised beef in Guinness, grilled local steaks and Astbury Falls rainbow trout. There is plenty of accommodation available if you want to stay over.

Open 5-11.30 (Fri & Sat 11am-11.30pm Sun 11-6) Closed: Sun eve ex BH **Bar Meals** L served Fri-Sun 12-2 D served Mon-Sat 6-9 Av main course £11.50 **Restaurant** D served Mon-Sat 6-9 booking required Fixed menu price fr £22.50 Av 3 course à la carte fr £25 ⊕ FREE HOUSE ◖ Holden's Golden Glow, Wood's Shropshire Lad, Hobson's Town Crier, Draught Guinness Ŏ Weston's Stowford Export. ▼ 10 **Facilities** Children's menu Play area Garden Parking **Rooms** 10

CRAVEN ARMS

The Sun Inn ▼

Corfton SY7 9DF ☎ 01584 861239
e-mail: normanspride@aol.com
dir: *On B4368, 7m N of Ludlow*

First licensed in 1613, this historic pub has a public bar with pool table, jukebox and dartboard, along with a lounge and restaurant. Landlord Norman Pearce brews the Corvedale ales in what was the pub's old chicken and lumber shed, using local borehole water; Mahoral cider, from just down the road, is another drinks option. Teresa Pearce uses local produce in a delicious array of traditional dishes, served with up to six fresh vegetables and a choice of chips or new potatoes. The pub has historic connection with the transportation of criminals to Australia.

Open all wk 12-2.30 6-11 (Sun 12-3 7-11) **Bar Meals** L served all wk 12-2 D served all wk 6-9 Av main course £9 **Restaurant** L served 12-2 D served 6-9 ⊕ FREE HOUSE ◖ Corvedale Normans Pride, Dark & Delicious, Julie's Ale, Katie's Pride, Farmer Rays Ŏ Mahoral. ▼ 14 **Facilities** Children's menu Play area Dogs allowed Garden Parking

IRONBRIDGE

The Malthouse ♜

The Wharfage TF8 7NH
☎ 01952 433712 📄 01952 433298
e-mail: enquiries@themalthouseironbridge.com
dir: *Telephone for directions*

An inn since the 1800s, the Malthouse is located in the village of Ironbridge next to the river, now a designated UNESCO World Heritage Site famous for its natural beauty and award-winning museums. Party menus are available for both the popular jazz bar and the restaurant, while the main menu ranges from lasagne or faggots to monkfish and pancetta baked and served with sweet chorizo, mussel and tomato cassoulet.

Open all wk **Bar Meals** food served all day **Restaurant** food served all day ⊕ PUNCH TAVERNS ◀ Directors, Greene King IPA, Badger. ☙ 10 **Facilities** Children's menu Dogs allowed Garden Parking

LUDLOW

The Roebuck Inn ★★★★ INN ⊛⊛

Brimfield SY8 4NE ☎ 01584 711230
e-mail: info@theroebuckludlow.co.uk
dir: *Just off A49 between Ludlow & Leominster*

Despite a façade that looks decidedly Victorian, this country inn dates from the 15th century. Its lounge bar retains the inglenook and wood panelling of the period, while the elegantly minimalist dining room is more contemporary. Customers have the choice of eating in either of these rooms from the imaginative menus of head chef-patron, Olivier Bossut. Expect his carte to offer starters of butternut squash risotto with aged Parmesan, roast pinenuts, cep oil; gateau of crab in a saffron beurre blanc; and main courses of saddle of lamb Wellington with Jerusalem artichoke and liquorice sauce; and fillet of beef en croûte with truffle sauce. Twice monthly, on Wednesday evenings, the Roebuck presents a French night in association with Ludlow's French Pantry, which specialises in providing the very best in regional food and wines from France.

Open all wk 11.30-3 6-mdnt (Sun eve times vary) **Bar Meals** L served Mon-Sat 11.30-2.30 D served Mon-Sat 6.30-9 Av main course £13.50 **Restaurant** L served all wk 11.30-2.30 D served Mon-Sat 6.30-9 ⊕ MARSTONS ◀ Bank's Bitter, Marstons Pedigree plus guests. **Facilities** Children's menu Dogs allowed Garden Parking **Rooms** 3

MUCH WENLOCK

The Feathers Inn ⬤

Brockton TF13 6JR
☎ 01746 785202 📠 01746 712717
e-mail: feathersatbrockton@googlemail.com
dir: *From Much Wenlock follow signs to Ludlow on B4378 for 3m*

A vast inglenook, big mirrors, stone busts, reclaimed timbers from old ships and local art are all features of this Grade II listed, 16th-century pub. The Feathers also incorporates a mini shop, a children's cookery school, a ladies' luncheon club with cookery demonstrations on Friday lunchtimes, and a takeaway food service. Menus are based on fresh, largely local ingredients, with a regularly updated specials board, traditional Sunday roasts, and good value early suppers. Wines are sourced from all over the world.

Open 12-2 6.30-11 Closed: 26 Dec, 1-4 Jan, Mon **Bar Meals** L served Tue-Sun 12-2 D served Tue-Sun 6.30-11 Av main course £12 **Restaurant** L served Tue-Sun 12-2 D served Tue-Sun 6.30-11 Fixed menu price fr £10 Av 3 course à la carte fr £16 ⊕ FREE HOUSE ◄ Hobsons Ale, Guinness, Boddingtons, Worfield Brewery Ales. ♈ 6 **Facilities** Children's menu Garden Parking

MUCH WENLOCK

Longville Arms

Longville in the Dale TF13 6DT
☎ 01694 771206 📠 01694 771742
e-mail: jill.livingstone@btconnect.com
dir: *From Shrewsbury take A49 to Church Stretton, then B4371 to Longville*

Prettily situated in an Area of Outstanding Natural Beauty in Shropshire, ideally placed for walking and touring, this welcoming country inn has been carefully restored. Solid elm or cast-iron-framed tables, oak panelling and wood-burning stoves are among the features that help to generate a warm, friendly ambience. Favourite main courses on the bar menu and specials board include steak and ale pie, mixed fish platter, and a range of steaks. There are tethering facilities for horses and dogs are welcome.

Open all wk 12-3 6.30-11.30 (Sun 12-3 6.30-10.30) **Bar Meals** L served all wk 12-2.30 D served all wk 6.30-9.30 Av main course £10 **Restaurant** L served Sun & BH 12-2.30 D served Fri-Sat & BH 6.30-9.30 Fixed menu price fr £9.95 Av 3 course à la carte fr £22 ⊕ FREE HOUSE ◄ Local guest ales. **Facilities** Children's menu Play area Dogs allowed Garden Parking

MUNSLOW

The Crown Country Inn ★★★★ INN ◎◎ ☂

SY7 9ET ☎ 01584 841205
e-mail: info@crowncountryinn.co.uk
dir: *On B4368 between Craven Arms & Much Wenlock*

In a lovely setting below the rolling hills of Wenlock Edge, this Grade II listed building, retains sturdy oak beams, flagstone floors and prominent inglenook fireplace. Meals are served in the main bar, the Bay dining area, and the Corvedale Restaurant. Top quality local produce from trusted sources features in the dishes, many of which can be both starter or main course, such as risotto of prawns, basil and crayfish tails topped with dried cherry tomatoes; or roast breast of free-range Breckland duck with dauphinoise potatoes. The cheeseboard lists a dozen English and Welsh cheeses, while for something sweet there's home-made ice cream.

Open Closed: Xmas, Sun eve, Mon **Bar Meals** L served Tue-Sun 12-2 booking required D served Tue-Sat 6.45-8.45 booking required Av main course £15 **Restaurant** L served Tue-Sun 12-2 booking required D served Tue-Sat 6.45-8.45 booking required Fixed menu price fr £18 Av 3 course à la carte fr £26 ⊕ FREE HOUSE ◀ Holden's Black Country Bitter, Holden's Golden Glow, Holden's Special Bitter, Three Tuns Brewery XXX ♂ Mahoral. ☗ 7 **Facilities** Children's menu Play area Garden Parking **Rooms** 3

SHREWSBURY

The Mytton & Mermaid Hotel ★★★ HL ◎◎ ☂

Atcham SY5 6QG
☎ 01743 761220 🖷 01743 761292
e-mail: admin@myttonandmermaid.co.uk
dir: *From M54 junct 7 signed Shrewsbury, at 2nd rdbt take 1st left signed Ironbridge/Atcham. In 1.5m hotel on right after bridge*

Food is a major attraction at this country house hotel on the banks of the Severn; its chef holds two AA rosettes for the quality of his cooking. The Grade II listed building's tastefully decorated interior recalls the atmosphere of its coaching inn days. Mad Jack's Bar, named after a colourful local squire, offers dishes such as naturally smoked haddock with crushed potatoes and hollandaise, or local venison and Shropshire Lad casserole with blue cheese dauphinoise and parsnip crisps.

Open all day all wk 7am-11pm Closed: 25 Dec **Bar Meals** L served all wk 12-2.30 D served all wk 6.30-10 Av main course £13.95 **Restaurant** L served all wk 12-2.30 booking required D served all wk 7-10 booking required Fixed menu price fr £29.50 Av 3 course à la carte fr £27.50 ⊕ FREE HOUSE ◀ Shropshire Lad, Shropshire Gold, Hobsons Best. ☗ 12 **Facilities** Children's menu Garden Parking **Rooms** 18

WENTNOR

The Crown Inn

SY9 5EE ☎ 01588 650613 🖹 01588 650436
e-mail: crowninn@wentnor.com
dir: *From Shrewsbury A49 to Church Stretton, follow signs over Long Mynd to Asterton, right to Wentnor*

Outdoor enthusiasts of all persuasions will appreciate the location of this 17th-century coaching inn below the Long Mynd. Its homely atmosphere, which owes much to log fires, beams and horse brasses, makes eating and drinking here a pleasure. Meals are served in the bar or separate restaurant. Typical daily changing, traditional home-made dishes include pork tenderloin filled with marinated fruits; pan-fried breast of duck with a burnt orange sauce; and grilled sea bass with couscous.

Open all wk noon-3 6-11 (Sat noon-mdnt Sun noon-10) Closed: 25 Dec **Bar Meals** L served Mon-Fri 12-2 D served Mon-Fri 6-9 Av main course £7.50 **Restaurant** L served Sat-Sun 12-9 D served Sat-Sun 12-9 ⊕ FREE HOUSE ◧ Hobsons, Old Speckled Hen, Three Tuns, Wye Valley ⌀ Westons Scrumpy. **Facilities** Children's menu Play area Garden Parking

WHITCHURCH

Willeymoor Lock Tavern ♀

Tarporley Rd SY13 4HF ☎ 01948 663274
dir: *2m N of Whitchurch on A49 (Warrington to Tarporley road)*

A former lock keeper's cottage idyllically situated beside the Llangollen Canal. Low-beamed rooms are hung with a novel teapot collection; there are open log fires and a range of real ales. Deep-fried fish and a choice of grills rub shoulders with traditional steak pie, chicken curry and vegetable chilli. Other options include salad platters, children's choices and gold rush pie for dessert.

Open all wk 12-2.30 6-11 (Sun 12-2.30 6-10.30) Closed: 25 Dec & 1 Jan **Bar Meals** L served all wk 12-2 D served all wk 6-9 **Restaurant** L served all wk 12-2 D served all wk 6-9 ⊕ FREE HOUSE ◧ Abbeydale, Moonshine, Weetwood, Oakham JHB, Best & Eastgate, Timothy Taylor Landlord. ♀ 8 **Facilities** Children's menu Play area Garden Parking **Notes** no credit cards

WISTANSTOW

The Plough ♥

SY7 8DG ☎ 01588 673251
e-mail: richardsys@btconnect.com
web: www.ploughwistanstow.co.uk
dir: 1m N of Craven Arms. Turn off A49 to Wistanstow

Beers don't have to travel far to end up being drawn through century-old hand-pumps in the simply furnished bar of this traditional country pub. Located next to the Wood Brewery, it is effectively the brewery tap, serving Parish Bitter, Shropshire Lad and Wood's other real ales. An ethically sourced menu includes the ever-popular fish and chips (made with Wood's beer batter, of course); Shropshire sirloin and gammon steaks; and scampi, as well as children's choices. The specials board changes regularly and might feature home-made curries; and farmhouse pork, bacon and cheese pie. Local faggots, omelettes and baguettes appear on the lunchtime menu. On Sundays, as well as the regular menus, there are traditional beef, pork or free-range chicken roasts. Take your drinks and meals out to the patio and beer garden on fine days.

Open all wk noon-2.30 5-mdnt (Sun noon-11) **Bar Meals** L served all wk 12-2 D served all wk 6.30-9 Av main course £7.50 ⊕ WOOD BREWERY ◀ Wood's Shropshire Lad, Parish, Pot O' Gold ♂ Thatchers, Stowford Press. ♥ 9 **Facilities** Children's menu Dogs allowed Garden Parking

APPLEY

The Globe Inn ♥

TA21 0HJ ☎ 01823 672327
e-mail: globeinnappley@btconnect.com
dir: From M5 junct 26 take A38 towards Exeter. Village signed in 5m

The Globe is known for its large collection of Corgi and Dinky cars, Titanic memorabilia, old advertising posters and enamel signs. The Grade II listed inn dates back 500 years and is hidden in maze of lanes on the Somerset-Devon border. Produce is sourced locally and using organic and Fair Trade goods where possible. Food from baguettes to main courses (including plenty for vegetarian options), like twice baked broccoli soufflé; lamb hot pot pie; Moroccan chicken and chickpea tagine; and 3 different varieties of 'multi chilli'.

Open Closed: Mon (ex BH) **Bar Meals** L served Tue-Sun 12-2 booking required D served Tue-Sun 7-9.30 booking required Av main course £11.95 **Restaurant** L served Tue-Sun 12-2 booking required D served Tue-Sun 7-9.30 booking required Fixed menu price fr £19.95 Av 3 course à la carte fr £22 ⊕ FREE HOUSE ◀ Palmers 200, Exmoor Ales, Appleys Ale, Doom Bar, Tribute ♂ Thatchers Gold. ♥ 8 **Facilities** Children's menu Play area Garden Parking

ASHCOTT

Ring O'Bells ⚑

High St TA7 9PZ ☎ 01458 210232
e-mail: info@ringobells.com
dir: *M5 junct 23 follow A39 & Glastonbury signs.
In Ashcott turn left, at post office follow church &
village hall signs*

A free house run by the same family for 21
years. Parts of the building date from 1750, so
the traditional village pub interior has beams,
split-level bars, an old fireplace and a collection
of bells and horse brasses. Local ales and ciders
are a speciality, particularly guest ales from
local breweries, while all food is made on the
premises. Look to the good value specials board
for ham and lentil soup; roast guinea fowl with
apple and local cider sauce, then orange and
rhubarb cheesecake to finish. An attractive patio
and gardens are welcoming in warmer weather.

Open all wk noon-3 7-11 (Sun 7-10.30pm) Closed:
25 Dec **Bar Meals** L served all wk 12-2 D served
all wk 7-10 Av main course £8 **Restaurant** L
served all wk 12-2 D served all wk 7-10 ⊕ FREE
HOUSE ◀ guest ales. ⚑ 8 **Facilities** Children's menu
Play area Garden Parking

BABCARY

Red Lion ⚑

TA11 7ED
☎ 01458 223230 📄 01458 224510
e-mail: redlionbabcary@btinternet.com
dir: *Please telephone for directions*

The Red Lion is a beautifully refurbished, stone-
built free house, with rich, colour-washed walls,
heavy beams and simple wooden furniture
setting the tone in the friendly bar, whilst
French doors lead out into the garden from the
restaurant. Granary sandwiches, ciabattas and
hot pub favourites like fish pie and honey-glazed
Somerset ham, egg and chips are served in the
bar. In the restaurant, expect slow roasted pork
belly with celeriac purée; butternut squash and
sage risotto; and free range duck breast with wild
mushroom cream sauce.

Open all wk **Bar Meals** L served all wk 12-2.30
D served Mon-Sat 7-9.30 **Restaurant** L served
all wk 12-2.30 D served Mon-Sat 7-9.30 ⊕ FREE
HOUSE ◀ Teignworthy Reel Ale, O'Hanlons, Otter,
Bath Ales. ⚑ 12 **Facilities** Children's menu Play area
Dogs allowed Garden Parking

BATH

The Hop Pole

7 Albion Buildings, Upper Bristol Rd BA1 3AR
☎ 01225 446327
e-mail: hoppole@bathales.co.uk
dir: *20 min walk from City of Bath on A4 towards Bristol. Pub opp Victoria Park*

One of just nine pubs belonging to Bath Ales, a fresh young microbrewery, the beers rejoice in names such as Gem, Spa, Wild Hare and Barnstormer. Described as a country pub in the heart of a city, The Hop Pole has a stripped-down, stylish interior, and the lovingly restored, spacious beer garden to the rear is complete with patio heaters and pétanque pitch. Home-cooked food ranges from imaginative bar snacks and sandwiches through to full meals. Children are served smaller portions from the main menu. You could start with chicken liver parfait before moving on to medallions of monkfish with chargrilled Mediterranean vegetables, sun-dried tomatoes and pesto. Monday night is quiz night.

Open all day all wk noon-11 (Fri-Sat noon-mdnt) **Bar Meals** L served Mon-Sat 12-2, Sun 12-3 D served Mon-Sat 6-9 Av main course £8.75 **Restaurant** L served Mon-Sat 12-2, Sun 12-3 D served Mon-Sat 6-9 ⊕ BATH ALES LTD ◀ Bath Ales: Gem, Spa, Barnstormer, Festivity, Wild Hare. **Facilities** Children's menu Garden

BICKNOLLER

The Bicknoller Inn

32 Church Ln TA4 4EL ☎ 01984 656234
e-mail: james_herd@sky.com
dir: *Telephone for directions*

A 16th-century thatched country inn set around a courtyard with a large garden under the Quantock Hills. Inside you'll find traditional inglenook fireplaces, flagstone floors and oak beams, as well as a theatre-style kitchen and restaurant. Meals range from sandwiches and pub favourites like hake in beer batter (priced for an 'adequate' or 'generous' portion), to the full three courses with maybe smoked salmon; chicken supreme cooked in red wine, and warm treacle tart.

Open all wk noon-3 6-11 (Fri-Sun all day) Closed: Mon L ex BH **Bar Meals** L served Tue-Thu 12-3, Fri-Sun all day booking required D served Tue-Thu 6.30-10, Fri-Sun all day booking required **Restaurant** L served Tue-Thu 12-3, Fri-Sun all day booking required D served Tue-Thu 6.30-10, Fri-Sun all day booking required ⊕ PALMERS BREWERY ◀ Palmers Copper, Palmers IPA, Palmers Gold, guest ales ⚬ Thatchers Traditional. **Facilities** Children's menu Play area Dogs allowed Garden Parking

BLUE ANCHOR

The Smugglers ▽

TA24 6JS ☎ 01984 640385
e-mail: info@take2chefs.co.uk
dir: *Off A3191, midway between Minehead & Watchet*

'Fresh food, cooked well' is the simple philosophy at this friendly 300-year-old inn, standing just yards from Blue Anchor's sandy bay with a backdrop of the Exmoor Hills. Food, using fresh produce locally sourced, can be enjoyed in the Cellar Bar or the Dining Room. Baguettes, filled baked potatoes, pizzas, pastas, grills, curries, salads, speciality sausages and fish and seafood are available. Honey-roast ham and minted lamb cutlets are listed among the 'comfort food' selection. In fine weather diners eat in the large walled garden, where children can enjoy the animals at the nearby farm and the bouncy castle.

Open noon-3 6-11 Closed: Nov-Etr, Sun eve, Mon-Tue L **Bar Meals** L served all wk 12-2.15 D served all wk 6-9 Av main course £8.95 **Restaurant** L served all wk 12-2.15 D served all wk 6-9 ⊕ FREE HOUSE ◀ Smuggled Otter, Otter Ale. ▽ 6 **Facilities** Children's menu Play area Dogs allowed Garden Parking

CONGRESBURY

The White Hart Inn ▽

Wrington Rd BS49 5AR ☎ 01934 833303
e-mail: murat@simplywhitehart.co.uk
dir: *From M5 junct 21 take A370 through Congresbury, right towards Wrington. Inn in 2.3m on Wrington Road*

A handy M5 pit-stop a short drive from junction 21, this Badger dining pub has a secluded garden with views of the Mendip Hills, and the beamed bars are country-cosy with log fires in stone inglenooks. Refuel with simple, honest food such as steak and Badger ale pie, venison with blackberry and stilton sauce, or a lunchtime brie and bacon baguette, washed down with a pint of Tanglefoot. The gin list is impressive and don't miss the Turkish night – music and belly dancers.

Open all wk 11.30-3 6-11.30 (Fri-Sun 11.30-11.30) Closed: 25 Dec **Bar Meals** Av main course £8.95 food served all day **Restaurant** Av 3 course à la carte fr £17.50 food served all day ⊕ HALL & WOODHOUSE ◀ Badger, Tanglefoot ♂ Westons Stowford Press. ▽ 8 **Facilities** Children's menu Play area Dogs allowed Garden Parking

DINNINGTON

Dinnington Docks

TA17 8SX ☎ 01460 52397 📄 01460 52397
e-mail: hilary@dinningtondocks.co.uk
dir: *S of A303 between South Petherton & Ilminster*

Formerly known as the Rose & Crown, this traditional village pub on the old Fosse Way has been licensed for over 250 years. Rail or maritime enthusiasts will enjoy the large collection of memorabilia, and it is an ideal location for cycling and walking. Good quality cask ales and farmhouse cider are served, and freshly prepared food including the likes of crab cakes, Greek salad, faggots, snapper, steak, and lamb shank for two.

Open all wk 11.30-3.30 6-mdnt **Bar Meals** Av main course £6.95 food served all day **Restaurant** food served all day ⊕ FREE HOUSE ◀ Butcombe Bitter, Wadworth 6X, guest ales ♂ Burrow Hill, Stowford Press, Thatchers Gold. **Facilities** Children's menu Play area Family room Dogs allowed Garden Parking

DUNSTER

The Luttrell Arms ★★★ HL

High St TA24 6SG
☎ 01643 821555 📄 01643 821567
e-mail: info@luttrellarms.fsnet.co.uk
dir: *From A39 (Bridgewater to Minehead), left onto A396 to Dunster (2m from Minehead)*

Built in the 15th-century as a guest house for the Abbots of Cleeve, this beguiling hotel has retained all its atmospheric charms. Open fires and oak beams make the bar a welcoming place in winter, while the bedrooms are period pieces complete with leather armchairs and four-poster beds. A rib-sticking wild venison casserole with ale and horseradish sauce is just the thing for a chilly day, while in the more formal restaurant you could tuck into smoked haddock fishcakes, followed by wild pigeon and mushroom parcels with cider jus. Desserts include sticky ginger parkin with vanilla-steeped pineapple and ginger ice cream in the restaurant, and clotted cream rice pudding in the bar. **Open** all wk 8am-11pm **Bar Meals** L served all wk 11.30-3, all day summer D served all wk 7-10 **Restaurant** L served Sun 12-3 booking required D served all wk 7-10 booking required ⊕ FREE HOUSE ◀ Exmoor Gold Fox, Guest ale ♂ Cheddar Valley Cider. **Facilities** Children's menu Family room Dogs allowed Garden **Rooms** 28

EAST COKER

The Helyar Arms ★★★★ INN 🏅

Moor Ln BA22 9JR
☎ 01935 862332 📠 01935 864129
e-mail: info@helyar-arms.co.uk
dir: *3m from Yeovil. Take A57 or A30, follow East Coker signs*

Reputedly named after Archdeacon Helyar, a chaplain to Queen Elizabeth I, this Grade II listed building dates back in part to 1468. The kitchen makes full use of local produce, including wood pigeon, rabbit, venison, pheasant and fish from the south Devon coast. Lunchtime bar snacks include salads such as chicken and bacon with toasted pine nuts; and hot beef and blue cheese with cherry tomatoes and red onion. A full meal could start with game keeper's terrine or home-smoked duck breast with beetroot and lentil salad. Main courses include pub classics in addition to the likes of whole roasted local partridge or confit chicken with sautéed thyme potatoes.

Open all wk **Bar Meals** L served all wk 12-2.30 D served all wk 6.30-9.30 Av main course £7 **Restaurant** L served all wk 12-2.30 D served all wk 6.30-9.30 Av 3 course à la carte fr £25 ⊕ PUNCH TAVERNS ◀ Butcombe Bitter, Black Sheep, Hobgoblin Ö Stowford Press, Taunton Traditional. **Facilities** Children's menu Family room Dogs allowed Garden Parking **Rooms** 6

EXFORD

The Crown Hotel ★★★ HL 🏅 🍷

TA24 7PP
☎ 01643 831554 📠 01643 831665
e-mail: info@crownhotelexmoor.co.uk
web: www.crownhotelexmoor.co.uk
dir: *From M5 junct 25 follow Taunton signs. Take A358 then B3224 via Wheddon Cross to Exford*

This family-run, 17th-century hotel is surrounded by beautiful countryside and moorland. Welcoming log fires are lit in the lounge and bar in winter, while there are lovely water and terrace gardens for summer use. Quality ingredients are sourced locally where possible and cooked to order. In the bar you'll find dishes like Exmoor free-range duck leg and lentil salad; and pan-fried sea bass with creamed leek potatoes, black trumpet mushrooms, roasted shallots and orange sauce. There's also a two-rosette restaurant for fine dining. Outdoor pursuits round here include walking, hunting, horse-riding and shooting. Bring your horse or dog – both can be accommodated.

Open all day all wk noon-11pm **Bar Meals** L served all wk 12-2.30 winter, 12-5.30 summer D served all wk 6-9.30 Av main course £11 **Restaurant** D served all wk 7-9 Av 3 course à la carte fr £37.50 ⊕ FREE HOUSE ◀ Exmoor Ale, Exmoor Gold Ö Thatchers Gold, Cornish Rattler. 🍷 12 **Facilities** Children's menu Dogs allowed Garden Parking **Rooms** 17

HINTON ST GEORGE

The Lord Poulett Arms ☖

High St TA17 8SE ☎ 01460 73149
e-mail: steveandmichelle@lordpoulettarms.com
dir: *2m N of Crewkerne, 1.5m S of A303*

Beautifully restored, this 17th-century thatched pub fronts the street in one of Somerset's loveliest villages. The bar features bare flagstones and boarded floors and is furnished with a harmonious mixture of old oak and elm tables, and ladderback, spindleback and Windsor chairs. Most of the food is locally sourced: fish is organic or wild, free-range meat comes from the Somerset/Dorset border, and herbs are home-grown. The lunch menu offers soups, salads, gourmet sandwiches, bouillabaise and hot dishes like pan-roasted duck magret. In the evening you might expect and braised Somerset pork shoulder with carrot and ginger mash. In summer, enjoy a drink under the wisteria shaded pergola or dine in the wild flower meadow.

Open all wk noon-3 6.30-11 Closed: 26 Dec, 1 Jan **Bar Meals** L served all wk 12-2 booking required D served all wk 7-9 booking required Av main course £14 **Restaurant** L served all wk 12-2 booking required D served all wk 7-9 booking required Av 3 course à la carte fr £22 ⊕ FREE HOUSE ◀ Hopback, Branscombe, Cotleigh, Archers, Otter ♂ Thatchers Gold. ☗ 7 **Facilities** Children's menu Dogs allowed Garden Parking

ILCHESTER

Ilchester Arms ☖

The Square BA22 8LN
☎ 01935 840220 ▤ 01935 841353
e-mail: mail@ilchesterarms.com
dir: *From A303 take A37 signed Ilchester/Yeovil, left at 2nd Ilchester sign. Hotel 100yds on right*

An elegant Georgian fronted house with lots of character, this establishment was first licensed in 1686 and was owned between 1962 and 1985 by the man who developed Ilchester cheese. Attractive features include open fires and a secluded garden. An extensive bistro menu offers the likes of smoked haddock fishcakes to start, medallions of venison with juniper onion compote, game sauce and pommes Anna, and passion fruit tart, in addition to snacks and salads, battered cod and steaks in the bar.

Open all day all wk 7am-11pm Closed: 26 Dec **Bar Meals** L served Mon-Sat 12-2.30 D served Mon-Sat 7-9 Av main course £6.50 **Restaurant** L served all wk 12-2.30 D served Mon-Sat 7-9 Av 3 course à la carte fr £35 ⊕ FREE HOUSE ◀ Butcombe, Flowers IPA, Bass, local ales ♂ Thatchers Gold. ☗ 12 **Facilities** Children's menu Play area Family room Garden Parking

KILVE

The Hood Arms ★★★★ INN ⚲

TA5 1EA ☎ 01278 741210 📄 01278 741477
e-mail: info@thehoodarms.com
dir: *From M5 junct 23/24 follow A39 to Kilve. Village between Bridgwater & Minehead*

This traditional, friendly 17th-century coaching inn is set among the Quantock Hills and provides thirsty walkers with traditional ales in the beamed bar and there are bedrooms available. A good range of fresh fish includes whole sea bass with apple and almond butter, and always on the menu is the inn's famous beef and ale pie, and stilton-topped steaks. Vegetarians get their own choice of dishes.

Open all day all wk 12-11 **Bar Meals** Av main course £9 food served all day **Restaurant** food served all day ⊕ FREE HOUSE ◀ Guinness, Otter Head, Palmers Copperdale, Fullers London Pride, Guest ales ♂ Thatchers Gold. ⚲ 13 **Facilities** Children's menu Play area Family room Dogs allowed Garden Parking **Rooms** 12

LONG SUTTON

The Devonshire Arms ★★★ INN ◉ ⚲

TA10 9LP
☎ 01458 241271 📄 01458 241037
e-mail: mail@thedevonshirearms.com
dir: *Exit A303 at Podimore rdbt onto A372. Continue for 4m, left onto B3165.*

A fine-looking, stone-built former hunting lodge on a pretty village green. Step through its imposing portico, to discover unexpectedly contemporary styling complementing the large open fire and other original features. The pub is renowned for its daily changing menu based whenever possible on locally sourced produce. For lunch try a venison burger with local cheddar, home-cut chips and garlic mayonnaise. Desserts may include dark chocolate and pear clafoutis. Dinner dishes are equally mouthwatering, with half a dozen choices at each course. You can drink and dine in the courtyard, large walled garden or overlooking the green at the front.

Open all wk noon-3 6-11 Closed: 25-26 Dec **Bar Meals** L served all wk 12-2.30 booking required D served all wk 7-9.30 booking required Av main course £9.75 **Restaurant** D served all wk 7-9.30 booking required Av 3 course à la carte fr £25 ⊕ FREE HOUSE ◀ Teignworthy Real Ale, Bath Spa, Cheddar Potholer, Yeovil Stargazer. ⚲ 10 **Facilities** Children's menu Play area Dogs allowed Garden Parking **Rooms** 9

LOWER VOBSTER

Vobster Inn ★★★★ INN ◉ ♟

BA3 5RJ ☎ 01373 812920 📄 01373 812247
e-mail: info@vobsterinn.co.uk
dir: *4m W of Frome*

The original part of this long stone building
dates back to the 17th century, though there
was probably an inn here even before that. The
bar menu offers suggestions such as roast
chorizo sausages with fried eggs and crusty
bread. On the main menu you'll find a selection
of Spanish cured and smoked meats with salad,
olives, houmous and crusty bread; as well as
grilled open cap mushrooms with Welsh rarebit.
Typical among the mains options are mixed bean
cottage pie; and grilled rib-eye with herb butter,
mushrooms, cherry vine tomatoes and fries.
All desserts are home made, with choices like
pannacotta with fresh berries; and lemon posset.
Children are particularly welcome and have
their own menu - they are also encouraged to try
smaller portions from the main menus.

Open Closed: Sun eve Bar Meals L served all
wk 12-2 booking required D served Mon-Sat
6.30-9 booking required Av main course £12.50
Restaurant L served all wk 12-2 booking required D
served Mon-Sat 6.30-9 booking required Av 3 course
à la carte fr £22.50 ⊕ FREE HOUSE ◖ Butcombe
Blonde, Butcombe Bitter ⌀ Ashton Press. ♟ 8
Facilities Children's menu Family room Garden
Parking Rooms 3

MARTOCK

The Nag's Head Inn

East St TA12 6NF ☎ 01935 823432
dir: *Telephone for directions*

This 200-year-old former cider house is set in a
lovely hamstone street in a picturesque south
Somerset village. The large rear garden is partly
walled and has pretty borders and trees. Local
real ales, wines and food are served in both the
public and lounge bars, where crib, dominoes,
darts and pool are available. The pub also has a
skittle alley and a decked smoking area.

Open all wk 6-11 (Fri-Sun noon-mdnt) Bar
Meals L served all wk 12-2 D served Mon-Thu 6-8,
Sat-Sun 6-9 Av main course £5.50 Restaurant Av 3
course à la carte fr £14 ⊕ FREE HOUSE ◖ Guinness,
Worthington, Toby. Facilities Children's menu Family
room Dogs allowed Garden Parking

MONTACUTE

The Kings Arms Inn 🍷

49 Bishopston TA15 6UU ☎ 01935 822513
e-mail: info@thekingsarmsinn.co.uk
dir: *From A303 onto A3088 at rdbt signed Montacute. Hotel in village centre*

Mons Acutus (thus Montacute) is the steep hill at whose foot the hamstone-built Kings Arms has stood since 1632. Have a snack in the fire-warmed bar or outside in warmer weather, or something more substantial chosen from the daily-changing restaurant menu; the restaurant was recently refurbished. At this welcoming inn, all food is cooked on the premises using the freshest of ingredients and served throughout the day.

Open all wk noon-3 6-11.30 (Sun noon-3 Oct-Feb) **Bar Meals** L served all wk 12-3 D served all wk 6-9 Av main course £4.75 **Restaurant** D served all wk 6-9 booking required Fixed menu price fr £15 ⊕ GREENE KING ◀ Ruddles County, Abbot Ale, Old Speckled Hen. 🍷 10 **Facilities** Children's menu Dogs allowed Garden Parking

OVER STRATTON

The Royal Oak 🍷

TA13 5LQ ☎ 01460 240906
e-mail: info@the-royal-oak.net
dir: *Exit A303 at Hayes End rdbt (South Petherton). 1st left after Esso garage signed Over Stratton*

Blackened beams, flagstones, log fires, pews and settles set the scene in this welcoming old thatched inn built from warm Hamstone, which has the added attraction of a garden, children's play area and barbecue. Expect real ales, including Tanglefoot from the Badger brewery in Blandford Forum, and dishes ranging from beer battered haddock and chips with home-made tartare sauce to supreme of chicken in an apricot, ginger and white wine sauce.

Open Closed: Mon (ex BH) **Bar Meals** L served Tue-Sun 12-2 booking required D served Tue-Sun 6-9 booking required **Restaurant** L served Tue-Sun 12-2 booking required D served Tue-Sun 6-9 booking required ⊕ HALL & WOODHOUSE ◀ Badger Best, Tanglefoot, Sussex Best Bitter. 🍷 6 **Facilities** Children's menu Play area Family room Dogs allowed Garden Parking

PITNEY RUDGE

The Full Moon at Rudge ★★★ INN ⬤

BA11 2QF

☎ 01373 830936 📠 01373 831366
e-mail: info@thefullmoon.co.uk
dir: *From A36 (Bath to Warminster road) follow Rudge signs*

Strategically placed at the crossing of two old drove roads, this inn enjoys great views of Westbury White Horse. The venerable 16th-century building had been sympathetically updated and retains its small, stone-floored rooms furnished with scrubbed tables. Modern British cooking is the watchword with menus changing to reflect the seasons. Lamb chump chop with bubble and squeak and a rosemary jus or simple steak and kidney pie are examples of the fare. There are 17 comfortable bedrooms if you would like to stay over.

Open all day all wk 11.30-11 (Sun noon-10.30) Bar Meals L served Mon-Sat 12-2 D served Mon-Sat 6-9, Sun 7-9 Restaurant L served all wk 12-2 D served Mon-Sat 6-9 booking required ⬛ FREE HOUSE ◀ Butcombe Bitter, John Smith's, Potholer Ⓒ Stowford Press, Thatchers Cheddar Valley. ⬤ 6 Facilities Children's menu Dogs allowed Garden Parking Rooms 17

TRISCOMBE

The Blue Ball ⬤

TA4 3HE ☎ 01984 618242 📠 01984 618371
e-mail: info@blueballinn.co.uk
dir: *From Taunton take A358 past Bishops Lydeard towards Minehead*

A converted 18th-century thatched barn, the Blue Ball Inn is hidden away down a narrow lane in the Quantock Hills. Inside you will find A-frame wooden ceilings, solid beech furniture, log fires and, from the windows, superb views south to the Brendon Hills. On fine days you can take a seat outside in the large beer garden or on the patio. Typical dishes are marinated Moroccan lamb with Mediterranean vegetables, lemon couscous and harissa sauce; and corn-fed chicken with herb velouté and baby spring vegetables. Puddings are all home-made and might include dark chocolate tart, lemon and thyme pannacotta, and rhubarb syllabub with crushed meringue and shortbread.

Open all day noon-3.30 6.30-11 (Fri-Sat 12-11 Sun 12-9) Closed: 25-26 Dec eve, 1 Jan eve Bar Meals L served Mon-Sat 12-2.30, Sun 12-6 D served all wk 7-9.30 Av main course £8.50 Restaurant L served Tue-Sat 12-2.30, Sun 12-6 booking required D served Tue-Sun 7-9.30 booking required ⬛ PUNCH TAVERNS ◀ Cotleigh Tawny, Exmoor Gold & Stag, St Austell, Tribute, Otter Head Ale. ⬤ 8 Facilities Children's menu Dogs allowed Garden Parking

WEST HUNTSPILL

Crossways Inn ☞

Withy Rd TA9 3RA
☎ 01278 783756   📠 01278 781899
e-mail: crossways.inn@virgin.net
dir: *On A38 3.5m from M5*

The Crossways Inn is a 17th-century coaching inn that forms an integral part of village life. A new skittle alley and pool table are available and live music, themed meals, and unusual competitions are regular events. Produce comes from local sources wherever possible, and dishes are from the menu or specials blackboards, from snacks like deep-fried whitebait and traditional pies, to lasagne, grilled duck breast with grilled peaches, lemon butter chicken or mushroom and brie Wellington. There's a family room, skittle alley and secluded garden. Recent change of management.

Open all wk 10-3.30 6-mdnt Closed: 25 Dec **Bar Meals** Av main course £7 food served all day **Restaurant** food served all day ⊕ FREE HOUSE ◖ Interbrew Bass, Flowers IPA, Fuller's London Pride, Exmoor Stag, Cotleigh Snowy, Butcombe Gold, Branscombe Bitter ♨ Ashton Press. ☞ 8 **Facilities** Children's menu Play area Family room Dogs allowed Garden Parking

WEST MONKTON

The Monkton Inn ☞

Blundells Ln TA2 8NP ☎ 01823 412414
web: www.themonkton.co.uk
dir: *M5 junct 25 to Taunton, right at Creech Castle for 1m, left into West Monkton Village*

Owners Eddie Street and Guy Arnold have refurbished the interior and kitchen, and added a stylish patio area. Their mission statement requires staff to greet a customer within 30 seconds of entering, to "go the extra mile", and to have fun at work. Hear, hear! By serving freshly prepared, reasonably priced food they have built a loyal following. Lunch and dinner menus change daily, which makes for a great many possibilities. Randomly selected are medallions of local pork with bacon, leek and sausage mash, apple and honey cider sauce; poached chicken with sweet potato and butternut squash mash, rich tomato sauce and fresh asparagus; and fresh fillet of plaice deep-fried in tempura batter, with home-made chips and tartare sauce.

Open noon-3 6-11 (Sat-Sun noon-11) Closed: Sun eve, Mon L **Bar Meals** L served Tue-Sun 12-2 Av main course £6 **Restaurant** L served Tue-Sun 12-2 D served Mon-Sat 6.30-9.30 booking required Fixed menu price fr £14.50 ⊕ ENTERPRISE INNS ◖ Butcombe Bitter, Cotleigh Tawny Exmoor Ale, Exmoor Gold. ☞ 7 **Facilities** Children's menu Play area Garden Parking

WHEDDON CROSS

The Rest and Be Thankful Inn ★★★★ INN

TA24 7DR
☎ 01643 841222 🖷 01643 841813
e-mail: stay@restandbethankful.co.uk
dir: *5m S of Dunster*

Years ago, travellers were grateful for a break at this coaching inn, nearly 1,000 feet up in Exmoor's highest village. Old world charm blends with friendly hospitality in the bar and spacious restaurant, where log fires burn in winter and home-cooked food is served. In addition to the restaurant menu there is a weekly specials board, a light lunch menu and a traditional Sunday carvery. The pub also has a skittle alley and pool table. There are comfortable, well-equipped bedrooms available.

Open all wk 10-3 6-close Bar Meals L served all wk 12-2 D served all wk 7-9 Restaurant L served all wk 12-2 booking required D served all wk 7-9 booking required ⊕ FREE HOUSE ◀ Exmoor Ale, Proper Job, Tribute, Guinness. Facilities Children's menu Garden Parking Rooms 8

WIVELISCOMBE

White Hart ★★★★ INN ▼

West St TA4 2JP
☎ 01984 623344 🖷 01984 624748
e-mail:
reservations@whitehartwiveliscombe.co.uk
web: www.whitehartwiveliscombe.co.uk
dir: *M5 junct 26. Pub in town centre*

Facing the square in Wiveliscombe this 350-year-old former coaching inn has a reputation for high quality, freshly cooked food using locally sourced produce. An ever-changing menu includes the 'famous' White Hart burger with home-made chips. Other favourites are starters such as chargrilled local organic vegetable terrine with goats' cheese and pesto salad; main dishes like pan-fried free-range West Country duck breast on a confit of garlic mash with orange and rosemary sauce; and for dessert, sticky toffee pudding; or the board of local cheeses. Sundays bring traditional roasts.

Open all day all wk 10.30am-11pm (Fri-Sat 10am-mdnt) Bar Meals L served Tue-Sun 12-2 booking required D served all wk 6.30-9 booking required Av main course £8 Restaurant L served Tue-Sun 12-2 booking required D served all wk 6.30-9 booking required Av 3 course à la carte fr £22.50 ⊕ FREE HOUSE ◀ Cotleigh Tawny Owl, Exmoor Gold, Sharps Doom Bar, Fullers London Pride, Cotleigh Harrier Ö Rattler. ▼ 10 Facilities Children's menu Dogs allowed Garden Parking Rooms 16

YEOVIL

The Masons Arms ★★★★ INN

41 Lower Odcombe BA22 8TX
☎ 01935 862591 📄 01935 862591
e-mail: paula@masonsarmsodcombe.co.uk
dir: *A3088 to Yeovil, right to Montacute, through village, 3rd right after petrol station to Odcombe*

Built of local hamstone, and dating back to the 15th century, this is the oldest building in the village. The kitchen, producing freshly prepared traditional pub grub such as fish pie topped with chive mash; spicy meatball pasta; corned beef hash; and ham, egg and chips, while his daily-changing carte menu might feature lamb's liver and bacon, bubble 'n' squeak and onion gravy; sirloin steak with brandy, black pepper sauce and slow-cooked cabbage; cod fillet wrapped in prosciutto, provençale vegetables and pea purée; and red pepper and Parmesan risotto with oyster mushroom fritters. The comfortable en suite letting rooms are set back from the road in an extension overlooking the garden.

Open all wk noon-3 6-mdnt **Bar Meals** L served all wk 12-2 booking required D served all wk 6.30-9.30 booking required Av main course £10 **Restaurant** L served all wk 12-2 booking required D served all wk 6.30-9.30 booking required ⊕ FREE HOUSE ◀ Drew's Odcombe ♂ Westons Bounds Brand. **Facilities** Children's menu Dogs allowed Garden Parking **Rooms** 6

COLTON

The Yorkshireman 🍷

Colton Rd WS15 3HB ☎ 01889 583977
e-mail: theyorkshireman@btconnect.com
dir: *10m from Stafford*

To know why the former Railway Tavern changed its name, look no further than the fact that a Yorkshireman once owned it, and rechristened it in his own honour. Beers are brewed by Blythe's just up the road, the most popular being Palmer's Poison, named after Rugeley's famous serial-murdering doctor. Curled up on his bed in the corner of the bar you'll probably find Dahl, the pub's lazy greyhound. Locally sourced food can change daily to include gammon with free-range egg, fresh pineapple and chips; poached smoked haddock with sautéed new potatoes and creamy mustard and white wine sauce; and roasted pepper stuffed with pilau rice, and vegetable and chickpea tandoori. The Deli sells the Yorkshireman's own sauces and dishes, including fishcakes and beefburgers, to take away, plus local cheeses and vegetables.

Open all wk noon-2.30 5.30-11 (Sun noon-6) **Bar Meals** L served Mon-Sat 12-2.30, Sun 12-6 D served Mon-Sat 6-9.30 Av main course £10 **Restaurant** L served Mon-Sat 12-2.30, Sun 12-6 booking required D served Mon-Sat 6-9.30 booking required ⊕ FREE HOUSE ◀ Blythes, Black Sheep. 🍷 9 **Facilities** Children's menu Dogs allowed Garden Parking

STAFFORD

The Holly Bush Inn ☂

Salt ST18 0BX

☎ 01889 508234 📠 01889 508058

e-mail: geoff@hollybushinn.co.uk

web: www.hollybushinn.co.uk

dir: Telephone for directions

The Holly Bush is well known for the quality of its food and welcome. The pub's comfortably old-fashioned interior contains all the vital ingredients: heavy carved beams, open fires, attractive prints and cosy alcoves. The team are enthusiastic in their attempts to reduce food miles and support local producers (named on the menu). At lunchtime there is a good selection of sandwiches, hot sandwiches, toasties and filled jacket potatoes. On the main menu are traditional Staffordshire oatcakes filled with spiced black pudding and a herby tomato sauce; and a centuries' old recipe of slow cooked venison casserole. Other typical dishes include home-made steak and kidney pudding with onion gravy; braised lamb and apples. Local award-winning cheeses and a great selection of locally farmed steaks complete the picture. The chalkboard displays the vegetarian options.

Open all wk 12-11 (Sun 12-10.30) Bar Meals Av main course £10.50 food served all day ⊕ FREE HOUSE ◀ Adnams, Pedigree, guest ales. ☂ 12 Facilities Children's menu Garden Parking

STAFFORD

The Moat House ★★★★ HL ◉◉ ☂

Lower Penkridge Rd, Acton Trussell ST17 0RJ

☎ 01785 712217 📠 01785 715344

e-mail: info@moathouse.co.uk

dir: M6 junct 13 towards Stafford, 1st right to Acton Trussell

A Grade II listed mansion dating back to the 14th century, standing on a mound, scheduled as an Ancient Monument, beside the Staffordshire and Worcestershire Canal. Inside are oak beams and an inglenook fireplace, the stylish Brasserie Bar, and the Conservatory Restaurant. The food is listed on a variety of menus offering, for example, beef tomato and buffalo mozzarella salad with crushed basil and extra virgin olive oil; 28-day, dry-aged Staffordshire sirloin steak with thick-cut chips, onion rings, field mushroom, tomato and a pepper sauce; and seared fillet of salmon served on a bed of wilted spinach with a sauce vièrge and new potatoes.

Open all day all wk 10am-11pm Closed: 25 Dec Bar Meals L served all wk 12-2.15 D served Sun-Fri 6-9 Av main course £10 Restaurant L served all wk 12-2 booking required D served all wk 6.30-9 booking required Av 3 course à la carte fr £40 ⊕ FREE HOUSE ◀ Old Speckled Hen, Greene King IPA, Guinness. ☂ 16 Facilities Children's menu Family room Garden Parking Rooms 41

WETTON

Ye Olde Royal Oak

DE6 2AF ☎ 01335 310287

e-mail: brian@rosehose.wanadoo.co.uk
dir: A515 towards Buxton, left in 4m to Manifold
Valley-Alstonfield, follow signs to Wetton

The stone-built inn dates back over 400 years and features wooden beams recovered from oak ships at Liverpool Docks. It was formerly part of the Chatsworth Estate, and the Tissington walking and cycling trail is close by. Belvoir beers and other guest ales are served along with dishes such as home-made soup; large battered cod; and treacle sponge. Separate vegetarian and children's menus are available. The pub's moorland garden includes a campsite with showers and toilets.

Open Closed: Mon-Tue in winter Bar Meals L served Wed-Sun 12-2 D served Wed-Sun 7-9 Av main course £7.50 ⊕ FREE HOUSE Facilities Children's menu Family room Dogs allowed Garden Parking

WRINEHILL

The Hand & Trumpet ♥

Main Rd CW3 9BJ

☎ 01270 820048   📄 01270 821911

e-mail: hand.and.trumpet@brunningandprice.co.uk
dir: M6 junct 16 follow signs for Keele, continue onto A531, 7m on right

A relaxed country pub, The Hand & Trumpet has a comfortable interior with original floors, old furniture, open fires and rugs. A deck to the rear overlooks the sizeable grounds, which include a large pond. Six cask ales and over 70 malt whiskies are served, along with a locally sourced menu of dishes such as braised lamb shoulder with honey roasted vegetables, rosemary and redcurrant gravy; or wild mushroom, celeriac, leek and thyme pie.

Open all day all wk 11.30-11 (Sun 11.30-10.30) Closed: 25 Dec Bar Meals L served all wk 12-10 booking required D served all wk 12-10 booking required Av main course £12.95 food served all day ⊕ FREE HOUSE ◀ Deuchars IPA, Hawkshead Lakeland Gold, Guest ales ♂ Stonehouse. ♥ 22 Facilities Children's menu Family room Dogs allowed Garden Parking

BURY ST EDMUNDS

The Linden Tree

7 Out Northgate IP33 1JQ ☎ 01284 754600
e-mail: lindentree@live.com
dir: *Opposite railway station*

Built to serve the railway station, this is a big,
friendly Victorian pub, with stripped pine bar,
dining area, non-smoking conservatory and
charming garden. The family-orientated menu
ranges from beef curry, home-made pies, and
liver and bacon, to crab thermidor, fresh sea
bass, and mushroom and lentil moussaka.
Youngsters will go for the burgers, scampi,
or pork chipolatas. Freshly filled ciabattas at
lunchtime.

Open all wk noon-11 (Fri-Sat 11-11 Sun noon-10)
Closed: 25 Dec **Bar Meals** L served all wk 12-2.30
D served all wk 6-9.30 **Restaurant** L served all wk
12-2.30 booking required D served all wk 6-9.30
booking required ⊕ GREENE KING ◀ Greene King,
IPA & Old Speckled Hen, guest. **Facilities** Children's
menu Play area Dogs allowed Garden

GREAT BRICETT

Red Lion

Green Street Green IP7 7DD
☎ 01473 657799 📄 01473 658492
e-mail: janwise@fsmail.net
dir: *4.5m from Needham Market on B1078*

This charming 17th-century building may
look like a traditional village pub and it was,
arguably, just another hostelry until Jan Wise
came along and turned it into East Anglia's only
vegetarian pub. She has a fixed rule: nothing is
served that means killing an animal, so there's
no Sunday carvery, no mixed grill, no scampi in
a basket. Wanting to 'celebrate the fantastic
flavours that only vegetables can provide', Jan
uses her 30 years' experience as a vegetarian
caterer to create internationally-inspired starters
such as dim sum, nachos or houmous, perhaps
followed by oyster mushroom, leek and pine nut
parcel; roasted vegetable and brie tart; or African
sweet potato stew. She's back on more familiar
territory with her desserts, which typically
include chocolate brownies, rhubarb crumble and
summer pudding. Not only is it advisable to book,
you'll also need a healthy appetite.

Open Closed: Mon **Bar Meals** L served Tue-Sun
12-2 D served Tue-Sat 6-9 Av main course £7.90
⊕ GREENE KING ◀ Greene King IPA, Old Speckled
Hen. **Facilities** Children's menu Play area Dogs
allowed Garden Parking

HALESWORTH

The Queen's Head 🍷

The Street, Bramfield IP19 9HT
☎ 01986 784214
e-mail: qhbfield@aol.com
dir: 2m from A12 on A144 towards Halesworth

A lovely old building in the centre of Bramfield on the edge of the Suffolk Heritage Coast near historic Southwold. The enclosed garden is ideal for children. The pub's interior welcomes with scrubbed pine tables, exposed beams, a vaulted ceiling in the bar and enormous fireplaces. The menu which proudly names the farms and suppliers from which the carefully chosen ingredients are sourced. Local produce notwithstanding, there's a definite cosmopolitan twist to many dishes, and vegetarian options are a particular strength: mushrooms baked in cream and garlic au gratin could be followed by fresh tagliatelle with pesto, roast red peppers and grilled goats' cheese. Local turkey, wild mushroom, bacon and chestnut pie or fillets of sea bass with rocket pesto mayonnaise are fine main course examples.

Open all wk 11.45-2.30 6.30-11 (Sun noon-3 7-10.30) Closed: 26 Dec Bar Meals L served all wk 12-2 D served Mon-Fri 6.30-9.15, Sat 6.30-10, Sun 7-9 Av main course £10.95 Restaurant Av 3 course à la carte fr £20.95 ⊕ ADNAMS ◄ Adnams Bitter, Broadside. 🍷 8 Facilities Children's menu Family room Dogs allowed Garden Parking

HOLBROOK

The Compasses

Ipswich Rd IP9 2QR
☎ 01473 328332 📠 01473 327403
e-mail: compasses.holbrook@virgin.net
dir: From A137 S of Ipswich, take B1080 to Holbrook, pub on left. From Ipswich take B1456 to Shotley. At Freston Water Tower right onto B1080 to Holbrook. Pub 2m right

Holbrook is bordered by the rivers Orwell and Stour, and this traditional country pub, which dates from the 17th century, is on the Shotley peninsula. A good value menu includes ploughman's, salads and jacket potatoes; pub favourites such as chilli con carne or chicken with cashew nuts; and a fish selection including seafood lasagne. Party bookings are a speciality, and look out for Wine of the Week deals. Pensioners' weekday lunches complete this pub's honest offerings.

Open all wk 11.30-2.30 6-11 (Sun noon-3 6-10.30) Closed: 25-26 Dec, 1 Jan, Tue eve Bar Meals L served all wk 12-2.15 booking required D served Wed-Mon 6-9.15 booking required Restaurant L served all wk 12-2.15 booking required D served Wed-Mon 6-9.15 booking required ⊕ PUNCH TAVERNS ◄ Greene King IPA, Adnams Bitter, Guinness Ŏ Aspall. Facilities Children's menu Play area Garden Parking

IXWORTH

Pykkerell Inn ♟

38 High St IP31 2HH

☎ 01359 230398   📄 01359 230398

dir: *On A143 from Bury St Edmunds towards Diss*

This former coaching inn dates from 1530 and still retains most of its original beams, inglenook fireplace and other features. The wood-panelled library is just off the lounge, and the 14th-century barn encloses a patio and barbecue. The extensive menu includes vegetarian options and children's meals, as well as traditional Sunday roast lunch. Menu boards highlight a variety of fresh fish, and may include red snapper, monkfish and Dover sole.

Open noon-3 5.30-11.30 Closed: Mon L **Bar Meals** L served Tue-Sun 12-2 D served all wk 7-9 ⊕ GREENE KING ◀ Greene King IPA, Abbot Ale, Old Speckled Hen. ♟ 6 **Facilities** Children's menu Dogs allowed Garden Parking

KETTLEBURGH

The Chequers Inn

IP13 7JT

☎ 01728 723760 & 724369

📄 01728 723760

e-mail: info@thechequers.net

dir: *From Ipswich A12 onto B1116, left onto B1078 then right through Easton*

The Chequers is set in beautiful countryside on the banks of the River Deben. The landlord serves a wide range of cask ales, including two guests. In addition to snack and restaurant meals, the menu in the bar includes local sausages and ham with home-produced free-range eggs. The riverside garden can seat up to a hundred people.

Open all wk **Bar Meals** L served all wk 12-2 D served all wk 7-9.30 Av main course £6.50 **Restaurant** L served all wk 12-2 D served all wk 7-9.30 Av 3 course à la carte fr £18 ⊕ FREE HOUSE ◀ Greene King IPA, Black Dog Mild, 3 guest ales Ⓞ Aspall. **Facilities** Children's menu Play area Dogs allowed Garden Parking

LAXFIELD

The Kings Head ⚑

Gorams Mill Ln IP13 8DW ☎ 01986 798395
e-mail: bob-wilson5505@hotmail.co.uk
dir: *On B1117*

Beautifully situated overlooking the river, the garden of this thatched 16th-century alehouse was formerly the village bowling green. Beer is still served straight from the cask in the original tap room, whilst high-backed settles and wooden seats add to the charming atmosphere. Traditional home-cooked dishes complement the à la carte menu and chef's specials and, on warmer evenings, the rose gardens and arbour are perfect for al fresco dining.

Open all wk Bar Meals L served all wk 12-2.30 D served Mon-Sat 7-9.30 Av main course £7.50 Restaurant L served all wk 12-2.30 booking required D served Mon-Sat 7-9.30 booking required Fixed menu price fr £7.50 Av 3 course à la carte fr £15 ⊕ ADNAMS ◀ Adnams Best & Broadside, Adnams seasonal, guest ales � Aspall. ⚑ 8 Facilities Children's menu Play area Family room Dogs allowed Garden Parking

LIDGATE

The Star Inn

The Street CB8 9PP
☎ 01638 500275   ▤ 01638 500275
e-mail: tonyaxon@aol.com
dir: *From Newmarket clocktower in High St follow signs towards Clare on B1063. Lidgate 7m*

This pretty, pink-painted Elizabethan building is made up of two cottages with gardens front and rear; inside, two traditionally furnished bars with heavy oak beams, log fires and pine furniture. Here you'll find a renowned Spanish restaurant offering Mediterranean cuisine. The Star is popular with Newmarket trainers on race days, and with dealers and agents from all over the world during bloodstock sales. The menu offers appealingly hearty food: starters like Catalan spinach; and Mediterranean fish soup might precede Spanish meatballs; or hake a la vasca. English tastes are also catered for, with dishes such as smoked salmon and avocado; roast lamb with garlic; and fillet steak in pepper sauce.

Open all wk noon-3 6-mdnt Closed: 25-26 Dec, 1 Jan Bar Meals L served Mon-Sat 12-3 booking required D served Mon-Sat 7-10 booking required Av main course £11.50 Restaurant L served all wk 12-3 booking required D served Mon-Sat 7-10 booking required Fixed menu price fr £14 Av 3 course à la carte fr £28 ⊕ GREENE KING ◀ Greene King IPA, Ruddles County, Abbot Ale. Facilities Children's menu Garden Parking

MILDENHALL

The Olde Bull Inn ★★★ HL ⊚ ▾

The Street, Barton Mills IP28 6AA
☎ 01638 711001 🖷 01638 712003
e-mail: bookings@bullinn-bartonmills.com
dir: *Off the A11 between Newmarket and Mildenhall, signed Barton Mills*

Beautifully refurbished in contemporary style in 2007, the new-look Bull Inn is a popular pit-stop for travellers heading for Norwich or the Norfolk coast. Everything is freshly prepared on the premises, so stay in the bar for classic award-winning Newmarket bangers and mash, a ciabatta filled with home-baked ham and mustard, or Denham Estate wild boar casserole served with dumplings. Linger over three courses in the Oak Room restaurant, perhaps following prawn and crayfish cocktail with braised lamb shank, and finishing with lemon tart. Well-appointed, individually designed bedrooms have flat-screen TVs, smart designer fabrics, and fresh bathrooms.

Open all day all wk 8am-11pm **Bar Meals** L served all wk 12-9 D served all wk 12-9 Av main course £8.75 food served all day **Restaurant** L served Sun 12-3 D served all wk 6-9 Av 3 course à la carte fr £22 ⊕ FREE HOUSE ◀ Adnams Broadside, Greene King IPA, Brandon Brewery Rusty Bucket, Humpty Dumpty, Wolf. ▾ 8 **Facilities** Children's menu Family room Garden Parking **Rooms** 14

MONKS ELEIGH

The Swan Inn ⊛⊛ ▾

The Street IP7 7AU ☎ 01449 741391
e-mail: carol@monkseleigh.com
dir: *On B1115 between Sudbury & Hadleigh*

The pub welcomed its first customers in the 16th century when the interior would have been open to the roof; and, even today, you can still see evidence of the former smokehole. Other historical features include the original wattle and daub that was exposed during renovation work; it can now be seen behind a glass panel. The regularly changing menus reflect local ingredients wherever possible. Expect to find game in season, locally picked vegetables and fresh fish from the Suffolk coast. Starters like creamy pea and asparagus soup and dressed Cromer crab might precede main course options such as roast monkfish wrapped in Parma ham and sage leaves on buttered samphire, or chargrilled sirloin steak with aubergine, cherry tomato and basil compote.

Open noon-2.30 7-11 Closed: 25-26 Dec, 1-2 Jan, Mon-Tue (ex BH) **Bar Meals** L served Wed-Sun 12-2 D served Wed-Sat 7-9 Av main course £10 **Restaurant** L served Wed-Sun 12-2 D served Wed-Sat 7-9 Fixed menu price fr £13.50 Av 3 course à la carte fr £25 ⊕ FREE HOUSE ◀ Greene King IPA, Adnams Bitter, Broadside Ö Aspall, Thatchers Katy. ▾ 20 **Facilities** Children's menu Garden Parking

SNAPE

The Golden Key ☙

Priory Ln IP17 1SQ ☎ 01728 688510
e-mail: info@snape-golden-key.co.uk
dir: *Telephone for directions*

The 17th-century building has seen many changes over the last couple of years with complete redecoration inside and out to provide an attractive and comfortable dining pub. Locally sourced food is key to the seasonal menus, which include fresh fish daily from Aldeburgh; Hogwarts Large Black rare-breed pork; and Simply Snape Jacob lamb. Typical dishes are dressed Aldeburgh crab; wild rabbit casserole; and Emmerdale Farm Suffolk Red Poll steak, mushroom and ale pie. A small shop has been established selling a range of local products.

Open all wk Bar Meals L served Mon-Sat 12-2, Sun 12-2.30 booking required D served Mon-Sat 6.30-9, Sun 7-9 booking required Av main course £10 Restaurant L served Mon-Sat 12-2, Sun 12-2.30 booking required D served Mon-Sat 6.30-9, Sun 7-9 booking required ⊕ ADNAMS ◀ Adnams Bitter, Broadside, Explorer, Old, Oyster Stout Ò Aspall. ☙14 Facilities Children's menu Family room Dogs allowed Garden Parking

SOUTHWOLD

The Randolph ☙ ☙

41 Wangford Rd, Reydon IP18 6PZ
☎ 01502 723603 ░ 01502 722194
e-mail: reception@therandolph.co.uk
dir: *A1095 from A12 at Blythburgh 4m, Southwold 9m from Darsham train station*

This grand late-Victorian establishment with large gardens was built by Adnams the local brewer and named after Lord Randolph Churchill, Sir Winston's father. There is a traditional bar but the interior has more of a gastro-pub ambience. Modern British menus offer simple dishes full of flavour, such as deep-fried cod in Adnams batter with hand-cut chips; and confit of duck legs served on an egg noodle and vegetable stir-fry with hoi sin sauce.

Open all wk Bar Meals L served all wk 12-2 D served all wk 6.30-9 Av main course £10.95 Restaurant L served all wk 12-2 booking required D served all wk 6.30-9 booking required Av 3 course à la carte fr £21.50 ⊕ ADNAMS PLC ◀ Adnams Bitter, Adnams Broadside, Explorer, Old Ale Ò Aspall. ☙6 Facilities Children's menu Garden Parking

WALBERSWICK

The Anchor ⍟⍟ ♟

Main St IP18 6UA

☎ 01502 722112 🖹 01502 724464

e-mail: info@anchoratwalberswick.com

dir: *Please telephone for directions*

A 1920s Arts and Crafts building located within earshot of the sea and run with passion and a zealous dedication to local ingredients, and skill in the kitchen. The short, perfectly seasonal menu pairs each flavour-packed dish with a different suggestion for beer and wine by the glass. Cooking is unpretentious, striking an interesting modern note, yielding the likes of double-baked Green's cheddar soufflé with caramelised onions, braised Blythburgh pork belly with Savoy cabbage and cider jus, and Hoegaarden braised rabbit's legs and peppered loin with buttered leeks and turnip gratin. Expect a relaxed atmosphere and a contemporary feel to the spruced-up bar, with its blue, sand and stone décor reflecting its seaside location, and rear dining room. The splendid rear terrace and garden overlook a beach-hut-dotted horizon.

Open all wk **Bar Meals** L served all wk 12-3 D served all wk 6-9 Av main course £13.25 **Restaurant** L served all wk 12-3 booking required D served all wk 6-9 booking required Av 3 course à la carte fr £24.50 ◀ Adnams Bitter, Broadside, Seasonal ⍟ Aspalls. ♟ 16 **Facilities** Children's menu Family room Dogs allowed Garden Parking

WALBERSWICK

Bell Inn ♟

Ferry Rd IP18 6TN

☎ 01502 723109 🖹 01502 722728

e-mail: thebell@adnams.co.uk

dir: *From A12 take B1387, follow to beyond village green, bear right down track*

The inn dates back 600 years and is located near the village green, beach and the ancient fishing harbour on the River Blyth. The large garden has beach and sea views, while the building's great age is evident from the interior's low beams, stone-flagged floors, high wooden settles and open fires. Food is all home cooked with local produce featuring strongly, particularly fresh fish. Specialities include starters of locally smoked sprats or Suffolk smokies – flaked smoked haddock in a creamy cheese sauce – both served with granary toast and a salad garnish. There are non-fish dishes too, like baked Suffolk ham or lamb burger in toasted ciabatta.

Open all wk **Bar Meals** L served all wk 12-2 D served all wk 7-9 ⊕ ADNAMS ◀ Adnams Bitter, Broadside, Regatta, Old Ale, Explorer, Spindrift ⍟ Aspall. ♟ 15 **Facilities** Children's menu Family room Dogs allowed Garden Parking

WESTLETON

The Westleton Crown ★★★ HL ⚜️⚜️ ℗

The Street IP17 3AD
☎ 01728 648777 📄 01728 648239
e-mail: reception@westletoncrown.co.uk
web: www.westletoncrown.co.uk
dir: *A12 N, turn right for Westleton just after Yoxford. Hotel opposite on entering Westleton*

Over the years this attractive brick-built pub has evolved into a well-appointed inn, combining historic character with contemporary charm. An extensive menu includes innovative daily specials and classic dishes with a twist, all freshly prepared from the best local produce available. Starters and lighter dishes may include free-range Blythburgh ham terrine with piccalilli, and baked butternut squash and onion tart. Main courses embrace braised shank of lamb with ratatouille, and local venison with sage creamed potatoes and blueberry sauce. Save some space for accomplished desserts like caramelised blackberry crème brûlée.

Open all day all wk 7am-11pm (Sun 7.30am-10.30pm) **Bar Meals** L served all wk 12-2.30 D served all wk 7-9.30 Av main course £15 food served all day **Restaurant** L served all wk 12-2.30 D served all wk 7-9.30 ⊕ FREE HOUSE ◀ Adnams Bitter, range of real ales. ℗ 9 **Facilities** Children's menu Dogs allowed Garden Parking **Rooms** 25

COMPTON

The Withies Inn ℗

Withies Ln GU3 1JA
☎ 01483 421158 📄 01483 425904
dir: *Telephone for directions*

Set amid unspoiled country on Compton Common, just below the Hog's Back, this low-beamed, 16th-century pub has been carefully modernised to incorporate a small restaurant. There is also a splendid garden where meals are served in the pergola. Snacks are available in the bar, while in the restaurant there is a selection from the chargrill, and dishes such as poached halibut with prawns and brandy sauce; home-cooked steak, kidney and mushroom pie; and steak Diane flambé.

Open 11-3 6-11 (Fri 11-11) Closed: Sun eve **Bar Meals** L served all wk 12-2.30 D served Mon-Sat 7-10 **Restaurant** L served all wk 12-2.30 D served Mon-Sat 7-10 ⊕ FREE HOUSE ◀ TEA, Sussex, Adnams. ℗ 8 **Facilities** Children's menu Dogs allowed Garden Parking

ELSTEAD

The Woolpack 🍷

The Green GU8 6HD
☎ 01252 703106 📠 01252 705914
e-mail: woolpack.elstead@yahoo.co.uk
dir: A3 S, take Milford exit, follow signs for Elstead on B3001

The Woolpack is surrounded by hundreds of acres of common land, attracting ramblers galore, especially at lunchtime, and their arrival in the bar is often heralded by the rustle of protective plastic shopping bags over their muddy boots. In the carpeted bar you'll find open log fires, low beams, high-backed settles, window seats and spindle-backed chairs. Large blackboards display frequently changing main meals, sandwiches, ploughman's and burgers. Menus are planned around the best local produce, taking account of the seasons, and choices range from a traditional sausages and mash to pan-fried sea bass with couscous. Leave room for home-made desserts.

Open all wk noon-3 5.30-11 (Sat-Sun noon-11)
Bar Meals L served all wk 12.2.30 booking required D served all wk 7-9.30 booking required Av main course £12 Restaurant L served all wk 12-2.30 booking required D served all wk 7-9.30 booking required Av 3 course à la carte fr £24 ⊕ PUNCH TAVERNS ◀ Greene King Abbot Ale, Hobgoblin, Youngs, Spitfire, London Pride ♂ Old English. 🍷 40
Facilities Children's menu Family room Dogs allowed Garden Parking

EPSOM

White Horse 🍷

63 Dorking Rd KT18 7JU ☎ 01372 726622
e-mail: enquiries@whitehorseepsom.com
dir: On A24 next to Epsom General Hospital

The town's oldest surviving pub focuses on four areas - real ales, freshly cooked traditional British food, being family friendly and, as host of the Epsom Jazz Club on Tuesday evenings, live entertainment. Typical starters are hot smoked salmon pâté or creamy garlic mushrooms: mains include chef's own pie of the week, fresh fish of the week and curry of the day; or braised lamb shank on herb mash. A carvery is available on Saturday and Sunday.

Open Closed: Mon until 6pm Bar Meals Av main course £8 food served all day Restaurant food served all day ⊕ PUNCH TAVERNS ◀ guest ales. 🍷 7
Facilities Children's menu Play area Family room Dogs allowed Garden Parking

FARNHAM

The Bat & Ball Freehouse ☘

15 Bat & Ball Ln, Boundstone GU10 4SA
☎ 01252 792108
e-mail: info@thebatandball.co.uk
dir: *From A31 Farnham bypass follow signs for Birdworld. Left at Bengal Lounge into School Hill. At top over staggered x-rds into Sandrock Hill Rd. After 0.25m left into Upper Bourne Lane, signed*

Tucked down a lane in a wooded valley south of Farnham, this 150-year-old inn is worth hunting out. The interior features oak beams, a roaring fire on colder days, and plenty of cricketing memorabilia. Outside is a children's play area and a lovely garden with vine-topped pergola that backs onto the Bourne stream. Expect excellent ales, a choice of six at any one time, and a varied selection of home-cooked food: perhaps Wensleydale, apple and walnut pâté followed by coq au vin, home-made pie or half duck slow roasted in orange, apricots and vermouth.

Open all wk 11-11 (Sun noon-10.30) Bar Meals L served Mon-Sat 12-2.15, Sun 12-3 booking required D served Mon-Sat 7-9.30, Sun 6-8.30 booking required Av main course £10.50 ⊞ FREE HOUSE ◀ Youngs Bitter, Tongham TEA, Triple FFF, Harvey's Sussex Bitter, Hop Back. ☘ 8 Facilities Children's menu Play area Family room Dogs allowed Garden Parking

LONG DITTON

The Ditton ☘

64 Ditton Hill Rd KT6 5JD ☎ 020 8339 0785
e-mail: goodfood@theditton.co.uk
dir: *Please telephone for directions*

The old Plough & Harrow has been given a facelift to return the pub to its former glory and a trendy new name, the rambling village pub now sports a fresh, contemporary feel throughout the bar and interconnecting dining areas. The focus is on family dining and wide-ranging menus take in classic bar snacks, a mezze menu, home-made pies, roasts on Sundays, and more adventurous dishes like pan-fried pork with mash and sherry sauce. The barbecue menu draws the crowds to the large garden on warm summer days.

Open all day all wk noon-11 Bar Meals L served all wk 12-9 D served all wk 12-9 Av main course £8.95 food served all day Restaurant L served Sat-Sun 12-9 booking required D served Mon-Sat 12-9 booking required Av 3 course à la carte fr £22.50 ⊞ ENTERPRISE INNS ◀ Bombardier, Youngs, Tanglefoot. ☘ 8 Facilities Children's menu Play area Dogs allowed Garden Parking

MICKLEHAM

King William IV 🍷

Byttom Hill RH5 6EL ☎ 01372 372590
dir: *From M25 junct 9, A24 signed to Dorking, pub just before Mickleham*

The former ale house, built in 1790 for workers on Lord Beaverbrook's estate, has a panelled snug and larger back bar with an open fire, cast iron tables and grandfather clock. The terraced garden, ideal for summer dining, offers panoramic views of the Mole Valley. The chef proprietor serves good food alongside real ales, with specials such as roast pheasant breast with red wine jus; and seared king scallops on crayfish in tomato sauce. An ideal location for outstanding local walks.

Open all wk Closed: 25 Dec Bar Meals L served Mon-Fri 11.45-2, Sat 12-2, Sun 12-5 booking required D served Tue-Sat 7-9 booking required Av main course £10 Restaurant L served Mon-Fri 11.45-2, Sat 12-2, Sun 12-5 booking required D served Tue-Sat 7-9 booking required Av 3 course à la carte fr £17 ⊕ FREE HOUSE ◀ Hogs Back TEA, Adnams Best, guest ales ♻ Stowford Press. 🍷 11 Facilities Children's menu Garden Parking

NEWDIGATE

The Surrey Oaks 🍷

Parkgate Rd RH5 5DZ
☎ 01306 631200 📄 01306 631200
e-mail: ken@surreyoaks.co.uk
dir: *From A24 follow signs to Newdigate, at T-junct turn left, pub 1m on left*

Picturesque oak-beamed pub located one mile outside the village of Newdigate. Parts of the building date back to 1570, and it became an inn around the middle of the 19th century. There are two bars, one with an inglenook fireplace, as well as a restaurant area, patio and beer garden with boules pitch. The great selection of beers are mainly from micro-breweries. A typical specials board features Barnsley lamb chop with minted gravy, chicken and ham pie, and grilled plaice with parsley butter.

Open all wk 11.30-2.30 5.30-11 (Sat 11.30-3 6-11 Sun noon-10.30) Bar Meals L served Mon-Fri 12-2, Sat-Sun 12-2.15 D served Tue-Sat 6.30-9.30 Av main course £9 Restaurant L served Mon-Fri 12-2, Sat-Sun 12-2.15 D served Tue-Sat 6.30-9.30 ⊕ ADMIRAL TAVERNS ◀ Harveys Sussex Best, Surrey Hills Ranmore Ale, rotating guest ales ♻ Moles Black Rat, Weston's Country Perry. 🍷 8 Facilities Children's menu Play area Dogs allowed Garden Parking

STAINES

The Swan Hotel ♥

The Hythe TW18 3JB
☎ 01784 452494 📄 01784 461593
e-mail: swanhotel@fullers.co.uk
dir: *Just off A308, S of Staines Bridge. 5m from Heathrow*

This 18th-century inn stands just south of Staines Bridge and was once the haunt of river bargemen who were paid in tokens which could be exchanged at the pub for food and drink. It has a spacious, comfortable bar, and a menu based on traditional home-cooked food. Examples range from sausage and mash; pot-roast lamb shank; and steak and ale pie, to seafood risotto or vegetarian noodle bowl.

Open all wk 11-11 **Bar Meals** L served Mon-Sat 12-3, Sun 12-8 D served Mon-Sat 6-10, Sun 12-8 **Restaurant** L served Mon-Sat 12-3, Sun 12-8 D served Mon-Sat 6-10, Sun 12-8 ⊕ FULLER SMITH TURNER PLC ◀ Fuller's London Pride, ESB, Discovery. ♥ 10 **Facilities** Children's menu Dogs allowed Garden

WEST HORSLEY

The King William IV ♥

83 The Street KT24 6BG
☎ 01483 282318 📄 01483 282318
e-mail: kingbilly4th@aol.com
dir: *On The Street off A246 (Leatherhead to Guildford)*

When laws limiting the consumption of gin were passed in the 1830s, the King William IV began a swift trade in ale through its street-level windows. Fortunately, many of the original Georgian features have been preserved, giving this traditional countryside local a warm and welcoming atmosphere, augmented by open fires in winter and a light and airy conservatory restaurant. Today it's popular with walkers, not least for the large garden and terrace to the rear, with colourful tubs and floral baskets. The well-priced menu ranges over reliable starters such as deep-fried French brie or crispy garlic mushrooms, and leads on to equally popular mains like seared tuna, or marinated minty lamb rumps. Children can tuck into home-made lasagne and a shot of sugar-free 'safari juice'.

Open all day all wk 11.30am-mdnt (Sun noon-10.30) **Bar Meals** L served all wk 12-3 D served Mon-Sat 6.30-9.30 Av main course £9.50 **Restaurant** L served all wk 12-3 D served Mon-Sat 6.30-9.30 Fixed menu price fr £9.50 ⊕ ENTERPRISE INNS ◀ Shere Drop, Courage Best. ♥ 12 **Facilities** Children's menu Family room Dogs allowed Garden Parking

DANEHILL

The Coach and Horses ♟

RH17 7JF

☎ 01825 740369 📄 01825 740369
dir: *From East Grinstead, S through Forest Row on A22 to junct with A275 (Lewes road), right on A275, 2m to Danehill, left onto School Lane, 0.5m, pub on left*

Set on the edge of Ashdown forest with access to miles of footpaths, The Coach and Horses has provided hospitality since 1847. The original bars remain busy with locals: open fires and neatly tended gardens add colour to a characterful setting: expect half-panelled walls, highly polished wooden floorboards and vaulted beamed ceilings. Food plays a key role in its success. Typical choices include confit rabbit terrine with shallot chutney; spicy Portland crab and saffron risotto with Parmesan; and hot chocolate fondant with pistachio crème Anglaise. In addition to the main menu and blackboard dishes, sandwiches are available at lunchtime. **Open** all wk 11.30-3 6-11 (Sat-Sun 11.30-11) **Bar Meals** L served all wk 12-2 D served Mon-Sat 7-9 Av main course £12.50 **Restaurant** L served all wk 12-2 D served Mon-Sat 7-9 Av 3 course à la carte fr £23.75 ⊕ FREE HOUSE ◀ Harveys Best & Old Ale, Wadworth IPA, WJ King & Co, Hammerpot, Dark Star ♻ Stowford Press. ♟10 **Facilities** Children's menu Play area Dogs allowed Garden Parking

EAST CHILTINGTON

The Jolly Sportsman ♟

Chapel Ln BN7 3BA

☎ 01273 890400 📄 01273 890400
e-mail: thejollysportsman@mistral.co.uk
dir: *From Lewes take A275, left at Offham onto B2166 towards Plumpton, take Novington Ln, after approx 1m left into Chapel Ln*

Secluded and romantic, this sympathetically upgraded dining inn is tucked away down a quiet no-through road surrounded by downland. The bar retains some of the character of a Victorian ale house, while the dining room strikes a cool, modern pose, and there is a terrace with Moroccan-tiled tables overlooking the garden. Typical dishes are mussel, tomato and herb risotto; roast partridge with cabbage, bacon and Lyonnaise potatoes; and almond custard fritter with roast plums.

Open Closed: 25-26 Dec, Mon ex BH **Bar Meals** L served Tue-Sat 12.15-2.30, Sun 12.15-3 D served Tue-Thu & Sun 7-9.30, Fri-Sat 7-10 booking required Av main course £13.50 **Restaurant** L served Tue-Sat 12.15-2.30, Sun 12.15-3 booking required D served Tue-Thu & Sun 7-9.30, Fri-Sat 7-10 booking required Fixed menu price fr £15.75 Av 3 course à la carte fr £25 ⊕ FREE HOUSE ◀ Dark Star Hophead, guest ales. ♟9 **Facilities** Children's menu Play area Dogs allowed Garden Parking

HARTFIELD

Anchor Inn

Church St TN7 4AG ☎ 01892 770424
dir: *On B2110*

A 14th-century inn at the heart of Winnie the Pooh country, deep within the scenic Ashdown Forest. Inside are stone floors enhanced by a large inglenook fireplace. Sandwiches and salads are among the bar snacks, while for something more substantial you could try whole Dover sole; grilled pork loin on a bed of spaghetti; or medallions of beef fillet. Puddings include crème brûlée; ice cream gâteau; and orange marmalade bread and butter pudding.

Open all day all wk **Bar Meals** L served all wk 12-2 booking required D served all wk 6-10 booking required Av main course £8 **Restaurant** L served all wk 12-2 booking required D served all wk 6-10 booking required ⊕ FREE HOUSE ◀ Harveys Sussex Best Bitter, Larkins. **Facilities** Children's menu Family room Dogs allowed Garden Parking

ICKLESHAM

The Queen's Head ♟

Parsonage Ln TN36 4BL
☎ 01424 814552 📄 01424 814766
dir: *Between Hastings & Rye on A259. Pub in village on x-rds near church*

A 17th-century tile-hung building, full of exposed oak beams, the pub has a magnificent view across the Brede valley to Rye. The traditional atmosphere has been conserved, with vaulted ceilings, large inglenook fireplaces, church pews, old farm implements, and a bar from the old Midland Bank in Eastbourne. Typical of the home-made dishes are a choice of pies; Thai vegetable curry; steaks and grills; salads and snacks. Gardens include a playhouse, climbing frame and boule pitch.

Open all wk 11-11 (Sun 11-10.30) **Bar Meals** L served Mon-Fri 12-2.30, Sat-Sun 12-9.30 D served Mon-Fri 6-9.30, Sat-Sun 12-9.30 Av main course £8.95 ⊕ FREE HOUSE ◀ Rother Valley Level Best, Greene King Abbot Ale, Harveys Best, Dark Star, Ringwood 49r ♂ Biddenden. ♟ 10 **Facilities** Children's menu Play area Garden Parking

RINGMER

The Cock ☕

Uckfield Rd BN8 5RX

☎ 01273 812040   📠 01273 812040

e-mail: matt@cockpub.co.uk

web: www.cockpub.co.uk

dir: *On A26 approx 2m N of Lewes just outside Ringmer*

Built in the 16th-century, this former coaching inn was a mustering point during the Civil War for the siege of Arundel. Original oak beams, flagstone floors and a blazing fire set a cosy scene. Harveys ales and guest beers accompany an extensive menu. Frequent specials include pot roasted pheasant, organic sausage and onion pie, whole fresh brill, and vegetarian quiche. The west-facing restaurant and garden have views to the South Downs and some wonderful sunsets.

Open all wk 11-3 6-11.30 (Sun 11-11) Closed: 26 Dec **Bar Meals** L served Mon-Sat 12-2, Sun 12-9.30 D served Mon-Sat 6-9.30, Sun 12-9.30 Av main course £9.50 **Restaurant** L served Mon-Sat 12-2, Sun 12-9.30 booking required D served Mon-Sat 6-9.30, Sun 12-9.30 booking required Av 3 course à la carte fr £18.50 ⊕ FREE HOUSE ◀ Harveys Sussex Best Bitter, Sussex XXXX Old Ale, Fuller's London Pride, Dark Star Hophead Ŏ Westons 1st Quality. ♚ 9 **Facilities** Children's menu Play area Dogs allowed Garden Parking

RYE

Mermaid Inn ★★★ HL 🏵 ☕

Mermaid St TN31 7EY

☎ 01797 223065   📠 01797 225069

e-mail: info@mermaidinn.com

dir: *A259, follow signs to town centre, then into Mermaid St*

Destroyed by the French in 1377 and rebuilt in 1420 (on foundations dating back to 1156), the Mermaid is steeped in history and stands among the cobbled streets of Rye. It remains strong on romantic appeal, with beams hewn from ancient ships' timbers, antique furnishings, linenfold panelling, and huge fireplaces carved from French stone ballast rescued from the harbour. Food is served in the bar and atmospheric restaurant, and in the summer you can relax under sunshades on the patio. Bar food ranges from sandwiches or baked fish pie, to smoked haddock and salmon fishcakes and sirloin steak with chips and blue cheese sauce.

Open all wk noon-11 **Bar Meals** L served all wk 12-2.30 D served all wk 6-9 Av main course £8.50 **Restaurant** L served all wk 12-2.30 booking required D served all wk 7.30-9.30 booking required Fixed menu price fr £24 Av 3 course à la carte fr £35 ⊕ FREE HOUSE ◀ Greene King Old Speckled Hen, Courage Best, Fuller's London Pride. ♚ 11 **Facilities** Children's menu Garden Parking **Rooms** 31

THREE LEG CROSS

The Bull 🍷

Dunster Mill Ln TN5 7HH
☎ 01580 200586 📄 01580 201289
e-mail: enquiries@thebullinn.co.uk
dir: From M25 exit at Sevenoaks toward Hastings, right at x-rds onto B2087, right onto B2099 through Ticehurst, right for Three Legged Cross

The Bull is based on a 14th-century Wealden hall house, set in a hamlet close to Bewl Water. The interior features oak beams, inglenook fireplaces, quarry tiled floors, and a mass of small intimate areas in the bar. The extensive gardens are popular with families who enjoy the duck pond, petanque pitch, aviary and children's play area. Menus offer pub favourites ranging from freshly baked baguettes and bar snacks to hearty dishes full of comfort, such as bangers and mash and treacle tart.

Open all wk noon-11 Closed: 25-26 Dec eve **Bar Meals** L served Mon-Fri 12-2.30, Sat 12-3, Sun 12-8 D served Mon-Sat 6.30-9, Sun 6.30-8 **Restaurant** L served Mon-Fri 12-2.30, Sat 12-3, Sun 12-8 D served Mon-Sat 6.30-9, Sun 6.30-8 ⊕ FREE HOUSE ◀ Harveys, Sussex Best, Harveys Armada, Timothy Taylor, 1066, guest ales ⚲ Stowford Press. 🍷 7 **Facilities** Children's menu Play area Dogs allowed Garden Parking

WADHURST

The Best Beech Inn 🍷

Mayfield Ln TN5 6JH ☎ 01892 782046
dir: 7m from Tunbridge Wells. On A246 at lights turn left onto London Rd (A26), left at mini rdbt onto A267, left then right onto B2100. At Mark Cross signed Wadhurst, 3m on right

The unusually-named Best Beech Inn is going from strength to strength. The inn dates back to 1680, and has been sympathetically refurbished in recent years to preserve the essentially Victorian character of its heyday. The result is a place bursting with personality, characterised by comfy chairs, exposed brickwork and open fireplaces. The fine à la carte restaurant offers excellent European cuisine with a French influence. For those who prefer a more informal atmosphere, there is the bar bistro with a comprehensive menu available from the blackboard.

Open all day all wk noon-11pm **Bar Meals** L served Mon-Sat 12-3, Sun 12-4 booking required D served Mon-Sat 6-9.30 booking required **Restaurant** L served Mon-Sat 12-3, Sun 12-4 booking required D served Mon-Sat 6-9.30 booking required ⊕ SHEPHERD NEAME ◀ Kent Best, Master Brew. 🍷 7 **Facilities** Children's menu Family room Dogs allowed Garden Parking

WARTLING

The Lamb Inn ☻

BN27 1RY ☎ 01323 832116
web: www.lambinnwartling.co.uk
dir: *A259 from Polegate to Pevensey rdbt. Take 1st
left to Wartling & Herstmonceux Castle. Pub 3m
on right*

Since 1640 The Lamb has provided a welcome
rest stop to everyone from 18th-century
smugglers to today's birdwatchers, walkers and
locals who enjoy the nearby Pevensey Levels and
surrounding countryside. Everything is made
on the premises, including the bread, and,
as far as possible, makes use of top quality
produce sourced locally. Fish from Hastings and
Newhaven is offered daily on the specials board.
Begin with smoked mackerel, prawn and crayfish
terrine with horseradish cream and Melba toast;
followed by chargrilled Barnsley chop with
dauphinoise potatoes, garlic and parsley butter.
For dessert, try lemon and sultana bread and
butter pudding with clotted cream.

Open all wk Closed: Sun eve, Mon in winter **Bar
Meals** L served all wk 12-2.15 booking required D
served Tue-Sat 7-9 booking required Av main course
£8.95 **Restaurant** L served all wk 12-2.15 booking
required D served Tue-Sat 7-9 booking required
Fixed menu price fr £11.95 Av 3 course à la carte fr
£22.95 ◀ Harveys, Red River, Horsham Best, Toff's,
Level Best. ☻ 8 **Facilities** Children's menu Dogs
allowed Garden Parking

AMBERLEY

Black Horse ☻

High St BN18 9NL ☎ 01798 831700
dir: *Please telephone for directions*

A traditional 17th-century tavern with a lively
atmosphere in a beautiful South Downs village.
Look out for the display of sheep bells donated
by the last shepherd to have a flock on the local
hills. Food is served in the large restaurant
and bar or in the beer garden complete with
pond, and there's plenty of choice for everyone
including a children's menu. Great beer, good
local walks, and nice views of the South Downs.
Dogs (on leads) are welcome in the bar.

Open all day all wk **Bar Meals** L served all wk
12-3 D served Sun-Thu 6-8.30, Fri-Sat 6-9.30 Av
main course £10 **Restaurant** L served Sun only
booking required D served Sun-Mon & Wed-Thu
6-8.30, Fri-Sat 6-9.30 booking required ⊕ ADMIRAL
TAVERNS ◀ Greene King IPA, Harveys Sussex, guest
ale. ☻ 9 **Facilities** Children's menu Dogs allowed
Garden

BALCOMBE

The Cowdray

RH17 6QD ☎ 01444 811280
e-mail: alexandandy@hotmail.co.uk
dir: *Please telephone for directions*

Just a mile from the M23 (junct 10a), the once run-down village boozer has been transformed into cosy dining pub, with Alex and Andy Owen, who once worked for Gordon Ramsay, re-opening the doors in early 2008. Expect wood floors, a fresh, crisp decor, and a pub menu that's a cut above average and boasts 85% Sussex produce. Follow wild mushroom risotto with pan-fried squid with chorizo, prawns and clams, or Old Spot pork belly with root vegetables, and pear Tatin.

Open all wk noon-3 5.30-11 Closed: 25 Dec eve, 1 Jan eve **Bar Meals** L served Mon-Sat 12-3, Sun 12-4 D served Mon-Thu 6-9, Fri-Sat 6-10 Av main course £8.50 **Restaurant** L served Mon-Sat 12-3, Sun 12-4 booking required D served Mon-Thu 6-9, Fri-Sat 6-10 booking required Av 3 course à la carte fr £25 ⊕ GREENE KING **Facilities** Children's menu Play area Family room Dogs allowed Garden Parking

DUNCTON

The Cricketers ♀

GU28 0LB ☎ 01798 342473
dir: *On A285, 3m from Petworth, 8m from Chichester*

Dating back to the 16th century, this attractive white-painted pub is situated in spectacular walking country at the western end of the South Downs. Rumoured to be haunted, the inn has changed little over the years. There is a delightful and very popular garden with extensive deck seating and weekend barbecues. The menus sometimes change four times a day, offering good hearty meals like beer-battered haddock or rib-eye steak, both with hand-cut chips; all washed down with quality real ales from micro-breweries. An ideal stop-off point for coach parties visiting Goodwood.

Open all day all wk **Bar Meals** L served Mon-Fri 12-2.30, Sat-Sun 12-6 D served Mon-Fri 6-9, Sat-Sun 12-9 **Restaurant** L served Mon-Fri 12-2.30, Sat-Sun 12-6 D served Mon-Fri 6-9, Sat-Sun 12-9 ⊕ FREE HOUSE ◀ Betty Stogs, Horsham Best, Arundel Gold, Guest ale ♂ Thatchers Heritage. ♀ 8 **Facilities** Children's menu Play area Dogs allowed Garden Parking

FLETCHING

The Griffin Inn 🍷

TN22 3SS

☎ 01825 722890 📠 01825 722810

e-mail: info@thegriffininn.co.uk

dir: *M23 junct 10 to East Grinstead, then A22, then A275. Village signed on left, 15m from M23*

The Griffin's superbly landscaped gardens boast one of the best views in Sussex, looking out over the Ouse Valley towards Sheffield Park. Indeed, in the summer months, the terrace forms an important part of the restaurant. Old beams, wainscotting, open fires and pews make up the character of the main bar. Menus change daily, with the emphasis on organic, locally sourced ingredients wherever possible. Modern British dishes are given a Mediterranean twist, and a typical meal might start with spiced beef carpaccio with black olives and caper dressing; followed by roast rack of Sussex lamb, chargrilled courgette and cavalo nero. Puddings include pears with mascarpone and pine nuts.

Open all wk noon-11 Closed: 25 Dec **Bar Meals** L served Mon-Fri 12-2.30, Sat-Sun 12-3 D served all wk 7-9.30 Av main course £11.50 **Restaurant** L served Mon-Fri 12-2.30, Sat-Sun 12-3 booking required D served Mon-Sat 7-9.30 booking required Fixed menu price fr £30 Av 3 course à la carte fr £30 FREE HOUSE Harvey Best, Kings of Horsham, Hepworths. 🍷 15 **Facilities** Children's menu Play area Garden Parking

GUN HILL

The Gun Inn 🍷

TN21 0JU

☎ 01825 872361 📠 01622 851881

e-mail: enquiries@thegunhouse.co.uk

dir: *5m S of Heathfield, 1m off A267 towards Gun Hill. 4m off A22 between Uckfield & Hailsham*

A lovely 17th-century building set in delightful East Sussex countryside, with extensive views from a pretty terrace and garden. Wood dominates the interior, with beams, a beautiful wooden floor, and lots of hideaway places for quiet eating and drinking. From the menu come starters like stuffed mushroom with stilton and bacon, while main dishes include home-made Dublin pie (beef, mushrooms and Guinness gravy), and chef's favourite Sussex beef cuts (rib-eye, sirloin) with sauce of your choice. The Old Coach House behind The Gun has been transformed into a farmer's market.

Open noon-3 6-11 (Sat-Sun noon-11) **Bar Meals** L served Mon-Fri 12-3, Sat-Sun 12-10 D served Mon-Fri 6-9.30, Sat-Sun 12-10 Av main course £9.95 **Restaurant** L served Mon-Fri 12-3, Sat-Sun 12-10 D served Mon-Fri 6-9.30, Sat-Sun 12-10 Fixed menu price fr £10 Av 3 course à la carte fr £19 FREE HOUSE Harveys, Guinness, Youngs. 🍷 13 **Facilities** Children's menu Play area Garden Parking

LICKFOLD

The Lickfold Inn ☙

GU28 9EY ☎ 01798 861285

e-mail: lickfold@evanspubs.co.uk

dir: *From A3 take A283, through Chiddingfold, 2m on right signed 'Lurgashall Winery', pub in 1m*

This thriving free house dates back to 1460, and period features include an ancient timber frame with attractive herringbone-patterned bricks, and a huge central chimney. Inside are two restaurant areas with oak beamed ceilings, and a cosy bar dominated by a large inglenook fireplace, Georgian settles and moulded panelling. Look for the recurring garlic motif, reflecting the village's Anglo-Saxon name, 'leac fauld', which means an enclosure where garlic grows. The pub is heavily food oriented, offering tempting lunchtime sandwiches, Sunday roasts, and seasonal dishes. Expect Lickfold Inn fish pie; grilled aubergine with spinach and ricotta; and roast guinea fowl in bacon with potato rosti and redcurrant sauce. Fifty per cent of the pub's profits go to a children's hospice.

Open all day all wk noon-11 (Sun noon-5) Closed: 25 Dec **Bar Meals** Av main course £10 food served all day **Restaurant** Av 3 course à la carte fr £26 food served all day ∰ FREE HOUSE ◀ Hogs Back TEA, Guinness, Old Speckled Hen. ☙ 12 **Facilities** Children's menu Dogs allowed Garden Parking

LURGASHALL

The Noah's Ark ☙

The Green GU28 9ET ☎ 01428 707346

e-mail: amy@noahsarkinn.co.uk

dir: *B2131 from Haslemere follow signs to Petworth/ Lurgashall. A3 from London towards Portsmouth. At Milford take the A283 signed Petworth. Follow signs to Lurgashall*

Set in a picturesque village, beneath Blackdown Hill, this attractive 16th-century inn overlooks the cricket green. The revitalised interior is full of charm and character, thanks to the enthusiastic owners, with old beams and a large inglenook fireplace. Three ales are offered along with a regularly changing guest beer, and traditional British food with a contemporary twist and the occasional French influence. Ingredients are carefully sourced from the best local suppliers for dishes ranging from Sussex beef bourguignon to Noah's ale battered cod and chips.

Open all day Closed: Mon (ex Summer) **Bar Meals** L served Tue-Sat 12-2.30 booking required D served Tue-Sat 7-9.30 booking required Av main course £13 **Restaurant** L served Tue-Sun 12-2.30 booking required D served Tue-Sat 7-9.30 booking required ∰ GREENE KING ◀ Greene King IPA , Abbot, Guest ale ⬧ Stowford Press. ☙ 8 **Facilities** Children's menu Family room Dogs allowed Garden Parking

OVING

The Gribble Inn ♟

PO20 2BP
☎ 01243 786893   🖹 01243 786893
e-mail: dave@thegribble.co.uk
dir: *From A27 take A259. After 1m left at rdbt, 1st right to Oving, 1st left in village*

Named after local schoolmistress Rose Gribble, the inn retains all of its 16th-century charm. Large open fireplaces, wood burners and low beams set the tone. There's no background music at this peaceful hideaway, which is the ideal spot to enjoy any of the half dozen real ales from the on-site micro-brewery. Liver and bacon; spinach lasagne with red peppers; and special fish dishes are all prepared and cooked on the premises.

Open all wk 11-3 5.30-11 (Fri-Sun 11-11) **Bar Meals** L served all wk 12-2.30 D served all wk 6.30-9.30 Av main course £9 **Restaurant** L served all wk 12-2.30 booking required D served all wk 6.30-9.30 booking required ⊕ HALL & WOODHOUSE ◀ Gribble Ale, Reg's Tipple, Fursty Ferret, Badger First Gold, Pigs Ear. ♟ 10 **Facilities** Children's menu Family room Dogs allowed Garden Parking

PETWORTH

The Black Horse

Byworth GU28 0HL ☎ 01798 342424
dir: *A285 from Petworth, 2m, turn right signed Byworth, pub 50yds on right*

An unspoilt 16th-century village pub, once part of the old tanneries, The Black Horse retains a rustic feel with exposed beams, flagstone floors, scrubbed wooden tables and open fires. The former kitchen has been transformed into a snug dining area including the original Aga, whilst the large garden offers views to the South Downs. Expect a range of home-made fresh pizza, light bites and daily specials. A function room and separate bar accommodates larger parties.

Open all day all wk 11-11 (Sun 12-11) **Bar Meals** L served all wk 12-3 D served Mon-Thu 6-9, Fri-Sat 6-9.30, Sun 6-8.30 **Restaurant** L served all wk 12-3 booking required D served Mon-Thu 6-9, Fri-Sat 6-9.30, Sun 6-8.30 booking required ⊕ FREE HOUSE ◀ Fuller's London Pride, Sharp's Doom Bar, Flowerpots, Hophead. **Facilities** Children's menu Dogs allowed Garden Parking

POYNINGS

Royal Oak Inn 🍷

The Street BN45 7AQ
☎ 01273 857389 📠 01273 857202
e-mail: ropoynings@aol.com
dir: *N on A23 just outside Brighton, take A281 signed Henfield & Poynings, then follow signs into Poynings*

Tucked away in a fold of the South Downs below the Devil's Dyke, the Royal Oak has eye-catching window blinds and cream-painted exterior and roaring winter fires within. Solid oak floors and old beams hung with hop bines blend effortlessly with contemporary decor and comfy sofas. The menu combines local and seasonal produce with sometimes ambitious international twists. Starters and light meals include sharing and sandwich platters, or more elaborate preparations such as potted Selsey crab with spring onion and garlic, lemon and lime toasts. For a main course you might choose hand-made Henfield sausages, creamed potato, rich gravy and red onion jam. Puddings are ordered at the bar – pear, apple and ginger crumble perhaps.

Open all day all wk 11-11 (Sun 11.30-10.30) **Bar Meals** food served all day **Restaurant** food served all day FREE HOUSE Harveys Sussex, Abbot Ale, Greene King Morland Old Speckled Hen, Fuller's London Pride Westons Herefordshire Country Perry, Old Rosie Scrumpy. 🍷 12 **Facilities** Children's menu Play area Dogs allowed Garden Parking

SHIPLEY

George & Dragon 🍷

Dragons Green RH13 7JE ☎ 01403 741320
dir: *Signed from A272 between Coolham & A24*

Set amid beautiful Sussex countryside, this 17th-century cottage is a haven of peace and quiet, especially on balmy summer evenings when the garden is a welcome retreat. Its interior is all head-banging beams and inglenook fireplaces, with an excellent choice of real ales at the bar. Food-wise, expect pub classics such as local ham with egg and chips or a Yorkshire pudding filled with sausage, mash and gravy. Shipley is famous for its smock mill.

Open all wk **Bar Meals** L served all wk 12-2 booking required D served all wk 6-9 Av main course £7.50 **Restaurant** L served all wk 12-2 D served all wk 6-9 HALL & WOODHOUSE Badger Best, Sussex Best, Hall and Woodhouse Fursty Ferret & Pickled Partridge, Guest ale Westons Stowford Press. 🍷 8 **Facilities** Children's menu Play area Family room Dogs allowed Garden Parking

SLINDON

The Spur ♥

BN18 0NE

☎ 01243 814216   ▤ 01243 814707
dir: *Off A27 on A29 outside Slindon*

Nestling on top of the South Downs, just outside the village of Slindon, sits this 17th-century pub. Inside this free house is an open-plan bar and restaurant, warmed by log fires that create a friendly atmosphere. If you book in advance you can use the skittle alley, or enjoy a game of pool or other pub games.

Open all wk 11.30-3 6-11 (Sun noon-3 7-10.30) Bar Meals L served all wk 12-2 D served Sun-Tue 7-9, Wed-Sat 7-9.30 Av main course £11.50 Restaurant L served all wk 12-2 booking required D served Sun-Tue 7-9, Wed-Sat 7-9.30 booking required Av 3 course à la carte fr £24 ⊕ FREE HOUSE ◀ Greene King IPA, Courage Directors. ♥ 9 Facilities Children's menu Dogs allowed Garden Parking

STEDHAM

Hamilton Arms/Nava Thai Restaurant ♥

Hamilton Arms School Ln GU29 0NZ

☎ 01730 812555   ▤ 01730 817459
e-mail: hamiltonarms@hotmail.com
web: www.thehamiltonarms.co.uk
dir: *Off A272 between Midhurst & Petersfield*

The Hamilton Arms is one of the first traditional English country pubs to serve authentic Thai food. The pub is set in a pretty village in beautiful South Downs countryside, and is also the base for a charitable trust to help prevent child prostitution in Thailand. The huge menu offers soups, curries, salads and speciality meat, seafood and vegetarian dishes, also available to takeaway. Oriental beers, too, are available alongside local real ales. There is a patio to enjoy in warmer weather.

Open 11-3 6-11 (Sun noon-4 7-11, Fri-Sat 11am-11.30pm) Closed: Mon (ex BH) Bar Meals L served Tue-Sun 12-2.30 D served Tue-Sun 6-10 Restaurant L served Tue-Sun 12-2.30 D served Tue-Sun 6-10 booking required ⊕ FREE HOUSE ◀ Ballard's Best, Fuller's London Pride, Everards Tiger Best, Fuller's HSB, Wadworth 6X, Sussex King, Barnes Ŏ Westons Vintage. ♥ 8 Facilities Children's menu Play area Dogs allowed Garden Parking

WEST CHILTINGTON

The Queens Head ♀

The Hollow RH20 2JN
☎ 01798 812244 📄 01798 815039
e-mail: enquiries@thequeenshead.info
dir: *Please telephone for directions*

A traditional, mainly 17th-century country pub
with two bars, a restaurant and ample outside
space. The interior is pure textbook —beams,
low ceilings, an open fire and a bar serving
three well-kept real ales. Mainly locally sourced,
freshly cooked traditional dishes include Harvey's
beer-battered haddock and chips with mushy
peas; Caesar salad with chicken and bacon;
slow-roasted lamb shank with fresh herb mash;
and mushroom Stroganoff with rice. Up to five
home-made pies appear as specials.

Open all day all wk noon-11 (Mon 5-11 ex BH
noon-11 Sun noon-10.30) **Bar Meals** L served
Tue-Sat 12-2.30, Sun & BH 12-4 D served Tue-Sat
6-9.30 Av main course £10.50 **Restaurant** L served
Tue-Sat 12-2.30, Sun & BH 12-4 D served Tue-Sat
6-9.30 Av 3 course à la carte fr £18 ⊕ ENTERPRISE
INNS PLC ◁ Harveys Sussex Best Bitter, Fuller's
London Pride, Ballards Best Bitter, Itchen Valley
Godfathers, Langhams Halfway to Heaven. ♀ 7
Facilities Children's menu Dogs allowed Garden
Parking

ALCESTER

The Holly Bush

37 Henley St B49 5QX
☎ 01789 762482 & 0788 4342363
e-mail: thehollybushpub@btconnect.com
dir: *M40 junct 15 for Warwick/Stratford, take A46
to Stratford*

The 17th-century Holly Bush has been
transformed from a one-bar boozer to a thriving
pub serving great ales and delicious food.
Menus blend traditional pub classics with more
contemporary dishes and the emphasis on using
locally sourced ingredients. Extensive menus
range from lunchtime sandwiches, ham, egg
and chips, and beer-battered cod and chips, to
chorizo and clam risotto, roast pork belly with
apple mash and sweet cabbage, and monkfish
wrapped in Parma ham with pea mash and
red wine sauce. For pudding, perhaps try the
chocolate mousse with fresh raspberries. This is
a cracking pub run with passion and panache —
and there's a great garden, too.

Open all day all wk noon-mdnt (Fri-Sat noon-1am)
Bar Meals L served Mon-Sat 12-2.30, Sun 12-4
D served Tue-Sat 7-9.30 Av main course £7.50
Restaurant L served Mon-Sat 12-2.30, Sun 12-4
D served Tue-Sat 7-9.30 Av 3 course à la carte
fr £23 ⊕ FREE HOUSE ◁ Sharpe's Doom Bar,
Black Sheep, Purity Gold, Purity Mad Goose, Uley
Bitter ♂ Local farm cider. **Facilities** Children's menu
Dogs allowed Garden

193

ETTINGTON

The Houndshill ♥

Banbury Rd CV37 7NS
☎ 01789 740267 📠 01789 740075
dir: *On A422 SE of Stratford-upon-Avon*

Family-run inn situated at the heart of England, making it a perfect base for exploring popular tourist attractions such as Oxford, Blenheim, Stratford and the Cotswolds. The pleasant tree-lined garden is especially popular with families. Typical dishes range from poached fillet of salmon, and faggots, mash and minted peas, to supreme of chicken and ham and mushroom tagliatelle. Alternatively, try cold ham off the bone or home-made steak and kidney pie.

Open all wk **Closed:** 25-28 Dec **Bar Meals** L served all wk 12-2 D served all wk 7-9.30 Av main course £7.50 **Restaurant** L served all wk 12-2 D served all wk 7-9.30 Av 3 course à la carte fr £15 ⊕ FREE HOUSE ◼ Hook Norton Best, Spitfire. ♥ 7 **Facilities** Children's menu Play area Dogs allowed Garden Parking

NAPTON ON THE HILL

The Bridge at Napton ♥

Southam Rd CV47 8NQ ☎ 01926 812466
e-mail: info@thebridgeatnapton.co.uk
dir: *At Bridge 111 on Oxford Canal on A425, 2m from Southam & 1m from Napton on the Hill*

This is an ideal place to moor the narrow boat, though travellers by car or bike are equally welcome. Built as a stabling inn at Bridge 111 on the Oxford canal, the pub has a restaurant, three bars and a large garden, plus its own turning point for barges. There are some excellent ales, and food choices range from Aberdeen Angus beefburger with chips to the likes of honey-roasted belly pork with caramelised onions.

Open noon-3 6-11 (Sun noon-8) **Closed:** Mon (ex BH & summer school hols) **Bar Meals** L served Mon-Sat 12-2, Sun 12-7 booking required D served Mon-Sat 6-9, Sun 12-7 booking required Av main course £9 **Restaurant** L served Mon-Sat 12-2, Sun 12-7 booking required D served Mon-Sat 6-9, Sun 12-7 booking required ⊕ PUNCH TAVERNS ◼ Guinness, John Smith, Black Sheep, Guest ales. ♥ 6 **Facilities** Children's menu Play area Family room Dogs allowed Garden Parking

RATLEY

The Rose and Crown

OX15 6DS ☎ 01295 678148
e-mail: k.marples@btinternet.com
dir: *Follow Edgehill signs, 7m N of Banbury (13m SE of Stratford-upon-Avon) on A422*

Following the Battle of Edgehill in 1642, a Roundhead was discovered in the chimney of this 12th-century pub and beheaded in the hearth. His ghost reputedly haunts the building. Enjoy the peaceful village location and the traditional pub food, perhaps including beef and ale pie, scampi and chips, chicken curry and the Sunday roast, plus vegetarian options.

Open Closed: Mon L Bar Meals L served Tue-Sun 12-2.30 booking required D served Mon-Sat 6.30-9 booking required Av main course £9.95 ⊕ FREE HOUSE ◀ Wells Bombardier, Eagle IPA, Greene King Old Speckled Hen, Guest ale. Facilities Children's menu Family room Dogs allowed Garden Parking

RUGBY

Old Smithy ♚

1 Green Ln, Church Lawford CV23 9EF
☎ 02476 542333
e-mail: smithy@king-henry-taverns.co.uk
dir: *Take the Coventry to Rugby Road, The Old Smithy is on the green in Church Lawford*

Anyone asked to draw their idyllic 'roses round the door' village pub might produce something looking like The Old Smithy. As with all King Henry's Taverns pubs, the menu features a huge choice of traditional favourites, such as gammon steak, fish and seafood, to haddock in batter; chicken dishes, and a selection for those with larger appetites, including Brontosaurus lamb shank. Vegetarians will welcome a six-way choice, including tomato and basil penne pasta.

Open all day all wk noon-11 Bar Meals Av main course £3 food served all day Restaurant food served all day ⊕ KING HENRY'S TAVERN ◀ Guinness, IPA, Marstons Pedigree. ♚ 15 Facilities Children's menu Play area Family room Garden Parking

SHIPSTON ON STOUR

The Red Lion ★★★★ INN ◉ ☙

Main St, Long Compton CV36 5JS
☎ 01608 684221 📠 01608 684968
e-mail: info@redlion-longcompton.co.uk
web: www.redlion-longcompton.co.uk
dir: On A3400 between Shipston on Stour & Chipping Norton

This Grade II listed inn blends old-world charm with a smart contemporary feel. High backed settles, stone walls and oak beams set the scene, with warming log fires in winter. The bar is full of atmosphere, and the menu and blackboard specials cater for all tastes, from sandwiches like crayfish, rocket and lemon mayonnaise on ciabatta to an open goats' cheese omelette with caramelised onions, spinach and salad. Starters include wild boar terrine with spiced pear chutney, whilst main course dishes range from venison with roasted winter vegetables to pan-fried scallops with creamed parsnips, crisp pancetta and a vermouth and chive sauce. Round off with treacle tart and clotted cream.

Open all wk 11-11 **Bar Meals** L served Mon-Thu 12-2.30, Fri-Sun 12-9.30 D served Mon-Thu 6-9, Fri-Sun 12-9.30 Av main course £15.95 **Restaurant** L served Mon-Thu 12-2.30, Fri-Sun 12-9.30 D served Mon-Thu 6-9, Fri-Sun 12-9.30 Fixed menu price fr £11.95 ⊕ FREE HOUSE ◀ Hook Norton Best, Adnams, Timothy Taylor. ☙ 7 **Facilities** Children's menu Play area Dogs allowed Garden Parking **Rooms** 5

STRATFORD-UPON-AVON

The One Elm ☙

1 Guild St CV37 6QZ ☎ 01789 404919
e-mail: theoneelm@peachpubs.com
dir: In town centre

Standing on its own in the heart of town, the One Elm has two dining rooms: downstairs is intimate, even with the buzzy bar close by, while upstairs feels grander. The menu features chargrilled côte de boeuf for two, Aberdeen Angus rump steak, and tuna, as well as other main courses. The deli board offers all-day nuts and seeds, cheeses, charcuterie and antipasti. The secluded terrace induces in some a feeling of being abroad.

Open all wk 11-11 (Thu-Sat 11am-mdnt) Closed: 25 Dec **Bar Meals** Av main course £11 food served all day **Restaurant** Av 3 course à la carte fr £18 food served all day ⊕ PEACH PUB CO ◀ London Pride, UBU Purity, Purity Gold. ☙ 9 **Facilities** Children's menu Dogs allowed Garden Parking

STRETTON ON FOSSE

The Plough Inn ⬤

GL56 9QX ☎ 01608 661053
e-mail: saravol@aol.com
dir: *From Moreton-in-Marsh, 4m on A429 N. From Stratford-upon-Avon, 10m on A429 S*

A classic village pub built from mellow Cotswold stone, The Plough has the requisite bare beams and real fire, plus a friendly resident cat, Alfie, to add to the welcome. It's a family-run affair, with French chef and co-owner Jean Pierre in charge of the kitchen. Expect traditional French cooking from the specials board, while other choices might include beer-battered cod with chips and salad. There's a spit roast in the inglenook on Sundays (September-May).

Open all wk 11.30-2.30 6-11.30 (Sun 12-2.30 7-11) Closed: 25 Dec eve **Bar Meals** L served all wk 12-2 D served Mon-Sat 7-9 Av main course £9.95 ⊕ FREE HOUSE ◀ Hook Norton, Ansells Mild, Spitfire, Purity, local ales Ⓞ Old Katy, Black Rat, Thatchers Traditional. ⬤ 9 **Facilities** Children's menu Play area Garden Parking

TEMPLE GRAFTON

The Blue Boar Inn ⬤

B49 6NR ☎ 01789 750010 🖹 01789 750635
e-mail: info@theblueboar.co.uk
dir: *From A46 (Stratford to Alcester) turn left to Temple Grafton. Pub at 1st x-rds*

The oldest part of the inn is 17th century, and has been an alehouse since that time. The restaurant features a 35-foot glass-covered well, home to a family of koi carp, from which water was formerly drawn for brewing. There are four open fires in the bar and restaurant areas, and a patio garden with views of the Cotswold Hills. A menu of traditional dishes is served, with variety provided by daily specials prepared from local produce, game in particular.

Open all day all wk **Bar Meals** L served all wk 12-3 D served all wk 6-10 **Restaurant** L served all wk 12-3 D served all wk 6-10 ⊕ MARSTONS PUB COMPANY ◀ Marstons Banks Original, Pedigree, Guinness Ⓞ Thatchers Gold. ⬤ 6 **Facilities** Children's menu Garden Parking

WITHYBROOK

The Pheasant ♥

Main St CV7 9LT

☎ 01455 220480 📄 01455 221296

e-mail: thepheasant01@hotmail.com

dir: *7m from Coventry*

This well-presented 17th-century free house stands beside the brook where withies were once cut for fencing. An inglenook fireplace, farm implements and horse-racing photographs characterise the interior. Under the same ownership since 1981, the pub has a varied menu with a wealth of popular choices. Alongside a blackboard of specials, a typical menu includes pan-fried pork cutlets, fisherman's pie, braised faggots, and chicken and mushroom pie. Outside tables overlook the Withy Brook.

Open all wk 11-3 6-11.30 (Sun & BH 11-11) Closed: 25-26 Dec **Bar Meals** L served Mon-Sat 12-2, Sun 12-9 booking required D served Mon-Sat 6-10, Sun 12-9 booking required **Restaurant** L served Mon-Sat 12-2, Sun 12-9 booking required D served Mon-Sat 6-10, Sun 12-9 booking required ⊕ FREE HOUSE ◀ Courage Directors, Theakstons Best, John Smiths Smooth. ♥ 9 **Facilities** Children's menu Dogs allowed Garden Parking

CHADWICK END

The Orange Tree ♥

Warwick Rd B93 0BN

☎ 01564 785364 📄 01564 782988

e-mail: theorangetree@lovelypubs.co.uk

dir: *3m from Knowle towards Warwick*

A pub/restaurant in peaceful countryside, only minutes away from the hustle and bustle of the National Exhibition Centre. The interior is light, airy and warm with open kitchens, stone-fired ovens and log burning fires. Comfort springs to mind here too, where sharing plates of antipasti or Greek mezze can be followed by fired pizzas – try the sloppy Guiseppe with hot spiced beef and green peppers. Alternatively half a dozen different pastas range from tagliatelle bolognese to macaroni with smoked haddock and cauliflower cheese. Other sections on the carte promise grills, spit-roast chicken from the rotisserie, salads and dishes such as braised beef in Barolo from the oven.

Open all day all wk 11-11 Closed: 25 Dec **Bar Meals** L served all wk 12-2.30 D served all wk 6-9.30 Av main course £13.50 **Restaurant** L served all wk 12-2.30 booking required D served all wk 6-9.30 booking required Av 3 course à la carte fr £25 ⊕ FREE HOUSE ◀ IPA, Old Hooky, Black Sheep ♂ Thatchers. ♥ 8 **Facilities** Children's menu Play area Dogs allowed Garden Parking

ARRETON

The White Lion

PO30 3AA ☎ 01983 528479
e-mail: chrisandkatelou@hotmail.co.uk
dir: *B3056 (Newport to Sandown road)*

Sited in an outstandingly beautiful conservation area, this 300-year-old former coaching inn offers a genuinely hospitable welcome. Oak beams, polished brass and open fires set the cosy tone inside, while a safe outside seating area enjoys views of the Arreton scenery. Well-priced pub grub is served all day, ranging from traditional snacks to specials such as nasi goreng - Indonesian spicy rice with chicken and prawns. Favourite puddings of spotted dick and jam roly poly sell out quickly.

Open all day all wk **Bar Meals** Av main course £7.95 food served all day **Restaurant** Av 3 course à la carte fr £10 food served all day ⊕ ENTERPRISE INNS ◀ Badger Best, Fuller's London Pride, Timothy Taylor Landlord, John Smiths Smooth, Flowers Best. **Facilities** Children's menu Play area Family room Dogs allowed Garden Parking

BEMBRIDGE

The Crab & Lobster
Inn ★★★★ INN ⬤

32 Foreland Field Rd PO35 5TR
☎ 01983 872244 ⬛ 01983 873495
e-mail: crab.lobster@bluebottle.com
dir: *From Bembridge Village, 1st left after Boots down Forelands Rd to Windmill Hotel. Left into Lane End Rd, 2nd right into Egerton Rd, left into Forelands Rd & immediately right into Foreland Field Rd*

Originally a fisherman's cottage, this refurbished, award-winning beamed pub sits just yards from the popular 65-mile coastal path. A raised deck and patio area offer superb sea views. Locally caught seafood is one of the pub's great attractions; typical choices include a pint of prawns; lobster salad; home-made crab cakes; and seafood platters. For meat eaters there are pub classics such as steaks or ham, egg and chips.

Open all wk summer 11-11 (Sun 11-10.30) winter 11-3 6-11 (Sun 6-10.30) **Bar Meals** L served all wk 12-2.30 booking required D served Sun-Thu 6-9, Fri-Sat 6-9.30 booking required Av main course £8.50 **Restaurant** L served all wk 12-2.30 booking required D served Sun-Thu 6-9, Fri-Sat 6-9.30 booking required ⊕ ENTERPRISE INNS ◀ Interbrew Flowers Original, Goddards Fuggle-Dee-Dum, Greene King IPA, John Smiths. ⬤ 12 **Facilities** Children's menu Dogs allowed Garden Parking **Rooms** 5

BONCHURCH

The Bonchurch Inn

Bonchurch Shute PO38 1NU
☎ 01983 852611   ◈ 01983 856657
e-mail: gillian@bonchurch-inn.co.uk
dir: *Off A3055 in Bonchurch*

In its quiet, off the road location, this small family-run free house inn lies tucked away in a secluded Dickensian-style courtyard. You won't be disturbed by juke boxes or gaming machines, for little has changed here since this former coaching inn and stables was granted its first licence in the 1840s. Food is available lunchtime and evenings in the bar; choices range from sandwiches and ploughman's to fresh fish, juicy steaks and Italian specialities.

Open all wk 11-3 6.30-11 Closed: 25 Dec **Bar Meals** L served all wk 12-2 D served all wk 6.30-9 booking required Av main course £10 **Restaurant** D served all wk 7-8.45 booking required ⊕ FREE HOUSE ◀ Courage Directors, Best. **Facilities** Children's menu Family room Dogs allowed Garden Parking

COWES

The Folly ♟

Folly Ln PO32 6NB ☎ 01983 297171
dir: *Telephone for directions*

Reached by land and water, and very popular with the boating fraternity, the Folly is one of the island's more unusual pubs. Timber from an old sea-going French barge was used in the construction, and wood from the hull can be found in the bar. The menus are wide ranging with something for everyone. House specialities include venison Wellington, prime British beef ribs and slow cooked lamb.

Open all wk **Bar Meals** Av main course £8 food served all day **Restaurant** food served all day ⊕ GREENE KING ◀ Greene King IPA, Old Speckled Hen, Goddards Best Bitter. ♟ 10 **Facilities** Children's menu Dogs allowed Garden Parking

GODSHILL

The Taverners ☎

High St PO38 3HZ ☎ 01983 840707
web: www.thetavernersgodshill.co.uk
dir: *Please telephone for directions*

Tucked away in picture-perfect Godshill, the Island's 'honeypot' village, the Taverners has been wowing locals and tourists with top-notch pub food since locals Roger Serjent and Lisa Choi took over in May 2008. Changing menus champion local seasonal produce, from local allotment fruit and vegetables and Bembridge crab to village-reared organic pork and lamb. Take baked crab pot, braised ox cheek with horseradish mash, finishing with treacle tart, with roast rib of beef for Sunday lunch. One to watch!

Open all day all wk 11-11 (Fri 11am-mdnt Sun 11-10.30) Closed: 1st 2wks Jan **Bar Meals** L served all wk summer 11.30-3.30, Mon-Sat 12-3, Sun 12-4 winter D served all wk summer 6-9.30, Mon-Sat winter 6-9 Av main course £10 **Restaurant** L served all wk summer 12-3.30, Mon-Sat 12-3, Sun 12-4 winter booking required D served Sun-Thu 6-9.30, Fri-Sat 6-10 summer, Sun-Thu 6-9, Fri-Sat 6-9.30 winter booking required Av 3 course à la carte fr £20 ⊕ PUNCH ◀ Undercliff, London Pride, John Smiths ⍥ Stowford Press, Old Rosie. ☎ 8 **Facilities** Children's menu Play area Family room Dogs allowed Garden Parking

NITON

Buddle Inn ☎

St Catherines Rd PO38 2NE ☎ 01983 730243
dir: *Take A3055 from Ventnor. In Niton take 1st left signed 'to the lighthouse'*

A spit away from the English Channel one way and the Coastal Path the other, this 16th-century, former cliff-top farmhouse can claim to be one of the island's oldest hostelries. Popular with hikers and ramblers (and their muddy boots and dogs), the interior has the full traditional complement - stone flags, oak beams and large open fire, as well as great real ales on tap. Simple but well prepared food is served, including beef Wellington and venison casserole. Recent change of hands.

Open all day all wk 11-11 (Fri-Sat 11-mdnt Sun noon-10.30) **Bar Meals** L served all wk 12-2.45 D served all wk 6-9 **Restaurant** L served all wk 12-2.45 D served all wk 6-9 ⊕ ENTERPRISE INNS ◀ Bombardier, Fortyniner, Spitfire. ☎ 8 **Facilities** Children's menu Family room Dogs allowed Garden Parking

NORTHWOOD

Travellers Joy

85 Pallance Rd PO31 8LS ☎ 01983 298024
e-mail: tjoy@globalnet.co.uk

Ruth and Derek Smith run this 300-year-old
alehouse, just a little way inland from Cowes.
They keep eight real ales on hand pump all year
round. Don't expect dishes described on the
menu as 'drizzled' or 'pan-roasted' here because
the food is home cooked and uncomplicated but
with all the trimmings - grilled gammon steak,
salmon steak, breaded plaice, double sausage
with egg, chips and beans, honey-roast ham,
home-made steak and kidney pie, and children's
meals. Outside is a pétanque terrain, pets' corner
and play area.

Open all wk **Bar Meals** L served all wk 12-2 D
served all wk 6.30-9.30 Av main course £6.45
⊕ FREE HOUSE ◀ Goddards Special Bitter, Courage
Directors, Ventnor Golden Bitter, Deuchars IPA, St
Austell Tribute. **Facilities** Children's menu Play area
Family room Dogs allowed Garden Parking

SHORWELL

The Crown Inn

Walkers Ln PO30 3JZ
☎ 01983 740293   📄 01983 740293
e-mail: info@crowninnshorwell.co.uk
dir: *Turn left at top of Carisbrooke High Street,
Shorwell approx 6m*

Set in a pretty village with thatched cottages, a
small shop, three manor houses, and the church
opposite. In summer a Wendy house, slide and
swings keep youngsters amused. The building
dates in part from the 17th century, and different
floor levels attest to many alterations. Log fires,
antique furniture and a friendly female ghost
complete the picture of this traditional family-run
pub. Beers on tap include an island brew, and
food consists of home-made favourites based on
locally sourced lamb, beef, plus game in winter
and fish in summer. Tempting pub grub, plus
an award-winning specials board offer cottage
pie, steak and kidney pie, and game dishes
when in season. There are also great fish, pasta
and vegetarian dishes too. Enjoy your meal
with a great selection of beers, including local
Goddards, Ringwood and Adnams Broadside.

Open all wk **Bar Meals** food served all day
⊕ ENTERPRISE INNS ◀ Goddards (local), Ringwood
Fortyniner, Ringwood Best, Doom Bar, Adnams
Broadside. **Facilities** Children's menu Play area
Family room Dogs allowed Garden Parking

VENTNOR

The Spyglass Inn ♟

The Esplanade PO38 1JX
☎ 01983 855338 📄 01983 855220
e-mail: info@thespyglass.com
dir: *Telephone for directions*

For centuries this area was a haunt of smugglers, and echoes of these activities can be seen in the huge collection of nautical memorabilia on the walls of this famous 19th-century inn. It has a superb position, right at the end of Ventnor Esplanade. Much of the food here is, naturally, fish, with home-made fish chowder, Ventnor crab and lobster, but other dishes might include several varieties of pie; local sausages; or ham and leek bake.

Open all day all wk 10.30am-11pm **Bar Meals** L served all wk 12-9.30 D served all wk 12-9.30 food served all day **Restaurant** L served all wk 12-9.30 D served all wk 12-9.30 food served all day ⊕ FREE HOUSE ◀ Ventnor Golden, Goddards Fuggle-Dee-Dom, Yates Undercliff Experience, Ringwood Best, Ringwood Fortyniner. ♟ 8 **Facilities** Children's menu Family room Dogs allowed Garden Parking

ALDBOURNE

The Crown at Aldbourne ★★★★ INN ♟

The Square SN8 2DU
☎ 01672 540214 📄 01672 541050
e-mail: info@crownataldbourne.co.uk
dir: *M4 Junct 15 go N on A419 direction of Swindon. At first junct Aldbourne is signed on B4192. The Crown is situated in centre of village opposite the pond*

Overlooking the village square and duck pond, the Crown is a spick-and-span 18th-century inn with a cosy, traditional beamed bar and a comfortable, wooden-floored dining room. Very much the village inn, smartly refurbished and with local Ramsbury Gold on tap, it offers a good selection of home-cooked dishes, from soup and sandwiches to Sunday roasts and a popular tapas menu, and four comfortable, well decorated bedrooms. The courtyard is a pleasant spot for summer sipping.

Open all wk noon-3 6-11 (Sat-Sun noon-11) **Bar Meals** L served all wk 12-3 D served Mon-Sat 7-9.30 **Restaurant** L served all wk 12-3 D served Mon-Sat 7-9.30 ⊕ ENTERPRISE INNS ◀ Spitfire Shepherds Neame, Sharp's Cornish Coaster, Ramsbury Gold ♂ Westons Stowford Press. ♟ 8 **Facilities** Children's menu Play area Dogs allowed Garden Parking **Rooms** 4

ALDERBURY

The Green Dragon ♟

Old Rd SP5 3AR ☎ 01722 710263
dir: *1m off A36 (Southampton to Salisbury road)*

There are fine views of Salisbury Cathedral from this 15th-century pub, which is probably named after the heroic deeds of Sir Maurice Berkeley, the Mayor of Alderbury, who slew a green dragon in the 15th century. Dickens wrote Martin Chuzzlewit here, and called the pub the Blue Dragon. An interesting and daily changing menu features home-made meat and vegetarian dishes using locally sourced produce.

Open all wk **Bar Meals** L served all wk 12-2 D served all wk 6.30-9.30 **Restaurant** L served all wk 12-2 D served all wk 6.30-9.30 ⊕ HALL & WOODHOUSE ◀ Badger First Gold, Tanglefoot, Fursty Ferret Ŏ Stowford Press. ♟ 14 **Facilities** Children's menu Dogs allowed Garden Parking

BOX

The Quarrymans Arms ♟

Box Hill SN13 8HN
☎ 01225 743569 📄 01225 742610
e-mail: john@quarrymans-arms.co.uk
dir: *Telephone for directions*

Built above Brunel's famous Box railway tunnel, this 300-year-old pub is packed with stone-mining memorabilia (take a tour of the old mine workings). Great views through the restaurant window of the valley, abundantly laced with marked paths and trails. In addition to the regular menu – sizzling stir-fry, pork Dijonnaise, tuna niçoise – look out for the vegetarian menu and specials board. Some good hand-pumped West Country beers, real ciders, good wines and over sixty malt whiskies are available.

Open all wk 11am-11.30pm **Bar Meals** L served all wk 11-3 booking required D served all wk 6- last booking booking required Av main course £10 **Restaurant** L served all wk 11-last booking required D served all wk 6-last booking booking required Av 3 course à la carte fr £19 ⊕ FREE HOUSE ◀ Butcombe Bitter, Wadworth 6X, Moles Best, Local guest ales Ŏ Stowford Press. ♟ 12 **Facilities** Children's menu Family room Dogs allowed Garden Parking

BRADFORD-ON-AVON

The Tollgate Inn ★★★★ INN 🏵🏵 ☖

Holt BA14 6PX

☎ 01225 782326 📄 01225 782805
e-mail: alison@tollgateholt.co.uk
dir: *M4 junct 18, A46 towards Bath, A363 to Bradford-on-Avon. B3107 towards Melksham, pub on right*

Built in the 16th century, this inn has been part weaving mill, part Baptist chapel, and even the village school. Regular customers are attracted by modern British cooking with Mediterranean influences, locally sourced and supplied whenever possible. Lunchtime light bites (Tuesday to Saturday only) include corned beef hash with fried egg; while the carte menu might feature goats' cheese bruschetta with figs and local honey followed by oven roasted halibut. The well-established garden and terrace (out of bounds to children under 12) is a tranquil place to eat when the weather permits.

Open 11.30-3 5.30-11 (Sun 11.30-3) Closed: Mon **Bar Meals** L served Tue-Sun 12-2 D served Tue-Sat 7-9 Av main course £13.50 **Restaurant** L served Tue-Sun 12-2 D served Tue-Sat 7-9 Fixed menu price fr £18.75 Av 3 course à la carte fr £22 ⊕ FREE HOUSE ◀ Exmoor Gold, Glastonbury Ales Mystery Tor, York Ales, Sharp's Doom Bar, Eden, Yorkshire Terrier Ö Thatchers Gold, Thatchers Scrumpy. ☖ 9 **Facilities** Children's menu Dogs allowed Garden Parking **Rooms** 4

BRINKWORTH

The Three Crowns ☖

SN15 5AF ☎ 01666 510366
dir: *From Swindon take A3102 to Wootton Bassett, then B4042, 5m to Brinkworth*

Facing the church across the village green, the Three Crowns extends into a large, bright conservatory and garden room, then out onto a heated patio and garden that offers extensive views of the Dauntsey Vale. In winter, a welcoming log fire burns in the lounge. When it's time to eat, the imaginative blackboard menus may offer locally smoked chicken with sherry and cream sauce; rack of English lamb with garlic breadcrumbs; poached halibut in white wine with a julienne of crispy leeks and seared scallops; or a baked vegetarian parcel with fresh tomato and basil sauce. The home-made dessert selection could feature strawberry shortbread; melon sorbet; or tangy lemon and Cointreau cheesecake.

Open all day all wk 10am-mdnt Closed: 25-26 Dec **Bar Meals** L served Mon-Sat 12-2, Sun 12-3 **Restaurant** L served Mon-Sat 12-2, Sun 12-3 D served all wk 6-9.30 ⊕ ENTERPRISE INNS ◀ Wadworth 6X, Greene King IPA, Wells Bombardier, Abbey Ales Bellringer Ö Stowford Press. ☖ 20 **Facilities** Children's menu Play area Dogs allowed Garden Parking

BROAD CHALKE

The Queens Head Inn 🍷

1 North St SP5 5EN

☎ 01722 780344 & 0870 770 6634

dir: *A354 from Salisbury towards Blandford Forum, at Coombe Bissett right towards Bishopstone, pub in 4m*

Attractive 15th-century-inn with friendly atmosphere and low-beamed bars, once the village bakehouse. On sunny days, enjoy the flower-bordered courtyard, whilst in colder weather the low beams and wood burner in the bar provide a cosy refuge. Menus include light snacks such as sandwiches, ploughman's lunches and home-made soups, as well as more substantial main courses: perhaps grilled trout with almonds, sirloin steak with a choice of vegetables, or wild game casserole.

Open all wk noon-3 6-11.30 (Fri-Sat 6-mdnt Sun noon-10.30) **Bar Meals** L served Mon-Sat 12-2.30, Sun 12-6 D served Mon-Sat 6-9, Sun 12-6 **Restaurant** L served Mon-Sat 12-2.30, Sun 12-6 D served Mon-Sat 6-9, Sun 12-6 ⊕ Hall & Woodhouse ◀ Badgers Best, Badger Tanglefoot, Hopping Hare ♂ Stowford Press. 🍷 7 **Facilities** Children's menu Family room Dogs allowed Garden Parking

HINDON

The Lamb at Hindon ★★★★ INN ⊛ 🍷

High St SP3 6DP

☎ 01747 820573 📄 01747 820605

e-mail: info@lambathindon.co.uk

dir: *From A303 follow signs to Hindon. At Fonthill Bishop right onto B3089 to Hindon. Pub on left*

Wisteria clings to one corner of the mellow 17th-century coaching inn, tucked away in a charming village. Inside, the bar is divided into several cosy areas and oozes old-world charm, with sturdy period furnishings, flagstone floors, terracotta walls hung with old prints and paintings, and a splendid old stone fireplace with a crackling log fire creates a warm, homely atmosphere, especially on cold winter nights. Add a chalkboard menu offering hearty modern pub dishes, then it's worth lingering over a meal by the fire. Typically, tuck into lambs' kidneys with balsamic shallots and red wine jus, followed by roast salmon with Jerusalem artichokes and Puy lentils, or slow-cooked salt beef with horseradish dumplings, and butterscotch tart for pudding.

Open all day all wk 7.30am-mdnt **Bar Meals** L served all wk 12-2.30 D served all wk 6.30-9.30 booking required Av main course £10 **Restaurant** L served all wk 12-2.30 D served all wk 6.30-9.30 booking required Av 3 course à la carte fr £25 ⊕ BOISDALE ◀ Youngs Bitter, Wells Bombardier, 2 guest ales. 🍷 6 **Facilities** Children's menu Family room Dogs allowed Garden Parking **Rooms** 14

LACOCK

The Rising Sun ♟

32 Bowden Hill SN15 2PP ☎ 01249 730363
e-mail: the.risingsun@btinternet.co.uk

The pub is located close to the National Trust
village of Lacock, on a steep hill, providing
spectacular views over Wiltshire from the large
garden. Beer festivals, live music, hog roasts
and barbecues are a regular feature, and games
and reading material are provided in the bar.
Thai curries and stir-fries are popular options,
alongside traditional liver, bacon and onions,
steaks, and beef, ale and Stilton pie. Enjoy a pint
of Moles ale or Black Rat cider.

Open all wk noon-3 6-11 Bar Meals L served
all wk 12-2 booking required D served all wk
6-9 booking required Restaurant L served all
wk 12-2 booking required D served all wk 6-9
booking required ⊕ MOLES BREWERY ◀ Moles
Best, Molecatcher, Tap Bitter, Rucking Mole,
guest ale Ŏ Thatchers Gold, Black Rat. ♟ 10
Facilities Children's menu Play area Dogs allowed
Garden Parking

LITTLE CHEVERELL

The Owl

Low Rd SN10 4JS ☎ 01380 812263
dir: *A344 from Stonehenge, then A360, after 10m left
onto B3098, right after 0.5m. Pub signed*

Sit in the pretty garden after dark and you'll
discover that this pub is aptly named. As
well as the hoot of owls, woodpeckers can be
heard in summer. A brook runs at the bottom
of the garden and there are views of Salisbury
Plain. The pub itself is a cosy hideaway with
oak beams and a fire in winter. Typical dishes
include lasagne; Thai chicken curry; sizzling beef
Szechwan; and stilton and mushroom pork.

Open all day all wk noon-11 Bar Meals L served all
wk 12-9 D served all wk 12-9 food served all day
⊕ ENTERPRISE INNS ◀ Hop Back Summer Lightning,
Bath Gem. Facilities Children's menu Play area Dogs
allowed Garden Parking

LOWER CHICKSGROVE

Compasses Inn ★★★★ INN ◉ ♟

SP3 6NB ☎ 01722 714318
e-mail: thecompasses@aol.com
dir: *On A30 (1.5m W of Fovant) take 3rd right to Lower Chicksgrove. In 1.5m turn left into Lagpond Lane, pub 1m on left*

This picture-perfect 14th-century thatched inn is full of character. Inside there's a long, low-beamed bar with stone walls, worn flagstone floors and a large inglenook fireplace with a wood-burning stove for colder days. Be sure to try the food: the kitchen team have won an AA rosette for their efforts. Dishes from the ever-changing blackboard menu are freshly made using seasonal produce. A meal might take in potted crab and avocado; venison steak with mixed berry sauce and dauphinoise potatoes; and brioche bread and butter pudding with banana and rum. The garden has a large grassed area with some lovely views and seats for 40 people. Five bedrooms are available, providing an ideal base for exploring the beautiful surrounding countryside.

Open all wk noon-3 6-11 (Sun noon-3 7-10.30) Closed: 25-26 Dec **Bar Meals** L served all wk 12-2 D served all wk 6.30-9 Av main course £15 ⊕ FREE HOUSE ◀ Keystone Large One & Solar Brew, Hidden Potential, Bass ♂ Stowford Press. ♟ 8 **Facilities** Children's menu Dogs allowed Garden Parking **Rooms** 5

LUDWELL

The Grove Arms ♟

SP7 9ND ☎ 01747 828328 🖹 01747 828960
e-mail: info@grovearms.com
dir: *On A30 (Shaftesbury to Salisbury road), 3m from Shaftesbury*

The Grove Arms is a 16th century village inn once owned by the aristocratic Grove family. David Armstrong-Reed, chef and owner, is passionate about local produce, which is sourced from local farms and estates. Dishes are freshly made, including the popular home-made breads and chutneys, and fresh fish features strongly. Popular dishes, such as meat pies, chicken curry, and Badger beer battered haddock with tartare sauce are also available to take away during the week.

Open all day all wk **Bar Meals** L served all wk 12-3 D served all wk 6-9.30 Av main course £7 **Restaurant** L served Mon-Fri 12-3, Sat-Sun 12-9.30 booking required D served Mon-Fri 6-9.30, Sat-Sun 12-9.30 booking required ⊕ HALL & WOODHOUSE ◀ Badger Gold, Festive Feasant, Hopping Hare. ♟ 6 **Facilities** Children's menu Family room Dogs allowed Garden Parking

MALMESBURY

Horse & Groom Inn 🍷

The Street, Charlton SN16 9DL
☎ 01666 823904
e-mail: info@horseandgroominn.com
web: www.horseandgroominn.com
dir: *M4 junct 17 follow signs to Cirencester on A429. Through Corston & Malmesbury. Straight on at Priory rdbt, at next rdbt take 3rd exit to Cricklade, then to Charlton*

This 16th-century coaching inn stands well back from the road from Malmesbury to Cricklade, fronted by a tree-sheltered lawn. You will still find the original stone flags and fireplaces in the popular Charlton Bar. Outside space is plentiful including a lovely walled garden and separate play area. Menus focus on sensibly priced, modern British cooking; roasted Cotswold chicken breasts marinated in lemon and thyme with truffle mash and Evesham asparagus; and grilled fillet of wild brown trout, herb-crushed potatoes and cherry tomato and fennel salad.

Open all wk 11-11 (Sun 11-10.30) Bar Meals L served Mon-Sat 12-2.30 D served Sun-Thu 6.30-9, Fri-Sat 6.30-9.30 Av main course £11 Restaurant L served Mon-Sat 12-2.30, Sun 12-3 D served Sun-Thu 6.30-9, Fri-Sat 6.30-9.30 Av 3 course à la carte fr £25 ◀ Archers, Morland Original, Old Speckled Hen, guest ales. 🍷 8 Facilities Children's menu Play area Dogs allowed Garden Parking

MARDEN

The Millstream 🍷

SN10 3RH
☎ 01380 848308 📄 01380 848337
e-mail: mail@the-millstream.net
dir: *Signed from A342*

The Millstream sits in lovely countryside in the Vale of Pewsey, within sight of both Salisbury Plain and the Marlborough Downs. It was tastefully refurbished a few years ago without losing its traditional feel: wooden floors, beamed ceilings, log fires and pretty muted colours create a cosy, welcoming interior. Books, games and comfy sofas add their own homely touch. A good choice of hand-pulled beers and an impressive wine list are an ideal accompaniment for the contemporary menu, where locally sourced seasonal produce, plus fish from Cornwall, hold sway. Look out for braised lamb shank, and spatchcock poussin, with all the trimmings.

Open noon-3 6-late (Fri-Sun noon-late) Closed: Mon (ex BH) Bar Meals L served Tue-Sat 12-3, Sun 12-4 booking required D served Tue-Sat 6.30-10 booking required Restaurant L served Tue-Sat 12-3, Sun 12-4 booking required D served Tue-Sat 6.30-10 booking required ⊕ WADWORTH ◀ 6X, Henry's IPA, Bishops Tipple, Malt & Hops Ö Stowford Press. 🍷 14 Facilities Children's menu Play area Family room Dogs allowed Garden Parking

MINETY

Vale of the White Horse Inn ♀

SN16 9QY

☎ 01666 860175   📄 01666 860175
dir: *On B4040 (3m W of Cricklade, 6m & E of Malmesbury)*

This eye-catching, beautifully restored inn overlooks its own lake. In summer, sitting out on the large raised terrace, it's hard to think of a better spot. The village bar still serves the local community well with a good selection of real ales and a range of sandwiches and simple bar meals. Upstairs, lunch and dinner are served in the stone-walled restaurant with its polished tables and bentwood chairs. The menus offer something for most tastes, with starters including leek, stilton and sun-dried tomato quiche, and crayfish tail and king prawn cocktail. Main courses range from beer-battered cod and chips to confit duck leg on braised red cabbage with mustard mash and Madeira sauce. Finish with crumble or treacle tart with ice cream.

Open all day all wk 11-11 **Bar Meals** L served all wk 12-2.30 D served all wk 6-9.15 Av main course £8 **Restaurant** L served all wk 12-2.30 D served all wk 6-9.15 Av 3 course à la carte fr £16.50 ⊕ FREE HOUSE ◀ Wadworth, Henrys IPA, Three Castle Vale Ale, Hancocks, Archers Chrystal Clear ♂ Stowford Press. ♀ 12 **Facilities** Children's menu Family room Dogs allowed Garden Parking

NUNTON

The Radnor Arms ♀

SP5 4HS ☎ 01722 329722
dir: *From Salisbury ring road take A338 to Ringwood. Nunton signed on right*

A popular pub in the centre of the village dating from around 1750. In 1855 it was owned by the local multi-talented brewer/baker/grocer, and bought by Lord Radnor in 1919. Bar snacks are supplemented by an extensive fish choice and daily specials, which might include braised lamb shank, wild mushroom risotto, tuna with noodles, turbot with spinach or Scotch rib-eye fillet, all freshly prepared. Fine summer garden with rural views. Hosts an annual local pumpkin competition.

Open all wk **Bar Meals** L served all wk 12-2.15 D served all wk 7-9 Av main course £8.95 **Restaurant** L served all wk 12-2.15 D served all wk 7-9 Av 3 course à la carte fr £25 ⊕ HALL & WOODHOUSE ◀ Badger Tanglefoot, Best, Golden Champion. ♀ 6 **Facilities** Children's menu Play area Family room Dogs allowed Garden Parking

PEWSEY

The Seven Stars ♥

Bottlesford SN9 6LU

☎ 01672 851325   📠 01672 851583

e-mail: info@thesevenstars.co.uk

dir: *Off A345*

This thatched 16th-century free house stands in a splendid seven acre garden. Its front door opens straight onto the low-beamed, oak-panelled bar, now tastefully refurbished. Expect well-kept ales and an extensive menu of home-cooked food. With pheasant and pigeon on the menu when available, typical dishes include roast pork belly; smoked haddock risotto; and mutton shepherd's pie with greens. Finish with rice pudding with Bramley compote and crumble topping, then walk it off with a stroll in the garden.

Open noon-3 6-11 Closed: Mon **Bar Meals** food served all day **Restaurant** food served all day ⊕ FREE HOUSE ◼ Wadworth 6X, Brakspear, London Pride, Guest ales ♂ Stowford Press. ♥ 6 **Facilities** Children's menu Dogs allowed Garden Parking

BEWDLEY

Little Pack Horse ♥

31 High St DY12 2DH

☎ 01299 403762   📠 01299 403762

e-mail: enquires@littlepackhorse.co.uk

dir: *From Kidderminster follow ring road & signs for Safari Park. Then follow signs for Bewdley over bridge, turn left, then right, right at top of Lax Lane. Pub in 20mtrs*

The interior of this historic timber-framed inn is warmed by cosy log fires and lit by candles at night. There are low beams, an elm bar, and a small outside patio for alfresco summer dining. There are a great selection of real ales and ciders, and the finest, local produce is sourced with an emphasis on seasonality. Expect an impressive range of roasts like Packhorse mix roast using lamb, beef, pork, turkey and slow roasted duck leg.

Open all wk noon-2.30 6-11.30 (Sat-Sun noon-mdnt) **Bar Meals** food served all day **Restaurant** food served all day ⊕ PUNCH TAVERNS ◼ Theakstons Best Wye Valley HPA, Dorothy Goodbodies Golden Ale, Black Sheep Bitter, Shepherd Neame Spitfire ♂ Stowford Press, Westons Organic, Thatchers Katy. ♥ 21 **Facilities** Children's menu Family room Dogs allowed Garden

DROITWICH

The Chequers ☻

Cutnall Green WR9 0PJ
☎ 01299 851292 📄 01299 851744
dir: *Telephone for directions*

A display of football memorabilia on the bar wall reveals that this is the home of Roger Narbett, chef to the England football team. He runs the Chequers with his wife Joanne, retaining its charming and traditional village pub atmosphere with open fire, panelled bar and richly coloured furnishings. Lunchtime sandwiches and toasted paninis are backed by classics such as Scotch beef steak pie with neeps, mash and onion gravy; and slow braised lamb with herb dumplings and root vegetables. The carte includes starters of carrot, sweet potato and red lentil soup with garlic toasty. Typical main courses may proffer breast of pot roast Jimmy Butler's belly of pork, while desserts like treacle tart with granny's thick custard should not be missed.

Open all wk Closed: 25 Dec, 1 Jan **Bar Meals** L served Mon-Sat 12-2, Sun 12-2.30 D served Mon-Sun 6.30-9.15 Av main course £10.75 **Restaurant** L served Mon-Sat 12-2, Sun 12-2.30 booking required D served Mon-Sun 6.30-9.15 booking required Fixed menu price fr £11.50 Av 3 course à la carte fr £18.50 ⊕ ENTERPRISE INNS ◀ Timothy Taylor, Enville Ale, Banks Bitter, Banks Mild, Hook Norton, Ruddles. ☻ 11 **Facilities** Children's menu Family room Dogs allowed Garden Parking

DROITWICH

The Honey Bee ☻

Doverdale Ln, Doverdale WR9 0QB
☎ 01299 851620
e-mail: honey@king-henrys-taverns.co.uk
dir: *Please telephone for directions*

'It's buzzin' at The Honey Bee but you won't get stung!' So say King Henry's Taverns, which owns this beekeeping-themed pub, with working beehives and a children's area containing an enormous beehive plaything. All the group's establishments offer a standard menu that covers most pub grub eventualities - steak and ale pie; whole roast chicken; pan-fried fillets of plaice; rump, fillet and rib steaks; lamb rogan josh; vegetarian balti; and broccoli and cream cheese bake.

Open all day all wk noon-10 **Bar Meals** Av main course £3 food served all day **Restaurant** food served all day ⊕ KING HENRY TAVERNS ◀ Guinness, Greene King IPA, Marstons Pedigree. ☻ 15 **Facilities** Children's menu Play area Family room Garden Parking

FLYFORD FLAVELL

The Boot Inn ★★★★ INN ♟

Radford Rd WR7 4BS

☎ 01386 462658   📄 01386 462547

e-mail: enquiries@thebootinn.com

web: www.thebootinn.com

dir: *From Worcester take A422 towards Stratford. Turn right to village*

Parts of this family-run coaching inn date back to the 13th century, as heavy beams and slanting doorways attest. The large bar area is comfortable, with pool table and TV in a separate room. Good food is served by friendly staff, and may include mains like minted lamb and spinach curry or grilled swordfish steak with pink peppercorn sauce. Outside are gardens front and back, with a heated patio and sheltered smoking area. Five charming bedrooms in the converted coach house complete the picture.

Open all wk noon-mdnt (25 Dec noon-2) **Bar Meals** L served all wk 12-2 D served all wk 6.30-10 **Restaurant** L served all wk 12-2 D served all wk 6.30-10 ⊕ PUNCH TAVERNS ◀ Old Speckled Hen, London Pride, John Smith's Tribute. ♟ 8 **Facilities** Children's menu Dogs allowed Garden Parking **Rooms** 5

KNIGHTWICK

The Talbot ♟

WR6 5PH

☎ 01886 821235   📄 01886 821060

e-mail: admin@the-talbot.co.uk

dir: *A44 (Leominster road) through Worcester, 8m W right onto B4197 at River Teme bridge*

The late 14th-century coaching inn has been owned by the Clift family for over 25 years and in that time they have developed their own style, firmly rooted in the traditions and produce of the Teme Valley. Nearly everything is made in house, including bread, preserves, black pudding, raised pies and so on. The inn has a large kitchen garden, which produces a wide range of salads, herbs and, of course, vegetables. Sausages, hams, bacon and cheeses are sourced from local suppliers. The Talbot is also the home of The Teme Valley Brewery, started in 1997, using hops grown in the parish. The cask conditioned ales are all available on hand pump in the bar.

Open all day all wk 7.30am-11.30pm Closed: 25 Dec pm **Bar Meals** L served all wk 12-2 D served all wk 6.30-9 Av main course £16 **Restaurant** D served all wk 6.30-9 booking required Fixed menu price fr £27 Av 3 course à la carte fr £38 ⊕ FREE HOUSE ◀ Teme Valley This, That , T'Other & Wot, Hobsons Best Bitter Choice. ♟ 9 **Facilities** Children's menu Dogs allowed Garden Parking

MALVERN

The Anchor Inn 🍷

Drake St, Welland WR13 6LN
☎ 01684 592317
e-mail: theanchor13@hotmail.com
dir: M50 junct 1, A38 follow signs for Upton upon Severn. Left onto A4104, through Upton upon Severn, 2.5m. Pub on right

The attractive 17th-century Anchor Inn has spectacular views of the Malvern Hills. There's a garden for warmer weather and a welcoming winter fire in the dining room. Fresh, quality food is cooked to order. Light bites and main meals are marked up on the chalkboard, with dishes such as pork loin stuffed with apple in stilton sauce, steak and kidney pie, and shank of lamb simmered in mint and rosemary gravy. Themed menus and quiz nights feature regularly. The inn has won awards from Britain in Bloom.

Open Closed: Sun eve **Bar Meals** L served all wk 12-2 D served Mon-Sat 7-9 booking required Av main course £9.99 **Restaurant** L served all wk 12-2 D served Mon-Sat 7-9 booking required ⊕ FREE HOUSE ◖ Black Sheep, Woods, Hook Norton, Greene King, Malvern Hills. 🍷 20 **Facilities** Children's menu Family room Garden Parking

MARTLEY

The Crown Inn

Berrow Green Rd WR6 6PA ☎ 01886 888840
dir: 7m W of Worcester on B4204

Once the scene of an unlikely gig by Eric Clapton, the Crown is a Victorian village pub with a large extension formed from redundant outbuildings, which now houses the dining area. In one bar is an open fire, Sky TV, pool table and jukebox, while the other has dining tables and French windows to the garden. This great community pub is on the Worcester Way, so many visitors tend to be walkers. Locally sourced, freshly cooked food includes 10oz Kobe beefburger; lamb and mint sausages; Thai fish curry; and penne pasta with creamy goats' cheese sauce.

Open all wk noon-11 (Fri-Sat noon-mdnt Sun noon-10.30) **Bar Meals** L served Mon-Sat 12-2, Sun 12-3 D served Mon-Sat 6-9 Av main course £8.50 **Restaurant** L served Mon-Sat 12-2, Sun 12-3 D served Mon-Sat 6-9 Av 3 course à la carte fr £17.65 ⊕ MARSTONS ◖ Banks Bitter, Banks Mild. **Facilities** Children's menu Play area Dogs allowed Garden Parking

LOW CATTON

The Gold Cup Inn ♀

YO41 1EA ☎ 01759 371354
dir: *1m S of A166 or 1m N of A1079, E of York*

Solid tables and pews - reputedly made from a single oak tree - feature in the restaurant of this 300-year-old, family-run free house. There's a large beer garden, and the adjoining paddock drops down to the River Derwent. On the menu expect to find braised beef in red wine gravy on mashed potato; grilled gammon with port and mushroom sauce; baked cod loins with herb crust; and deep-fried brie with cranberry and orange dip.

Open noon-2.30 6-11 (Sat-Sun noon-11) Closed: Mon L **Bar Meals** L served Tue-Fri 12-2.30, Sat-Sun 12-6 D served all wk 6-9 Av main course £8.25 **Restaurant** L served Sun 12-5.30 booking required D served all wk 6-9 booking required Fixed menu price fr £12.5 Av 3 course à la carte fr £20 ⊕ FREE HOUSE ◀ John Smiths, Theakstons. ♀ 15 **Facilities** Children's menu Play area Dogs allowed Garden Parking

AKEBAR

The Friar's Head ♀

Akebar Park DL8 5LY
☎ 01677 450201 & 450591
🖹 01677 450046
e-mail: info@akebarpark.com
dir: *From A1 at Leeming Bar onto A684, 7m towards Leyburn. Entrance at Akebar Park*

A typical stone-built Dales pub at the entrance to a stunning, peaceful holiday park, The Friar's Head overlooks beautiful countryside and grounds, where bowls or croquet can be played on the lawn. The large south-facing conservatory dining room called The Cloister is a stunning feature, particularly by candlelight, with its stone flags, lush planting and fruiting vines. Hand-pulled local ales are served, and typical dishes include beef and mushrooms in Dijon mustard cream sauce, and halibut steak with white wine cream sauce.

Open all wk 10-3 6-11.30 (Fri-Sun 10am-11.30pm Jul-Sep) Closed: 25 Dec, 26 Dec eve & 1 Jan **Bar Meals** L served all wk 12-2.30 D served all wk 6-9.30 **Restaurant** L served all wk 12-2.30 booking required D served all wk 6-9.30 booking required ⊕ FREE HOUSE ◀ John Smiths & Theakston Best Bitter, Black Sheep Best, Timothy Taylor Landlord. ♀ 14 **Facilities** Children's menu Garden Parking

ASENBY

Crab & Lobster ®® ₹

Dishforth Rd YO7 3QL

☎ 01845 577286 📠 01845 577109

e-mail: reservations@crabandlobster.co.uk

web: www.crabandlobster.co.uk

dir: *From A1(M) take A168 towards Thirsk, follow signs for Asenby*

Amid seven acres of garden, lake and streams stands this unique 17th-century thatched pub and adjacent small hotel. Equally famous for its innovative cuisine and special gourmet extravaganzas, the menus show influences from France and Italy, with occasional oriental spices too. Starters leave no doubt you are in seafood heaven: crispy fishcakes of local codling and oak-smoked salmon, with creamed greens and poached hen's egg; a classic prawn cocktail with lobster and langoustine; and steamed Shetland mussels. The theme continues into main courses with the likes of lobster, scallop and prawn thermidor; and crab-crusted Wester Ross salmon. For those who prefer meat, the range of locally-sourced ingredients will not disappoint.

Open all wk 11-11 **Bar Meals** L served all wk 12-2.30 D served Sun- Mon 7-9, Sat 6.30-9.30 Av main course £15 **Restaurant** Fixed menu price fr £16 Av 3 course à la carte fr £35 ⊕ FREE HOUSE ◀ John Smiths, Scots 1816, Golden Pippin, Guinness. ₹ 16 **Facilities** Children's menu Garden Parking

BROMPTON-BY-SAWDON

The Cayley Arms ₹

YO13 9DA ☎ 01723 859372

e-mail: joannabou@hotmail.co.uk

dir: *Situated on the A170 in Brompton-by-Sawdon between Pickering and Scarborough*

Standing in the heart of picturesque Brompton-by-Sawdon, the pub is named after pioneering aviator Sir George Cayley. Its cosy log fire and friendly atmosphere has been the centre of village life for over a century, and is well-known to travellers between Pickering and Scarborough. Chunky lunchtime sandwiches with home-made crisps and hot baguettes are supplemented by hot dishes like Yorkshire pudding and boozey beef. In the evening expect spinach and ricotta tortellini; fisherman's pie with potato topping; or oven-baked chicken with leek and blue cheese sauce.

Open noon-3 5-close (Mon 6-close) Closed: Mon L **Bar Meals** L served Tue-Sun 12-2 D served Mon-Sat 6-9 **Restaurant** L served Tue-Sat 12-2 D served Mon-Sat 6-9 ⊕ PUNCH TAVERNS ◀ Tetley Cask, Black Sheep Cask. ₹ 20 **Facilities** Children's menu Play area Dogs allowed Garden Parking

BYLAND ABBEY

Abbey Inn ★★★★★ RR ❀ ♓

YO61 4BD

☎ 01347 868204 📄 01347 868678

e-mail: abbeyinn@english-heritage.org.uk

web: www.bylandabbeyinn.com

dir: *From A19 Thirsk/York follow signs to Byland Abbey/Coxwold*

This award-winning gastro-pub uses only fresh seasonal Yorkshire produce, and the daily-changing menu might offer starters and light bites such as organic parsnip and honey soup; Gloucester Old Spot and chestnut sausages with creamed mash; or potted brown shrimps in blade mace butter with lemon and home-made granary bread. Main course dishes include crispy feta and spinach pastries with tomato and chickpeas; and pan-fried black bream with Yorkshire potato tartiflette, clams and samphire. Leave room for dessert: Yorkshire Parkin with black treacle ice cream is a typical choice. Children are offered the same healthy food but in half-size portions.

Open noon-2.30 6-11 (Sun noon-3) Closed: 25-26 Dec, 24 & 31 Dec eve, 1 Jan, Sun eve, Mon-Tue **Bar Meals** Av main course £14.50 **Restaurant** L served Wed-Sat 12-2.30, Sun 12-3 D served Wed-Sat 6-11 Fixed menu price fr £12.50 Av 3 course à la carte fr £20.95 ⊕ FREE HOUSE ◀ Black Sheep Best, Timothy Taylor. ♓ 8 **Facilities** Children's menu Garden Parking **Rooms** 3

HAWES

The Moorcock Inn ♓

Garsdale Head LA10 5PU

☎ 01969 667488 📄 01969 667488

e-mail: admin@moorcockinn.com

dir: *On A684 5m from Hawes, 15m from Sedbergh at junct for Kirkby Stephen (10m). Garsdale Station 1m*

A heart-warming 18th-century hostelry, where owners Caz and Simon welcome weary walkers with or without muddy boots and dogs. Candles glow in the windows, while inside fairy lights pick out a cosy blend of original stonework and bright colours, furnished with comfy sofas and traditional wooden chairs. Savour the pub's local ales around the wood-burning stove, or enjoy the spectacular views from the garden. Traditional fare ranges from Whitby scampi; lamb and root vegetable hotpot; to steak, mushroom and ale pie. Vegetarians and children are not forgotten with their own choices.

Open all day all wk 11am-mdnt **Bar Meals** food served all day **Restaurant** food served all day ⊕ FREE HOUSE ◀ Black Sheep, Copper Dragon, Boddingtons Cask, guest ales. ♓ 7 **Facilities** Children's menu Family room Dogs allowed Garden Parking

HELMSLEY

The Crown Inn ⬛ ★★★★ INN

Market Square YO62 5BJ ☎ 01439 770297

e-mail: info@tchh.co.uk

dir: *Please telephone for directions*

The family-run 16th-century inn overlooking Helmsley's beautiful square has been refurbished with style and taste, without losing the inn's historic charm. You can order a pint of Black Sheep and tuck into some fresh home-made food using local produce in the cosy bar and lounge, each warmed by an open log fire. Choose to stay to explore the North York Moors and visit nearby Castle Howard; you have the choice of smart, well-appointed rooms in the inn, or in a converted barn with views of Helmsley Castle.

Open all day all wk 7.30am-11.30pm **Bar Meals** Av main course £9 food served all day **Restaurant** Fixed menu price fr £14.95 Av 3 course à la carte fr £20 ⊕ FREE HOUSE ◖ Black Sheep, John Smith Cask, Guest ale. **Facilities** Children's menu Family room Dogs allowed Garden Parking **Rooms** 19

HOVINGHAM

The Worsley Arms Hotel ★★★ HL ⚲

Main St YO62 4LA

☎ 01653 628234 📄 01653 628130

e-mail: enquiries@worsleyarms.co.uk

dir: *On B1257 between Malton & Helmsley*

In 1841 Sir William Worsley thought he would turn the village of Worsley into a spa to rival Bath, and built a spa house and a hotel. However, he reckoned without the delicate nature of his guests who disliked the muddy track between the two. Inevitably the spa failed, but the hotel survived andy ou can eat in the restaurant or the Cricketer's Bar (the local team has played on the village green for over 150 years). Hambleton Stallion beer from nearby Thirsk is on tap, and food choices include seared Gressingham duck with celeriac and potato dauphinoise, Worsley Arms fishcakes with lemon fish cream, Waterford Farm sausages with mash and red onion confit, or rack of North Yorkshire lamb with fondant potato, roast garlic and fresh mint.

Open all day all wk **Bar Meals** L served all wk 12-2 booking required D served all wk 6.30-9 booking required Av main course £11 **Restaurant** L served Sun 12-2 booking required D served all wk 6.30-9 booking required Fixed menu price fr £29.50 Av 3 course à la carte fr £23.50 ⊕ FREE HOUSE ◖ Tetleys, Hambleton Ales. ⚲ 20 **Facilities** Children's menu Dogs allowed Garden Parking **Rooms** 20

LASTINGHAM

Blacksmiths Arms ☏

YO62 6TL

☎ 01751 417247 📠 01751 417247
e-mail: pete.hils@blacksmithslastingham.co.uk
dir: *7m from Pickering & 4m from Kirbymoorside.
A170 (Pickering to Kirbymoorside road), follow
Lastingham & Appleton-le-Moors signs*

This 17th-century pub stands opposite St Mary's
Church (renowned for its Saxon crypt) in the
National Park area. The stone-built free house
retains its original low-beamed ceilings and open
range fireplace, and outside there's a cottage
garden and decked seating area. Home-cooked
dishes prepared from locally supplied ingredients
include lamb casserole served with Yorkshire
pudding, and beer-battered jumbo cod. Snacks
range through panini, luxury salad, filled roll
platters and buckets of chips. Look out for daily
specials.

Open all day noon-11.30 Closed: Tue L (Nov-May)
Bar Meals L served all wk (not Tue Nov-May)
12-5 D served all wk 6.30-8.45 Av main course
£8.50 Restaurant L served Mon-Sat 12-2 (not
Tue Nov-May), Sun 12-5 booking required D
served all wk 6.30-8.45 booking required ⊕ FREE
HOUSE ◀ Theakstons Best Bitter, 2 rotating guest
ales. ☏ 10 Facilities Children's menu Family room
Garden

LEYBURN

Sandpiper Inn ☏

Market Place DL8 5AT

☎ 01969 622206 📠 01969 625367
e-mail: hsandpiper99@aol.com
dir: *From A1 take A684 to Leyburn*

Although it has been a pub for only 30 years, the
building that houses the Sandpiper Inn in is the
oldest in Leyburn, dating back to around 1640. It
has a beautiful summer garden, and inside, and
a dining room where an exciting and varied mix
of traditional and more unusual dishes is served.
Lunch brings sandwiches (brie, salami and
rocket for example); and Masham sausage and
mash with onion gravy. An evening meal could
start with warm pigeon on a butternut squash
risotto or terrine of game with apple chutney, and
continue with fish pie topped with Berwick Edge
cheese or slow-cooked Dales lamb with winter
vegetables and dauphinoise potatoes. Sunday
lunch includes roasted rib of Dales beef with
onion gravy and Yorkshire pudding.

Open 11.30-3 6.30-11 (Sun noon-2.30 7-10.30)
Closed: Mon & occasionally Tue Bar Meals L served
all wk 12-2.30 Av main course £8.50 Restaurant L
served all wk 12-2.30 booking required D served
all wk 6.30-9.30 booking required ⊕ FREE
HOUSE ◀ Black Sheep Best, Black Sheep
Special, Daleside, Copper Dragon, Archers. ☏ 8
Facilities Children's menu Family room Dogs allowed
Garden

MASHAM

The Black Sheep Brewery

HG4 4EN
☎ 01765 689227 & 680100
🖹 01765 689746
e-mail: sue.dempsey@blacksheep.co.uk
dir: *Off A6108, 9m from Ripon & 7m from Bedale*

Paul Theakston, of Masham's famous brewing family, founded the Black Sheep Brewery in the early nineties according to traditional brewing principles. The complex boasts a visitor centre where you can enjoy a 'shepherded' tour of the brewhouse, before popping into the cosy bistro and 'baa...r' to sample the ales. The beers also find their way into a range of hearty dishes, including steak and Riggwelter casserole served with jacket potato.

Open all wk 10.30-4.30 (Thu-Sat 10.30-late) **Bar Meals** food served all day **Restaurant** food served all day ⊕ BLACK SHEEP BREWERY ◀ Black Sheep Best Bitter, Riggwelter, Black Sheep Ale. **Facilities** Children's menu Family room Garden Parking

PICTON

The Station Hotel ☙

TS15 0AE ☎ 01642 700067
dir: *1.5m from A19*

'Hotel' by name only, this is family-run and family-friendly village pub has had the same owner for 20 years. Offering real food at reasonable prices, just about everything is home made from locally sourced produce, with one menu serving both bar and dining room. While the children enjoy the outdoor play area in the beer garden, parents can relax in front of the open fire and scan the extensive specials board over a pint of John Smiths.

Open all wk 6-11.30 (Sat noon-2.30 6-11.30 Sun noon-4 6-11.30) **Bar Meals** L served Sat 12-2.30, Sun 12-4 booking required D served all wk ⊕ FREE HOUSE ◀ John Smiths Cask, John Smiths Smooth, Guinness. ☙ 6 **Facilities** Children's menu Play area Garden Parking

REETH

Charles Bathurst Inn ★★★★ INN ☻

Arkengarthdale DL11 6EN
☎ 01748 884567 🖹 01748 884599
e-mail: info@cbinn.co.uk
web: www.cbinn.co.uk
dir: *From A1 leave at Scotch Corner, take A6108 to Richmond then B6270 to Reeth. At Buck Hotel turn N to Langthwaite, pass church on right, Inn 0.5m on right*

Cosy fires and antique pine furniture greet customers entering this 18th-century free house. The owners pride themselves on knowing the provenance of all their food, and the daily menu is written up on an imposing mirror hanging at the end of the room. Starters might include butternut squash and Parmesan risotto; and pan-fried mackerel on Greek salad. For a hearty lunch try steamed steak and red wine suet pudding with parsnip mash; or the lighter goats' cheese, tomato and red onion tartlet; followed, perhaps, by plum crumble with crème Anglaise.

Open all wk 11am-mdnt Closed: 25 Dec **Bar Meals** L served all wk 12-2 booking required D served all wk 6.30-9 booking required Av main course £11.95 **Restaurant** L served all wk 12-2 booking required D served all wk 6.30-9 booking required Av 3 course à la carte fr £22 ⊕ FREE HOUSE ◀ Theakstons, John Smiths Bitter, John Smiths Smooth, Black Sheep Best, Riggwelter. ☻ 12 **Facilities** Children's menu Play area Garden Parking **Rooms** 19

SUTTON-ON-THE-FOREST

The Blackwell Ox
Inn ★★★★ INN ☻ ☻

Huby Rd YO61 1DT
☎ 01347 810328 🖹 01347 812738
e-mail: enquiries@blackwelloxinn.co.uk
dir: *7m from centre of York off A1237. Take B1363, at T-junct left. Pub on right*

The Blackwell Ox blends modern elegance with period charm. Visitors will find hand-pulled ales and an open fire in the bar, as well as a terrace for sitting out in the warmer months. Meanwhile, restaurant diners can relax in the lounge area before or after their meal. The chef believes in simple, honest cooking, and sources local North Yorkshire produce to create his dishes. Substantial sandwiches appear at lunchtime, alongside a fixed price menu that might include confit of pork with cassoulet. A typical evening meal might start with pea and mint soup, followed by sea bass with braised endive, and finishing with lemon posset and butter shortbread.

Open all wk noon-3 5.30-11 (Sun close 10.30) **Bar Meals** Av main course £11.45 food served all day **Restaurant** Fixed menu price fr £10.95 Av 3 course à la carte fr £25 food served all day ⊕ FREE HOUSE ◀ Black Sheep, John Smiths Cask, Guinness, Timothy Taylor Landlord, Copper Dragon. ☻ 9 **Facilities** Children's menu Garden Parking **Rooms** 7

THORNTON WATLASS

The Buck Inn ★★★ INN ♀

HG4 4AH ☎ 01677 422461 📄 01677 422447
e-mail: innwatlass1@btconnect.com
web: www.buckwatlass.co.uk
dir: From A1 at Leeming Bar take A684 to Bedale,
then B6268 towards Masham. Village 2m on right,
by cricket green

Overlooking the village green and cricket pitch
this pub is a traditional, well run, friendly
institution with three separate dining areas - the
bar for informality, the restaurant for dining
by candlelight, and on busy days the large
function room is opened. The menu ranges
from traditional, freshly prepared pub fare to
exciting modern cuisine backed by daily changing
blackboard specials. Typical bar favourites
are Masham rarebit (Wensleydale cheese with
local ale topped with bacon and served with
pear chutney); or steak and ale pie. Hearty
daily specials may take in beef Wellington with
Madeira sauce; game casserole, and roast cod
with mash and saffron cream.

Open all wk 8am-mdnt Closed: 25 Dec eve **Bar
Meals** L served Mon-Sat 12-2, Sun 11-3 D served all
wk 6.30-9.30 Av main course £12.75 **Restaurant** L
served Mon-Sat 12-2, Sun 11-3 D served all wk
6.30-9.30 ⊕ FREE HOUSE ◀ Theakston Best, Black
Sheep Best, Theakston Black Bull, guest ales. ♀ 7
Facilities Children's menu Play area Family room
Dogs allowed Garden Parking **Rooms** 7

WEAVERTHORPE

The Star Country Inn

YO17 8EY
☎ 01944 738273 📄 01944 738273
e-mail: starinn.malton@btconnect.com
dir: From Malton take A64 towards Scarborough.
12m, at Sherborn right at lights. Weaverthorpe 4m,
inn opposite junct

This 200-year-old inn has a rustic interior with
large winter fires and a welcoming, convivial
atmosphere. Food is fresh and locally sourced
where possible, and pride is taken in everything
from fresh-baked breads to home-made ice
cream. Even the tomato ketchup is made on site!
A meal might include ham hock terrine followed
by beer battered Whitby fish with hand cut chips,
mushy peas and tartare sauce, while spicier
options include vegetable balti with pilau rice
or green Thai prawn curry. A classy selection of
specials might include pan-fried pigeon breast
with watercress salad and walnut dressing; or
pan-seared Shetland king scallops with curried
parsnip purée and parsnip chips.

Open all day noon-mdnt Closed: Mon **Bar Meals** L
served Tue-Sat 12-6, Sun 12-3 booking required Av
main course £8 food served all day **Restaurant** L
served Sun 12-3 booking required D served Tue-Sun
6-9 booking required ⊕ FREE HOUSE ◀ Bitter, John
Smiths, Wold Top, Theakstons. **Facilities** Children's
menu Garden Parking

BRADFIELD

The Strines Inn

Bradfield Dale S6 6JE ☎ 0114 2851247
dir: N off A57 between Sheffield & Manchester

Nestled amid the breathtaking moorland scenery of the Peak District National Park, overlooking Strines Reservoir, this popular free house feels a world away from nearby Sheffield but is in fact within its border. Although it was built as a manor house in the 13th century, most of the present building is 16th century. It has been an inn since 1771. Traditional home-made fare ranges from sandwiches, salads and jacket potatoes, to substantial Yorkshire puddings with a choice of fillings, plus grilled steaks, mammoth mixed grill, or pie of the day.

Open all wk 10.30-3 5.30-11 (Sat-Sun 10.30am-11pm) Closed: 25 Dec **Bar Meals** L served all wk 12-2.30 D served all wk 5.30-9 Av main course £8.25 ⊕ FREE HOUSE ◄ Marston's Pedigree, Kelham Island, Mansfield Cask, Bradfield Bitter, Old Speckled Hen. **Facilities** Children's menu Play area Dogs allowed Garden Parking

CADEBY

Cadeby Inn ♥

Main St DN5 7SW ☎ 01709 864009
e-mail: info@cadeby-inn.co.uk

Before being converted into a picturesque whitewashed pub, with a stone-walled traditional bar and a more contemporary restaurant with stylish yet comfortable chairs, this was a farmhouse. Sandstone walls enclose the large front garden, while a patio and smaller garden lie at the rear; ideal for enjoying a meal or a pint of John Smiths in the warmer weather. The lunch menu offers interesting sandwiches like classic minute steak and onion, or open sandwich of smoked salmon, prawn and lemon mayonnaise; or crisp warm brie with Waldorf salad and cranberry sauce. In the evening you might start with creamy parsnip and apple soup, followed by main courses such as Whitby cod fillet, creamy mash, parsley sauce and crisp bacon; confit duck leg, stew of white beans, Savoy cabbage, shallots and thyme; and simple wild mushroom and parmesan risotto.

Open all wk noon-11 **Bar Meals** L served all wk 12-5.30 food served all day **Restaurant** L served all wk 12-9.30 D served Mon-Sat 12-9.30, Sun 12-8 food served all day ⊕ FREE HOUSE ◄ John Smiths Cask, Black Sheep Best Bitter, Guinness. ♥ 6 **Facilities** Children's menu Garden Parking

DONCASTER

Waterfront Inn ☻

Canal Ln, West Stockwith DN10 4ET
☎ 01427 891223
dir: *From Gainsborough take either A159 N, then minor road to village. Or A631 towards Bawtry/ Rotherham, then right onto A161, then minor road*

Built in the 1830s overlooking the Trent Canal basin and the canal towpath, the pub is now popular with walkers and visitors to the nearby marina. Real ales and good value food are the order of the day, including pasta with home-made ratatouille, broccoli and cheese bake, deep fried scampi, half honey-roasted chicken, and lasagne.

Open noon-2.30 6-11 (Sat noon-11 Sun noon-9)
Closed: Mon (ex BH) **Bar Meals** L served Tue-Sun, 12-2.30 D served Tue-Sun 6.30-9 Av main course £7.99 **Restaurant** L served Tue-Sun 12-2.30 D served Tue-Sun 6.30-9 ⊕ ENTERPRISE INNS ◖ John Smiths Cask, Greene King Old Speckled Hen. ☻ 9 **Facilities** Children's menu Play area Dogs allowed Garden Parking

PENISTONE

Cubley Hall ☻

Mortimer Rd, Cubley S36 9DF
☎ 01226 766086   📠 01226 767335
e-mail: info@cubleyhall.co.uk
dir: *M1 junct 37, A628 towards Manchester, or M1 junct 35a, A616. Hall just S of Penistone*

Since the 1700s this place has been used for a variety of purposes, and original features such as ornate plasterwork, oak panelling and stained glass have survived. The restaurant, massively oak-beamed and solidly slate-floored, has old pine tables, chairs and pews. There are plenty of snacks and light meals, as well as main courses like 'classic British' pie of the day with shortcrust pastry, salted steak fries and a panache of vegetables; Whitby wholetail breaded scampi with homemade tartare sauce; risotto with mixed beans, fresh herbs, Parmesan and pesto; and seasonal salads. Ten daily specials on blackboards, several 'credit munch' options and a children's menu complete the picture.

Open all wk **Bar Meals** D served Mon-Fri until 9.30, Sat-Sun until 10 Av main course £8 food served all day **Restaurant** L served Sun 12.30-3.30 booking required D served Sun, last orders at 5.45 booking required Fixed menu price fr £9.75 Av 3 course à la carte fr £21 ⊕ FREE HOUSE ◖ Tetley Bitter, Burton Ale, Greene King Abbot Ale, Young's Special. ☻ 7 **Facilities** Children's menu Play area Family room Garden Parking

SHEFFIELD

The Fat Cat

23 Alma St S3 8SA
☎ 0114 249 4801 📠 0114 249 4803
e-mail: info@thefatcat.co.uk
dir: *Telephone for directions*

This reputedly haunted three-storey, back street pub was built in 1832, and is Grade II listed. Beer-wise, it's hard to imagine anywhere better: a constantly changing range of guest beers from across the country, especially from micro-breweries, makes for a real ale heaven. The smart interior is very much that of a traditional, welcoming city pub; outside there's an attractive walled garden complete with Victorian-style lanterns, bench seating and shrubbery. Real fires in winter complete the cosy feel. Home-cooked food from a simple weekly menu is available except on Sunday evenings — nutty mushroom pie or Mexican chicken casserole. Look out for special events such as beer and food evenings.

Open all wk noon-11 (Sat-Sun noon-mdnt) Closed: 25 Dec **Bar Meals** L served all wk 12-2.30 D served Mon-Sat 6-8 ⊕ FREE HOUSE 🍺 Timothy Taylor Landlord, Kelham Island Bitter, Pale Rider, Pride of Sheffield, Kelham Island Gold ♂ Stowford Press, Guest ciders. **Facilities** Children's menu Family room Dogs allowed Garden Parking

TOTLEY

The Cricket Inn 🍷

Penny Ln, Totley Bents S17 3AZ
☎ 0114 236 5256
e-mail: info@brewkitchen.co.uk
dir: *Follow A621 from Sheffield 8m. Turn right onto Hillfoot Rd, 1st left onto Penny Ln*

Being so close to the Peak District means that The Cricket is a natural choice for sustenance when you have completed your ten-mile tramp or fell run. Muddy running shoes, walking boots, children and dogs are all welcome. The building was originally a farmhouse which started selling beer to navvies building the Totley Tunnel on the nearby Sheffield to Manchester railway. It's a forward-looking venture that links the innovative beers with great pub food. Fill the odd corner with tasty snacks like fresh (rather than frozen) whitebait; main course offerings include steak and kidney pie with home-made ham hock. Whatever you order, the chips, fried in beef dripping the way nature intended, are not to be missed.

Open all wk 11-11 **Bar Meals** L served Mon-Fri 12-2.30, Sat-Sun all day D served Mon-Fri 5-8.30, Sat-Sun all day Av main course £12 **Restaurant** L served Mon-Fri 12-2.30, Sat-Sun all day D served Mon-Fri 5-8.30, Sat-Sun all day Fixed menu price fr £12 Av 3 course à la carte fr £20 ⊕ BREWKITCHEN LTD 🍷 8 **Facilities** Children's menu Dogs allowed Garden Parking

LINTON

The Windmill Inn ♥

Main St LS22 4HT
☎ 01937 582209 📄 01937 587518
web: www.thewindmillinnwetherby.co.uk
dir: *From A1 exit at Tadcaster/Otley junct, follow Otley signs. In Collingham follow Linton signs*

A coaching inn since the 18th century, the building actually dates back to the 14th century, and originally housed the owner of the long-disappeared windmill. Stone walls, antique settles, log fires, oak beams and lots of brass set the scene in which to enjoy good bar food prepared by enthusiastic licensees. Expect the likes of chicken breast on mustard mash with onion jus, sea bass on pepper mash with tomato and basil sauce, baked salmon on Italian risotto, or king prawns in lime and chilli butter. While you're there, ask to take a look at the local history scrapbook.

Open all wk 11-3 5.30-11 (Sat-Sun 11-11) Closed: 1 Jan **Bar Meals** L served Mon-Fri 12-2, Sat 12-2.30, Sun 12-5.45 Av main course £8.95 **Restaurant** L served Mon-Fri 12-2, Sat 12-2.30, Sun 12-5.45 D served Mon-Tue 5.30-8.30, Wed-Sat 5.30-9, Sun 12-5.45 Fixed menu price fr £9.95 Av 3 course à la carte fr £13.95 ⊕ SCOTTISH COURAGE ◀ John Smiths, Theakston Best, Daleside, Greene King Ruddles County. ♥ 12 **Facilities** Children's menu Dogs allowed Garden Parking

MYTHOLMROYD

Shoulder of Mutton ♥

New Rd HX7 5DZ ☎ 01422 883165
dir: *A646 Halifax to Todmorden, in Mytholmroyd on B6138, opposite rail station*

Award-winning Pennines' pub situated by a trout stream in the village where Ted Hughes was born. Popular with walkers, cyclists, families and visitors to the area, the pub's reputation for real ales and hearty fare using locally sourced ingredients remains intact after 33 years of ownership. The menu ranges from snacks and sandwiches to vegetarian quiche; filled giant Yorkshire pudding; Cumberland sausages; and beef in ale. Look out for the 17th-century counterfeit golden guineas on display in the bar.

Open Closed: Tue L **Bar Meals** L served Wed-Mon 11.30-2 D served Wed-Sun 7-8.15 Av main course £4.50 ⊕ ENTERPRISE INNS ◀ Black Sheep, Copper Dragon, Greene King IPA, Timothy Taylor Landlord, Castle Eden. ♥ 10 **Facilities** Children's menu Play area Family room Dogs allowed Garden Parking **Notes** no credit cards

SOWERBY

The Travellers Rest ▽

Steep Ln HX6 1PE
☎ 01422 832124   📄 01422 831365
dir: *M62 junct 22 or 24*

The stone-built Travellers Rest was built in 1730 and sits high on a steep hillside with glorious views, a dining terrace, duck pond, huge car park and helipad. The cosy stone-flagged bar boasts fresh flowers and an open fire, while in the restaurant, beams, animal print sofas, more warmth from a wood-burning stove, and exposed stonework continue the emphasis on comfort and relaxation. Dishes cooked to order from local produce are rooted in Yorkshire tradition yet refined with French flair, yielding an immaculate and happy mix of classic and contemporary cooking. Start with ham hock terrine with home-made piccalilli, belly pork with truffled new potatoes, or salmon tapas; continue with lamb loin with cabbage and Parma ham, or venison with sweet potato crisps. Resist the sticky toffee pudding if you can.

Open Closed: Mon-Tue **Bar Meals** L served Sat 12-2, Sun 12-7 D served Wed-Thu 5-9, Fri 5-9.30, Sat 5.30-9.30, Sun 12-7 **Restaurant** L served Sat 12-2, Sun 12-7 D served Wed-Thu 5-9, Fri 5-9.30, Sat 5.30-9.30, Sun 12-7 ⊕ FREE HOUSE ◀ Timothy Taylor Landlord, Timothy Taylor, Best Bitter. ▽ 8 **Facilities** Children's menu Dogs allowed Garden Parking

SOWERBY BRIDGE

The Alma Inn

Cotton Stones HX6 4NS ☎ 01422 823334
e-mail: info@almainn.com
dir: *Turn off A58 at Triangle Twixt Sowerby Bridge & Ripponden. Follow signs for Cotton Stones*

The old stone inn stands in a dramatic rural location in the heart of Calderdale with views across the glorious Rydale Valley from its terrace and garden. Inside, stone-flagged floors, oak beams, glowing fires, and rustic pine tables set the informal, traditional scene for supping pints of Taylor Landlord and, surprisingly, for tucking into Italian-inspired dishes. Expect great value pizzas and pasta dishes, or fillet steak Rossini, and pubby bar meals, from the Alma burger to fish pie.

Open all day all wk noon-11 **Bar Meals** Av main course £8 food served all day **Restaurant** Fixed menu price fr £7.50 Av 3 course à la carte fr £14 food served all day ⊕ FREE HOUSE ◀ Tetley Bitter, Timothy Taylor Landlord, Timothy Taylor Golden Best. **Facilities** Children's menu Dogs allowed Garden Parking

CASTEL

Hotel Hougue du Pommier ★★★ HL

Hougue du Pommier Rd GY5 7FQ
☎ 01481 256531 🖹 01481 256260
e-mail: hotel@houguedupommier.guernsey.net
dir: *Telephone for directions*

An 18th-century Guernsey farmhouse with the only feu du bois (literally 'cooking on the fire') in the Channel Islands. Eat in the beamed Tudor Bar with its open fire or the more formal restaurant. Menu options may include dishes from the spit-roast menu, baked aubergine and Mediterranean vegetable ragout; chargrilled supreme of chicken; or Chef's seafood fishcake. The 8-acre gardens have a swimming pool, barbecue and medieval area, where banquets are held the first Saturday of the month.
Open all day all wk **Bar Meals** L served all wk 12-2 booking required D served all wk 6.30-9 booking required Av main course £9.50 **Restaurant** L served all wk 12-2 booking required D served all wk 6.30-9 booking required Fixed menu price fr £19.50 Av 3 course à la carte fr £25 ⊕ FREE HOUSE ◀ John Smiths, Extra Smooth, Guernsey Best Bitter, Guinness. **Facilities** Children's menu Dogs allowed Garden Parking **Rooms** 40

ST MARTIN

Royal Hotel ♟

La Grande Route de Faldouet JE3 6UG
☎ 01534 856289 🖹 01534 857298
e-mail: johnbarker@jerseymail.co.uk
dir: *2m from Five Oaks rdbt towards St Martyn. Pub on right next to St Martin's Church*

A friendly atmosphere, value for money, and great food and drink are the hallmarks of this friendly local in the heart of St Martin. John Barker, the landlord, has been extending a welcome for 23 years at this former coaching inn. Roaring log fires warm winter visitors, and there's a sunny beer garden to relax in during the summer months. Among the traditional home-made favourites are steak and ale pie, fresh grilled trout, monkfish and prawn Thai curry, and vegetarian lasagne. Ploughman's lunches, filled jacket potatoes, grills and children's choices are also on offer.

Open all day all wk **Bar Meals** L served Mon-Sat 12-2.15 D served Mon-Sat 6-8.30 Av main course £8.50 **Restaurant** L served Mon-Sat 12-2.15 D served Mon-Sat 6-8.30 ⊕ RANDALLS VAUTIER ◀ John Smiths Smooth, Theakstons Cool, Guinness, Ringwood Real Ale. ♟ 9 **Facilities** Children's menu Play area Garden Parking

NETHERLEY

The Lairhillock Inn ♥

AB39 3QS

☎ 01569 730001   📠 01569 731175

e-mail: info@lairhillock.co.uk

dir: *From Aberdeen take A90. Right towards Durris on B9077 then left onto B979 to Netherley*

Set in beautiful rural Deeside, just 15 minutes drive from Aberdeen, this 200-year-old former coaching inn offers real fires in the lounge to keep out the winter chill. Dishes are robust and use fresh, quality, local and regional produce such as wild boar and venison from the Highlands and salmon from the Dee and Don. For lunch, try the Lairhillock lasagne; for a more formal dining option, try shredded confit duck leg and beetroot timbale, followed by chicken supreme filled with sage and sausagemeat. Quality abounds on the children's menu too, where spicy spare ribs and Finnan haddock fishcakes can be found.

Open all wk 11am-mdnt Closed: 25-26 Dec, 1-2 Jan **Bar Meals** L served all wk 12-2 booking required D served all wk 6-9.30 booking required Av main course £9.95 **Restaurant** D served Tue-Sat 7-9.30 booking required Av 3 course à la carte fr £27.50 ⊕ FREE HOUSE ◖ Timothy Taylor Landlord, Courage Directors, Cairngorm, Tradewinds, Greene King IPA. ♥ 7 **Facilities** Children's menu Dogs allowed Garden Parking

ARDUAINE

Loch Melfort Hotel ★★★ HL ◎◎ ♥

PA34 4XG ☎ 01852 200233

e-mail: reception@lochmelfort.co.uk

web: www.lochmelfort.co.uk

dir: *On A816, 20m s of Oban*

This award-winning hotel and restaurant offers a uniquely informal and relaxed atmosphere. Choose to dine in the formal Arduaine Restaurant, where tian of Asknish Bay crab with apple and sweet pepper sauce; or marinated Islay scallops with pea pesto, lime and chilli dressing might introduce main courses like pan-fried loin of Argyll venison with dauphinoise potatoes, creamed leeks and a thyme and juniper jus; or sea trout fillet with braised fennel, and pea and chervil risotto. The more relaxed atmosphere of the modern Chartroom 2 bar and bistro is the place to enjoy all-day drinks, teas, coffees and home baking, as well as light lunches and suppers. It has the finest views on the West Coast and serves home-made Scottish fare including plenty of locally landed seafood. You can sit outside and enjoy a drink in warmer weather or crowd around the cosy fire in winter and watch the waves crashing against the rocks.

Open all wk 11-11 **Bar Meals** L served all wk 12-2.30 D served all wk 6-8.30 Av main course £8.95 ⊕ FREE HOUSE ◖ 80/- Ale Belhaven, Fyne Ale. ♥ 8 **Facilities** Children's menu Play area Dogs allowed Garden Parking **Rooms** 25

KILFINAN

Kilfinan Hotel Bar

PA21 2EP

☎ 01700 821201   🖨 01700 821205
e-mail: kilfinanhotel@btconnect.com
dir: *8m N of Tighnabruaich on B8000*

The hotel, on the eastern shore of Loch Fyne set amid spectacular Highland scenery on a working estate, has been welcoming travellers since the 1760s. The bars are cosy with log fires in winter, and offer a fine selection of malts. There are two intimate dining rooms, with the Lamont room for larger parties. Menus change daily and offer the best of local produce: Loch Fyne oysters, of course, and langoustine grilled in garlic butter; cullen skink soup; and moules marinière, plus game, Aberdeen Angus beef and a variety of Scottish sweets and cheeses. Enjoy the views from the garden on warmer days.

Open all wk **Bar Meals** L served all wk 12.30-4 D served all wk 6.30-9.30 Av main course £7.95 **Restaurant** L served all wk 12.30-4 booking required D served all wk 6.30-9.30 booking required Av 3 course à la carte fr £22 ⊕ FREE HOUSE ◀ McEwens 70/-, McEwens 80/-. **Facilities** Children's menu Family room Dogs allowed Garden Parking

PORT APPIN

The Pierhouse Hotel & Seafood Restaurant ★★★ SHL ◉

PA38 4DE

☎ 01631 730302   🖨 01631 730509
e-mail: reservations@pierhousehotel.co.uk
dir: *A828 from Ballachulish to Oban. In Appin right at Port Appin & Lismore ferry sign. After 2.5m left after post office, hotel at end of road by pier*

With breathtaking views to the islands of Lismore and Mull, it would be hard to imagine a more spectacular setting. A selection of menus feature mussels and langoustines harvested from Loch Linnhe and Loch Etive; and lobsters and crab kept mouth-wateringly fresh in creels at the end of the pier. There are alternatives to seafood, such as Highland fillet steak served on creamy herb mash with a whisky and peppercorn sauce; and pappardelle with fresh mushrooms, herbs, white wine, garlic and cream topped with Gruyère cheese.

Open all wk 11-11 Closed: 25-26 Dec **Bar Meals** L served all wk 12.30-2.30 D served all wk 6.30-9.30 Av main course £9 **Restaurant** L served all wk 12.30-2.30 booking required D served all wk 6.30-9.30 booking required Fixed menu price fr £35 Av 3 course à la carte fr £23 ⊕ FREE HOUSE ◀ Calders 80/-, Belhaven Best, Guinness. **Facilities** Children's menu Family room Dogs allowed Garden Parking **Rooms** 12

STRACHUR

Creggans Inn ★★★ HL ◉◉ ♚

PA27 8BX

☎ 01369 860279   🖷 01369 860637

e-mail: info@creggans-inn.co.uk

dir: *A82 from Glasgow, at Tarbet take A83 towards Cairndow, left onto A815 to Strachur*

From the hills above this informal family-friendly free house on the shores of Loch Fyne, you can gaze across the Mull of Kintyre to the Western Isles beyond. A good selection of real ales, wines by the glass and malt whiskies are all served at the bar. There's a formal terraced garden and patio for alfresco summer enjoyment, and regional produce plays a key role in the seasonal menus: the famed Loch Fyne oysters of course, but also salmon from the same waters, smoked or grilled. Robust main courses may feature fillet of Aberdeenshire beef; haddock in a crisp beer batter; or pot-roasted chicken. Apple and bramble tart with home-made cinnamon ice cream makes a fulfilling conclusion.

Open all wk 11am-mdnt **Bar Meals** L served all wk 12-2.30 D served all wk 6-8.30 Av main course £9.50 **Restaurant** D served all wk 7-8.30 booking required Fixed menu price fr £37.50 ⊕ FREE HOUSE ◖ Fyne Ales Highlander, Atlas Latitude, Deuchars IPA, Harvieston Bitter & Twisted. ♚ 7 **Facilities** Children's menu Dogs allowed Garden Parking **Rooms** 14

KIRKCUDBRIGHT

Selkirk Arms Hotel ★★★ HL ♚

Old High St DG6 4JG

☎ 01557 330402   🖷 01557 331639

e-mail: reception@selkirkarmshotel.co.uk

web: www.selkirkarmshotel.co.uk

dir: *M74 & M6 to A75, halfway between Dumfries & Stranraer on A75*

Robert Burns is reputed to have written the Selkirk Grace at this privately owned hotel, and the proprietors have created their own real ale, The Selkirk Grace, in conjunction with Sulwath Brewers. There are two bars, and a great choice of dishes is offered in The Bistro or more intimate Artistas Restaurant, including pan-seared Kirkcudbright king scallops; slow roast lamb shank; and Eccelfechan butter tart. Accommodation is provided in 17 en suite bedrooms.

Open all wk **Bar Meals** L served all wk 12-2 D served all wk 6-9 Av main course £9.95 **Restaurant** L served Sun 12-2 booking required D served all wk 7-9 booking required Fixed menu price fr £19 Av 3 course à la carte fr £30 ⊕ FREE HOUSE ◖ Youngers Tartan, John Smiths Bitter, Criffel, Timothy Taylor Landlord, The Selkirk Grace. ♚ 8 **Facilities** Children's menu Dogs allowed Garden Parking **Rooms** 17

NEW ABBEY

Criffel Inn

2 The Square DG2 8BX

☎ 01387 850305 & 850244

📄 01387 850305

e-mail: criffelinn@btconnect.com

dir: A74/A74(M) exit at Gretna, A75 to Dumfries, A710 to New Abbey

A former 18th-century coaching inn set on the Solway Coast in the historic conservation village of New Abbey close to the ruins of the 13th-century Sweetheart Abbey. Expect a warm welcome and excellent home-cooked food using local produce. There's a lawned beer garden overlooking the corn-mill and square; ideal for touring Dumfries and Galloway.

Open all wk noon-2.30 5-11 (Mon-Tue 5-11 Fri-Sat noon-2.30 5-mdnt) **Bar Meals** L served Wed-Sun 12-2 D served Wed-Sun 5-8 Av main course £7.95 **Restaurant** L served Wed-Sun 12-2 D served Wed-Sun 5-8 ⊕ FREE HOUSE 🍺 Belhaven Best, McEwans 60-, Guinness. **Facilities** Children's menu Family room Dogs allowed Garden Parking

NEWTON STEWART

Creebridge House Hotel 🅰 ★★★ SHL

Minnigaff DG8 6NP

☎ 01671 402121 📄 01671 403258

e-mail: info@creebridge.co.uk

dir: From A75 into Newton Stewart, turn right over river bridge, hotel 200yds on left

A listed building dating from 1760, this family-run hotel is set in three acres of idyllic gardens and woodland at the foot of Kirroughtree forest. It was formerly the Earl of Galloway's shooting lodge and part of his estate. The refurbished Bridge's bar and brasserie offers malt whiskies, real ales and an interesting menu, perfect for an informal lunch. For a candlelit dinner the alternative dining venue is the Creebridge Garden Restaurant. The emphasis is on fresh Scottish produce, and both menus feature Kirkcudbrightshire beef, hung for 14 days, and an award-winning house speciality: best loin of lamb with creamed kale and roulade of braised shin. Fish dishes range from the brasserie's local sea bass set on chive mash with dill butter sauce, to the restaurant's seared Solway salmon with lemon risotto and chive velouté.

Open all wk noon-2 6-11.30 (Fri-Sat noon-2 6-1am) **Bar Meals** L served all wk 12-2 D served all wk 6-9 ⊕ FREE HOUSE 🍺 Tennents, Deuchars, Guinness, guest ales. **Facilities** Dogs allowed Garden Parking **Rooms** 18

BROUGHTY FERRY

The Royal Arch Bar ♀

285 Brook St DD5 2DS
☎ 01382 779741   📄 01382 739174
dir: *3m from Dundee. 0.5 min from Broughty Ferry rail station*

In Victorian times, the jute industry made Broughty Ferry the 'richest square mile in Europe'. Named after a Masonic lodge which was demolished to make way for the Tay road bridge, the pub dates from 1869. The deep, dry cellars are ideal for conditioning ale so look forward to a nice pint in the bar with its original hand-carved oak bar, sideboard and counter. An extensive selection of meals range from light snacks to three-course meals, served in the bar, lounge, restaurant or pavement café.

Open all wk Closed: 1 Jan **Bar Meals** L served Mon-Fri 12-2.15, Sat-Sun 12-5 booking required D served All wk 5-7.30 booking required Av main course £8 ⊕ FREE HOUSE ◀ McEwans 80/-, Belhaven Best, Guinness, Caledonian, Deuchars IPA. ♀ 12 **Facilities** Children's menu Family room Dogs allowed Garden

GATEHEAD

The Cochrane Inn

45 Main Rd KA2 0AP ☎ 01563 570122
dir: *From Glasgow A77 to Kilmarnock, then A759 to Gatehead*

There's a friendly, bustling atmosphere inside this traditional village centre pub, which sits just a short drive from the Ayrshire coast. The menus combine British and international flavours. At lunch this might translate as cullen skink with crayfish tails followed by penne Arrabiata or spicy lamb curry. In the evening, maybe crispy bacon and houmous on toast ahead of a hearty steak pie with carrots and mash.

Open all wk noon-2.30 5.30 onwards (Sun noon-9) **Bar Meals** food served all day **Restaurant** food served all day ⊕ FREE HOUSE ◀ John Smiths. **Facilities** Children's menu Garden Parking

RATHO

The Bridge Inn ♥

27 Baird Rd EH28 8RA

☎ 0131 333 1320 📠 0131 333 3480

e-mail: info@bridgeinn.com

dir: *From Newbridge at B7030 junct, follow signs for Ratho and Edinburgh Canal Centre*

An 18th-century former farmhouse was converted to create this canal-side pub in 1820. In addition to the restaurant and two bars, The Bridge Inn also has a restaurant barge on the canal, providing the perfect venue for special events. Dishes range from bar snacks and light bites, such as mushrooms stuffed with haggis and black pudding, battered, deep-fried and served with red onion marmalade, to main courses of smoked haddock fishcakes with lime and tarragon dressing, or pork and beef medallions with wholegrain mustard sauce.

Open all day all wk 11-11 (Fri-Sat 11am-mdnt) Closed: 25-26 Dec, 1-2 Jan **Bar Meals** L served Mon-Sat 11-9, Sun 12-30-9 D served Mon-Sat 11-9, Sun 12-30-9 Av main course £9 food served all day **Restaurant** L served Mon-Sat 12-2.30, Sun 12.30-8.30 booking required D served Mon-Sat 6.30-9.30, Sun 12.30-8.30 booking required Fixed menu price fr £9.50 Av 3 course à la carte fr £16 ⊕ FREE HOUSE ◀ Belhaven, Deuchars IPA, Tennents, Stewarts Pentland. ♀ 6 **Facilities** Children's menu Family room Garden Parking

ANSTRUTHER

The Dreel Tavern ♥

16 High Street West KY10 3DL

☎ 01333 310727 📠 01333 310577

e-mail: dreeltavern@aol.com

dir: *From Anstruther centre take A917 towards Pittenweem*

Complete with a local legend concerning an amorous encounter between James V and a local gypsy woman, the welcoming 17th-century Dreel Tavern has plenty of atmosphere. Its oak beams, open fire and stone walls retain much of the distant past, while home-cooked food and cask-conditioned ales are served to hungry visitors of the present. Peaceful gardens overlook Dreel Burn.

Open all wk 11am-mdnt **Bar Meals** L served all wk 12-3 D served all wk 5.30-9.30 **Restaurant** L served all wk 12-3 D served all wk 5.30-9.30 ⊕ FREE HOUSE ◀ Deuchars IPA, 2 guest ales. ♀ 20 **Facilities** Children's menu Family room Dogs allowed Garden Parking

AVIEMORE

The Old Bridge Inn ☕

Dalfaber Rd PH22 1PU ☎ 01479 811137
e-mail: nigel@oldbridgeinn.co.uk
dir: *Exit A9 to Aviemore, 1st left to Ski Rd, then 1st left again 200mtrs*

Set in the spectacular Scottish Highlands, in an area well-known for its outdoor pursuits, this friendly Aviemore pub overlooks the River Spey. Dine in the relaxing bars with roaring log fire, the comfortable restaurant, or in the attractive riverside garden. A tempting chargrill menu includes lamb chops in redcurrant jelly, Aberdeen Angus sirloin or rib-eye steaks, and butterflied breast of chicken marinated in yoghurt, lime and coriander. Other choices include braised guinea fowl with brandy or potato gnocchi with butternut squash in a filo basket. Fine cask ales and large selection of malt whiskies available.

Open all wk 11-11 (Fri-Sat 11am-mdnt Sun 12.30-11) Bar Meals L served all wk 12-2 D served all wk 6-9 Restaurant L served all wk 12-2 booking required D served all wk 6-9 booking required ⊕ FREE HOUSE ◀ Caledonian 80/-, Cairngorm Highland IPA, Deuchars IPA, Timothy Taylor, Atlas Avalanche. ☕ 18 Facilities Children's menu Play area Family room Garden Parking

CARRBRIDGE

The Cairn ▲ ★★★ INN ☕

PH23 3AS
☎ 01479 841212   📠 01479 841362
e-mail: info@cairnhotel.co.uk
dir: *Village centre on old A9 close to historic 1717 Pack Horse bridge*

The Highland village of Carrbridge and this family-run inn make the perfect base for exploring the Cairngorms, the Moray coast and the Malt Whisky Trail. In the homely, tartan-carpeted bar, you'll find cracking Isle of Skye and Cairngorm ales on handpump, blazing winter log fires, all-day sandwiches, and hearty bar meals, including sweet marinated herring with oatcakes, venison sausage casserole, and sticky toffee pudding.

Open all day all wk 11-11 (Fri-Sat 11am-1am) Bar Meals L served all wk 12-2 D served all wk 6-8.30 Av main course £7 ⊕ FREE HOUSE ◀ Cairngorm, Orkney. ☕ 8 Facilities Children's menu Dogs allowed Garden Parking Rooms 7

CAWDOR

Cawdor Tavern ♀

The Lane IV12 5XP
☎ 01667 404777 📠 01667 404777
e-mail: enquiries@cawdortavern.info
dir: *From A96 (Inverness-Aberdeen) take B9006 & follow Cawdor Castle signs. Tavern in village centre*

Formerly a joinery workshop for the Cawdor Estate, this pub features oak panelling from the castle in the lounge bar. Roaring log fires keep the place cosy and warm on long winter evenings, while the garden patio comes into its own in summer. A single menu is offered for both restaurant and bar, where refreshments include a choice of real ales and 100 malt whiskies. The pub's reputation for seafood draws diners from some distance for dishes like fresh Wester Ross salmon with potatoes and parsley butter. Other favourites include a trio of Scottish puddings — black pudding, white pudding and haggis served with home-made chutney; and prime beef steak pie and mash.

Open all wk 11-3 5-11 (Sat 11am-mdnt Sun 12.30-11) Closed: 25 Dec, 1 Jan **Bar Meals** L served Mon-Sat 12-2, Sun 12.30-3 D served all wk 5.30-9 booking required Av main course £8.95 **Restaurant** D served all wk 5.30-9 booking required Av 3 course à la carte fr £18.95 ⊕ FREE HOUSE ◀ Red McGregor, 3 Sisters, Orkney Dark Island, Raven Ale, Latitude Highland Pilsner. ♀ 8 **Facilities** Children's menu Family room Dogs allowed Garden Parking

GAIRLOCH

The Old Inn ♀

IV21 2BD
☎ 01445 712006 📠 01445 712933
e-mail: info@theoldinn.net
dir: *Just off A832, near harbour*

Gairloch's oldest hostelry enjoys a fabulous setting at the foot of the Flowerdale Valley looking out across the harbour to the isles of Rona, Raasay and Skye. Seafood is the main draw in an area where Loch Ewe scallops, Minch langoustines, mussels, brown crab and fresh fish are regularly landed. Tuck into Cullen skink, a soup of smoked haddock, potato and cream, before launching into pan-seared scallops with smoked bacon mash and tamarind sauce, or Cajun-spiced cod. Carnivores will not be disappointed with pork belly served with herb-roasted vegetables. A large grassy area by the pretty stream with picnic tables is an attractive place to eat and enjoy the views.

Open all day all wk 11am-mdnt (Sun noon-mdnt) **Bar Meals** L served all wk 12-2.30 (summer 12-4.30) D served all wk 5-9.30 Av main course £9.50 food served all day **Restaurant** D served all wk 6-9.30 booking required Fixed menu price fr £25 Av 3 course à la carte fr £17.50 ⊕ FREE HOUSE ◀ Adnams Bitter, Isle of Skye Red Cullin, Blind Piper, An Teallach, Deuchars IPA, Wildcat. ♀ 8 **Facilities** Children's menu Play area Family room Dogs allowed Garden Parking

INVERIE

The Old Forge

PH41 4PL

☎ 01687 462267 🖹 01687 462267

e-mail: info@theoldforge.co.uk

dir: *From Fort William take A830 (Road to the Isles) towards Mallaig. Take ferry from Mallaig to Inverie (boat details on website)*

Britain's most remote mainland pub, The Old Forge is accessible only by boat, and stands literally between heaven and hell (Loch Nevis is Gaelic for heaven and Loch Hourn is Gaelic for hell). It's popular with everyone from locals to hillwalkers, and is renowned for its impromptu ceilidhs. It is also the ideal place to sample local fish and seafood, and other specialities such as haunch of estate venison. There are nine boat moorings and a daily ferry from Mallaig.

Open all wk **Bar Meals** L served all wk 12-3 D served all wk 6-9.30 Av main course £10 food served all day **Restaurant** L served all wk 12-3 D served all wk 6-9.30 ⊕ FREE HOUSE ◀ 80 Shilling, Guinness, Red Cuillin, real ales. **Facilities** Children's menu Play area Family room Dogs allowed Garden Parking

NORTH BALLACHULISH

Loch Leven Hotel

Old Ferry Rd PH33 6SA

☎ 01855 821236 🖹 01855 821550

e-mail: reception@lochlevenhotel.co.uk

dir: *Off A82, N of Ballachulish Bridge*

With its relaxed atmosphere, beautiful loch-side setting, and dramatic views, this privately owned hotel lies in the heart of Lochaber, 'The Outdoor Capital of the UK', and proves popular with walkers and climbers. It began life over 300 years ago, accommodating travellers using the Ballachulish Ferry. Food is available in the restaurant and the bar, both of which offer spectacular views over the fast-flowing narrows to the mountains. Home-cooked meals are built around local produce, especially fresh seafood, game and other traditional Scottish dishes.

Open 11-11 (Thu-Sat 11am-mdnt Sun 12.30-11) **Closed**: afternoons in winter **Bar Meals** L served all wk 12-3 D served all wk 6-9 Av main course £8.95 **Restaurant** L served all wk 12-3 D served all wk 6-9 Fixed menu price fr £12.95 Av 3 course à la carte fr £15 ⊕ FREE HOUSE ◀ John Smith's Extra Smooth, MacEwans 80%. **Facilities** Children's menu Play area Family room Dogs allowed Garden Parking

PLOCKTON

The Plockton Hotel ★★★ SHL ♟

Harbour St IV52 8TN
☎ 01599 544274 📄 01599 544475
e-mail: info@plocktonhotel.co.uk
web: www.plocktonhotel.co.uk
dir: *On A87 to Kyle of Lochalsh take turn at Balmacara. Plockton 7m N*

The Pearson family's uniquely converted inn stands on the shores of Loch Carron, with stunning views of the loch to the surrounding Applecross hills – it's a location to die for. Menus are based on the very best of Highland produce, with seafood a major strength: locally caught langoustines and fresh fish landed at Gairloch and Kinlochbervie. This translates to smoked fish soup, roast monkfish wrapped in bacon, and traditional battered haddock and chips. Meat-eaters will not be disappointed with the Aberdeen Angus rib-eye steak platter served with a peppered whisky sauce. A fine range of malts is available to round off that perfect Highland day.

Open all day all wk 11am-mdnt (Sun 12.30pm-11pm) **Bar Meals** L served all wk 12-2.15 D served all wk 6-10 Av main course £9.75 **Restaurant** L served all wk 12-2.15 D served all wk 6-10 booking required Av 3 course à la carte fr £20 ⊕ FREE HOUSE ◼ Caledonian Deuchars IPA, Hebridean Gold - Isle of Skye Brewery, Harvieston Blonde Ale, Crags Ale. ♟ 6 **Facilities** Children's menu Family room Garden **Rooms** 15

PLOCKTON

Plockton Inn & Seafood Restaurant

Innes St IV52 8TW
☎ 01599 544222 📄 01599 544487
e-mail: info@plocktoninn.co.uk
dir: *On A87 to Kyle of Lochalsh take turn at Balmacara. Plockton 7m N*

The atmosphere of this attractive stone built inn is relaxed and friendly, with winter fires and a selection of more than 50 malt whiskies. Taking pride of place on the specials menus are fresh West Coast fish and shellfish and West Highland beef, lamb and game. Starters include hot Plockton prawns (landed by the barman himself) with garlic butter. Haggis and clapshot is a particular speciality served with neeps, tatties and home-made pickled beetroot. Seafood dishes take in hake fillet with pesto crust, as well as the famous seafood platter. Other dishes include venison in ale; and aubergine parmigiana. Among the desserts is lemon and ginger crunch pie, as well as a selection of Scottish cheeses.

Open all day all wk **Bar Meals** L served all wk 12-2.30 D served all wk 6-9 **Restaurant** D served all wk 6-9 booking required Av 3 course à la carte fr £18 ⊕ FREE HOUSE ◼ Greene King Abbot Ale, Fuller's London Pride, Isle Of Skye Blaven, Caledonian 80/-, Plockton Crag Ale. **Facilities** Children's menu Play area Dogs allowed Garden Parking

TORRIDON

The Torridon Inn ♥

IV22 2EY ☎ 01445 791242 📄 01445 712253
e-mail: Inn@thetorridon.com
dir: *From Inverness take A9 N, then follow signs to Ullapool. Take A835 then A832. In Kinlochewe take A896 to Annat. Pub 200yds on right after village*

Once a grand shooting lodge The Torridon enjoys one of the most impressive coastal positions in the Scottish Highlands. Newly refurbished, the cosy bar offers a Highland welcome from both staff and locals: choose from a range of over 60 malt whiskies, or recount the day's adventures over a pint of local real ale. Entertainment ranges from indoor games to regular traditional live music sessions. The inn has its own restaurant, where you can sample high quality, locally sourced food at any time. Local produce drives menus that might feature venison, salmon, haggis and home-made specials. Dinner could begin with caramelised onion tart with fresh rocket and olive oil, followed by game casserole served with creamy mashed potatoes and seasonal baby vegetables.

Open all wk Closed: Nov-27 Mar **Bar Meals** L served all wk, all day D served all wk 6-9 Av main course £13.50 food served all day **Restaurant** Av 3 course à la carte fr £22 ◀ Isle of Skye Brewery - Red Cuillin, Blaven, Torridon Ale, Cairngorm Brewery - Stag, Tradewinds. ♛ 8 **Facilities** Children's menu Play area Dogs allowed Garden Parking

GLENDEVON

An Lochan Tormaukin Country Inn and Restaurant ★★★★ INN ⊕ ♥

FK14 7JY ☎ 01259 781252 📄 01259 781526
e-mail: info@anlochan.co.uk
dir: *M90 junct 6 onto A977 to Kincardine, follow signs to Stirling. Exit at Yelts of Muckhard onto A823/Crieff*

This attractive whitewashed building was built in 1720 as a drovers' inn. Sympathetically refurbished throughout, it still bristles with real Scottish character and charm. Original features like stone walls, exposed beams and blazing winter fires in the cosy public rooms ensure a warm and welcoming atmosphere. Expect fresh, locally sourced food. Lunch might bring scallops, Stornoway black pudding and rocket followed by a home-made beef and venison burger with chips. In the evening, perhaps wild boar terrine, then Aberdeen Angus beef Wellington with spinach and wild mushrooms. Live music is a regular feature at the inn, and golfing breaks are available.

Open all day all wk **Bar Meals** L served all wk 12-3 D served all wk 5.30-9 food served all day **Restaurant** L served all wk 12-3 D served all wk 5.30-9 Fixed menu price fr £20.95 Av 3 course à la carte fr £19.90 ⊕ FREE HOUSE ◀ Bitter & Twisted, Thrappledouser ♂ Aspall. ♛ 8 **Facilities** Children's menu Dogs allowed Garden Parking **Rooms** 13

KINNESSWOOD

Lomond Country Inn ♥

KY13 9HN

☎ 01592 840253   📄 01592 840693

e-mail: info@lomondcountryinn.co.uk

dir: *M90 junct 5, follow signs for Glenrothes then Scotlandwell, Kinnesswood next village*

A small, privately owned hotel on the slopes of the Lomond Hills that has been entertaining guests for more than 100 years. The cosy public areas offer log fires, a friendly atmosphere, real ales and a fine collection of single malts. If you want to make the most of the loch views, choose the charming restaurant, a relaxing room freshly decorated in country house style. The focus is on serving well kept real ales such as Orkney Dark Island, and a mix of traditional and favourite pub dishes. Starters may feature home-made pâté; while main courses include steak and Guinness pie; mince and tatties; Cajun chicken breast; and home-made locally sourced game stew.

Open all day all wk 7am-1am Bar Meals L served all wk 7am-9pm D served all wk 5-9 Av main course £5.95 food served all day Restaurant L served all wk 7am-9pm D served all wk 5-9 Fixed menu price fr £9.95 Av 3 course à la carte fr £18.95 food served all day ⊕ FREE HOUSE ◀ Deuchars IPA, Calders Cream, Tetleys, Orkney Dark Island, Bitter & Twisted. ♥ 6 Facilities Children's menu Play area Family room Dogs allowed Garden Parking

LEITHOLM

The Plough Hotel ♥

Main St TD12 4JN

☎ 01890 840252   📄 01890 840252

e-mail: theplough@leitholm.wanadoo.co.uk

dir: *5m N of Coldstream on A697. Take B6461, Leitholm in 1m*

The only pub remaining in this small border village (there were originally two), the Plough dates from the 17th century and was once a coaching inn. Food is traditional with the likes of parsnip soup or pâté and Melba toast followed steak and Guinness pie; home-made lasagne; or local sausages with Yorkshire pudding. Tuesdays and Fridays are fish and chip nights.

Open all day all wk noon-mdnt Bar Meals Av main course £12 food served all day Restaurant food served all day ⊕ FREE HOUSE ◀ Guinness. ♥ 8 Facilities Children's menu Garden Parking

TIBBIE SHIELS INN

Tibbie Shiels Inn

St Mary's Loch TD7 5LH
☎ 01750 42231   🖹 01750 42302
dir: From Moffat take A708. Inn 14m on right

On the isthmus between St Mary's Loch and the Loch of the Lowes, this waterside hostelry is named after the woman who first opened it in 1826. Isabella 'Tibbie' Shiels expanded the inn from a small cottage to a hostelry capable of sleeping around 35 people, many of them on the floor! Famous visitors during her time included Walter Scott, Thomas Carlyle and Robert Louis Stevenson. Tibbie Shiels herself is rumoured to keep watch over the bar, where the selection of over 50 malt whiskies helps sustain long periods of ghost watching. Now under new ownership, meals can be enjoyed in either the bar or the dining room. The inn will also prepare packed lunches for your chosen activity – be it walking (the inn now lies on the coast-to-coast Southern Upland Way walking trail), windsurfing or fishing (residents fish free of charge).

Open all day all wk 9am-mdnt **Bar Meals** Av main course £10 food served all day **Restaurant** Fixed menu price fr £16 Av 3 course à la carte fr £20 food served all day ⊞ FREE HOUSE ◀ Broughton Greenmantle Ale, Belhaven 80/- Ŏ Stowford Press. **Facilities** Children's menu Play area Dogs allowed Garden Parking

WEST LINTON

The Gordon Arms ♟

Dolphinton Rd EH46 7DR
☎ 01968 660208   🖹 01968 661852
e-mail: info@thegordon.co.uk

Set in the pretty village of West Linton but within easy reach of the M74, this 17th-century inn has a real log fire in the cosy lounge bar, and a lovely sun-trap beer garden. Enjoy a local ale alongside your meal, which may start with feta cheese and cous cous fritters with a spicy red schoog, or cullen skink; continue with steak and ale pie, haggis, or collops of venison with a rustic butternut squash and sweet potato purée; and finish with sticky toffee pudding.

Open all day all wk 11-11 (Fri-Sat 11-1am Tue 11-mdnt) **Bar Meals** L served Mon-Fri 12-3, Sat-Sun all day D served Mon-Fri 6-9, Sat-Sun all day **Restaurant** L served Mon-Fri 12-3, Sat-Sun all day D served Mon-Fri 6-9, Sat-Sun all day ⊞ SCOTTISH & NEWCASTLE ◀ John Smiths, Guinness, real ales. ♟ 7 **Facilities** Children's menu Play area Dogs allowed Garden Parking

KIPPEN

Cross Keys Hotel

Main St FK8 3DN ☎ 01786 870293

e-mail: info@kippencrosskeys.co.uk

dir: *10m W of Stirling, 20m from Loch Lomond off A811*

Refurbished by owners Debby and Brian, this cosy inn now serves food and drink all day. Nearby Burnside Wood is managed by a local community woodland group, and is perfect for walking and nature trails. The pub's interior, warmed by three log fires, is equally perfect for resting your feet afterwards. Regular events include a weekly Tuesday folk night.

Open all day noon-11 (Fri-Sat noon-1am Sun noon-11) Closed: 25 Dec, 1-2 Jan, Mon Bar Meals L served Tue-Sun 12-9 D served Tue-Sun 12-9 food served all day Restaurant L served Tue-Sun 12-9 D served Tue-Sun 12-9 food served all day ⊕ FREE HOUSE ◀ Belhaven Best, Harviestoun Bitter & Twisted, Guinness. Facilities Children's menu Family room Dogs allowed Garden Parking

LINLITHGOW

Champany Inn - The Chop and Ale House ◉◉

Champany EH49 7LU

☎ 01506 834532 🖹 01506 834302

e-mail: reception@champany.com

dir: *2m N.E of Linlithgow on corner of A904 & A803*

At Champany Corner a collection of buildings, some 16th century, has been turned into two splendid restaurants. The more informal is the Chop and Ale House bar, while the elegant, octagonal restaurant offers dishes such as Highland black pudding with onion marmalade; or triple-smoked rump of beef with single-vineyard olive oil and fresh oregano. In winter try cullen skink, a soup made from smoked haddock. Walking from the bar to the restaurant takes you past a chilled counter filled with a selection of steaks for the charcoal grill. Although Aberdeen Angus holds centre-stage, the two-AA Rosette menu also offers baked chicken filled with smoked bacon and tarragon mousse; and grilled salmon, langoustines and deep-fried organic cod.

Open all wk noon-2 6.30-10 (Fri-Sun noon-10) Closed: 25-26 Dec, 1 Jan Bar Meals food served all day Restaurant food served all day ⊕ FREE HOUSE ◀ Belhaven. Facilities Children's menu Garden Parking

CARBOST

The Old Inn

IV47 8SR

☎ 01478 640205   📄 01478 640205
e-mail: reservations@oldinn.f9.co.uk

Two-hundred-year-old free house on the edge of
Loch Harport with wonderful views of the Cuillin
Hills from the waterside patio. Not surprisingly,
the inn is popular with walkers and climbers.
Open fires welcome winter visitors, and live
music is a regular feature. With a great selection
of real ales, the menu includes daily home-
cooked specials, with numerous fresh fish dishes,
including local prawns and oysters and mackerel
from the loch.

Open all day all wk 11am-mdnt Bar Meals L
served Mon-Sat 11-9, Sun 12.30-11.30 D served
Mon-Sat 11-9, Sun 12.30-11.30 food served all day
Restaurant L served Mon-Sat 11-9, Sun 12.30-11.30
D served Mon-Sat 11-9, Sun 12.30-11.30 food
served all day ⊕ FREE HOUSE ◀ Red Cuillin, Black
Cuillin, Hebridean ale, Cuillin Skye Ale, Pinnacle Ale.
Facilities Children's menu Family room Dogs allowed
Garden Parking

RED WHARF BAY

The Ship Inn ☗

LL75 8RJ

☎ 01248 852568   📄 01248 851013
dir: Telephone for directions

Wading birds in their hundreds flock to feed on
the extensive sands of Red Wharf Bay, making
The Ship's waterside beer garden a birdwatcher's
paradise on warm days. Before the age of steam,
sailing ships landed cargoes here from all over
the world; now the boats bring fresh Conwy
Bay fish and seafood to the kitchens of this
traditional free house. A single menu covers the
bars and the restaurant, and specials always
include a catch of the day. Starters range from
salmon fishcakes to hot-smoked duck and spring
onion salad with teriyaki dressing. A main course
of baked half shoulder of Welsh spring lamb with
celeriac dauphinoise could be rounded off by
lemon tart with fruit compote.

Open all wk Bar Meals L served all wk 12-2.30 D
served all wk 6-9 booking required Av main course
£10 Restaurant D served Sat-Sun booking required
Fixed menu price fr £17.50 Av 3 course à la carte fr
£20 ⊕ FREE HOUSE ◀ Brains SA, Adnams, guest
ales. ☗ 16 Facilities Children's menu Play area
Family room Garden Parking

CREIGIAU

Gwaelod-y-Garth Inn ☻

Main Rd, Gwaelod-y-Garth CF15 9HH
☎ 029 2081 0408 & 07855 313247
dir: *From M4 junct 32, N on A470, left at next exit, at rdbt turn right 0.5m. Right into village*

Meaning 'foot of the garth (mountain)', this welcoming pub was originally part of the Marquess of Bute's estate. Every window of the pub offers exceptional views, and it's a much favoured watering hole for ramblers, cyclists and hang-gliders as well as some colourful locals. Real ales change every week, and the pub offers Gwynt y Ddraig award-winning ciders. Starters might include mussels in a tomato and garlic sauce; and main courses like rack of lamb with a herb crust, or duck breast with a kumquat and blackcurrant sauce.

Open all wk 11am-mdnt (Sun noon-11) **Bar Meals** food served all day **Restaurant** L served Mon-Thu 12-2, Fri-Sat 11am-mdnt, Sun 12-3 booking required D served Mon-Sat 6.30-9 booking required ⊕ FREE HOUSE ◀ HPA (Wye Valley), Otley O1, RCH Pitchfork, Vale of Glamorgan, Crouch Vale Brewers Gold ⚲ Local cider. ☻7 **Facilities** Children's menu Family room Dogs allowed Garden Parking

LLANDDAROG

White Hart Thatched Inn & Brewery

SA32 8NT ☎ 01267 275395
e-mail: bestpubinwales@aol.com
web: www.thebestpubinwales.co.uk
dir: *6m E of Carmarthen towards Swansea, just off A48 on B4310, signed Llanddarog*

The Coles family invites you to try a pint from the micro-brewery that adjoins their ancient thatched free house. Built in 1371, the pub's thick stone walls and heavy beams enclose a cosy log fire and converted barn restaurant. The menu ranges far and wide, using the best of local produce. Expect Welsh lamb chops and Black Beef steaks from the grill; duck sizzling in orange sauce; and swordfish in Spanish sauce. In summer, the flower-filled patio garden is perfect for alfresco dining.

Open all wk 11.30-3 6.30-11 (Sun noon-3 7-10.30) **Bar Meals** L served all wk 11.30-3 D served all wk 6.30-11 **Restaurant** L served all wk 11.30-3 D served all wk 6.30-11 ⊕ FREE HOUSE ◀ Roasted Barley Stout, Llanddarog Ale, Bramling Cross. **Facilities** Children's menu Play area Garden Parking

LLANDEILO

The Angel Hotel ♥

Rhosmaen St SA19 6EN
☎ 01558 822765   📠 01558 824346
e-mail: capelbach@hotmail.com
dir: *In town centre next to post office*

This popular pub in the centre of Llandeilo has
something for everyone. Real ales are available
in the bar area, which hosts regular live music
nights. Upstairs, the Yr Eglwys function room
ceiling is decorated with soaring frescoes
inspired by Michelangelo's Sistine Chapel, and
at the rear is an intimate bistro with warm
terracotta walls, where dishes might include
warm chorizo and potato salad, followed by
slowly roasted Welsh beef in a sweet baby onion
gravy.

Open 11.30-3 6-11 Closed: Sun **Bar Meals** L served
Mon-Sat 11.30-2.30 D served Mon-Sat 6-9 Av main
course £5 **Restaurant** L served Mon-Sat 11.30-2.30
booking required D served Mon-Sat 6-9 booking
required Fixed menu price fr £9.95 Av 3 course à
la carte fr £16 ⊕ FREE HOUSE ◀ Evan Evans Ales,
Tetleys, Butty Bach. ♥ 12 **Facilities** Children's menu
Garden

LLWYNDAFYDD

The Crown Inn & Restaurant ♥

SA44 6BU ☎ 01545 560396
e-mail: www.the-crown-inn.moonfruit.com
dir: *Off A487 NE of Cardigan*

A traditional Welsh longhouse dating from 1799,
with original beams, open fireplaces and a
pretty restaurant. Rob and Monique, the young
owners, have been there for 18 months now, and
are having a great time. A varied menu offers
a good selection of dishes, including lamb and
root vegetable casserole with rosemary cobbler;
or whole trout stuffed with pine nuts and bacon
with rosemary and lemon butter. Blackboard
specials and bar meals are available lunchtimes
and evenings. Outside is a delightful, award-
winning garden. An easy walk down the lane
leads to a cove with caves and National Trust
cliffs.

Open all day all wk noon-11 **Bar Meals** L served all
wk 12-3 D served all wk 6-9 Av main course £8.95
Restaurant L served all wk 12-3 D served all wk
6-9 ⊕ FREE HOUSE ◀ Flowers IPA , Greene King Old
Speckled Hen, Honey Ales, Envill Ale, Fuller's London
Pride, guest ale. ♥ 11 **Facilities** Children's menu
Play area Family room Dogs allowed Garden Parking

DOLWYDDELAN

Elen's Castle

LL25 0EJ ☎ 01690 750207
e-mail: stay@hotelinsnowdonia.co.uk
dir: *5m S of Betws-Y-Coed, follow A470*

Once an 18th-century coaching inn and a part of
the Earl of Ancaster's Welsh Estate, this family-
run free house now boasts an old world bar with
a wood-burning stove. The intimate restaurant
offers breathtaking views of the mountains and
Lledr River, which can also be enjoyed from
the garden. Sample dishes include wild rice,
spinach and honey roast with summer vegetable
ratatouille; and Conwy valley lamb shank on
mashed potato and leek with rosemary jus.

Open vary by season Closed: 2wks Jan, wk days
in quiet winter periods **Bar Meals** L served all wk
12-2 (summer holidays) D served all wk 6.30-9
Av main course £7.95 **Restaurant** D served
all wk 6.30-9 Fixed menu price fr £17.50 Av 3
course à la carte fr £20 ⊕ Free House ◀ Brains,
Worthington, Black Sheep, Spitfire ♻ Stowford Press.
Facilities Children's menu Play area Family room
Dogs allowed Garden Parking

PRESTATYN

Nant Hall Restaurant & Bar ♥

Nant Hall Rd LL19 9LD
☎ 01745 886766 📄 01745 886998
e-mail: mail@nanthall.com
dir: *E towards Chester, 1m on left opposite large
car garage*

Nant Hall, a Grade II listed Victorian country
house in seven acres of grounds, operates as a
gastro-pub with a great variety of food, beers and
wines. The menu offers local and regional dishes
alongside recipes from around the world: Thai
green chicken curry, pan-seared fillet of salmon
with a creamy herb risotto, chargrilled steaks,
Chinese chicken and vegetable satay, or creamy
fish pie in a parsley sauce. The large outdoor
eating area is great in summer.

Open all day noon-11pm Closed: Mon **Bar Meals** Av
main course £9.95 food served all day **Restaurant**
Fixed menu price fr £10.95 Av 3 course à la carte
fr £15 food served all day ⊕ FREE HOUSE ◀ Bass
Smooth, Boddingtons. ♥ 14 **Facilities** Children's
menu Family room Garden Parking

RHEWL

The Drovers Arms, Rhewl ♗

Denbigh Rd LL15 2UD
☎ 01824 703163   🖹 01824 703163
dir: 1.3m from Ruthin on A525

A small village pub whose name recalls a past written up and illustrated on storyboards displayed inside. Main courses are divided on the menu into poultry, traditional meat, fish, grills and vegetarian; examples from each section are chicken tarragon; Welsh lamb's liver and onions; Vale of Clwyd sirloin steak; home-made fish pie; and mushroom stroganoff. Desserts include treacle sponge pudding.

Open all wk noon-3 5.30-11 (Sat noon-3 5.30-mdnt Sun noon-11pm Open all day Jun-Sep) Closed: Tue L **Bar Meals** L served all wk 12-2 booking required D served all wk 6-9 booking required **Restaurant** L served all wk 12-2 booking required D served all wk 6-9 booking required ⊕ J W Lees ◖ J W Lees bitter. ♗ 6 **Facilities** Children's menu Play area Garden Parking

BABELL

Black Lion Inn ♗

CH8 8PZ ☎ 01352 720239
e-mail: theblacklioninn@btinternet.com
dir: A55 junct 31 to Caerwys turn left at crossroads signed Babell. Travel 3m turn right at fork

Ancient inns spawn ghost stories, but the 13th-century Black Lion boasts more than its fair share. Ask about them when you visit, but don't be put off savouring a local real ale on the outside decking while the children enjoy the play area. Alternatively tuck into good home-cooked dishes like black pudding layered with crisp back bacon; and pork escalope with fresh asparagus sauce. Irish music keeps the spirits awake on the last Wednesday of the month.

Open all wk 6pm-close (Sat-Sun noon-close) **Bar Meals** L served Sat-Sun 12-9 D served Thu-Sun 6-9 Av main course £12.95 **Restaurant** L served Sat-Sun 12-9 D served Thu-Sun 6-9 Av 3 course à la carte fr £22 ⊕ FREE HOUSE ◖ Thwaites Lancaster Bomber, Thwaites Smooth Bitter, Purple Moose Brewery - Traeth Mawr, Thirstquencher Spitting Feathers. ♗ 7 **Facilities** Children's menu Play area Garden Parking

ABERDYFI

Penhelig Arms Hotel & Restaurant ♀

Terrace Rd LL35 0LT
☎ 01654 767215 📄 01654 767690
e-mail: info@penheligarms.com
dir: *On A493 W of Machynlleth*

The Penhelig Arms has been in business since the late 18th century, enjoying glorious views over the tidal Dyfi estuary. In the summer months many customers relax on the sea wall opposite the pub. Locals and visitors alike experience a warm welcome in the wood-panelled Fisherman's bar, where traditional ales and home-cooked bar meals are served. Alternatively take a seat in the popular waterfront restaurant, and choose between dishes such as half a dressed Aberdyfi lobster with salad and mayonnaise, or melon and crayfish tails with chilli and lime dressing? Follow up with the likes of grilled monkfish wrapped in pancetta; or roast rump of lamb with root vegetable mash and rosemary gravy.

Open all day all wk 11-11 Closed: 25-26 Dec **Bar Meals** L served all wk 12-2 D served all wk 6-9 booking required Av main course £12.50 **Restaurant** L served all wk 12-2 booking required D served all wk 7-9 booking required Fixed menu price fr £29 Av 3 course à la carte fr £25 ⊕ S A BRAIN & CO LTD ◀ Adnams Broadside, Brains Reverend James & SA, Brains SA, Everards Toger. ♀ 22 **Facilities** Children's menu Dogs allowed Garden Parking

LLANBEDR

Victoria Inn ★★★ INN ♀

LL45 2LD
☎ 01341 241213 📄 01341 241644
e-mail: junevicinn@aol.com
web: www.victoriainnllanbedr.co.uk
dir: *On A496 between Barmouth and Harlech*

Fascinating features for pub connoisseurs are the circular wooden settle, ancient stove, grandfather clock and flagged floors in the atmospheric bar of the Victoria. Home-made food is served in the lounge bar and restaurant, complemented by a range of Robinson's traditional ales. A children's play area has been incorporated into the well-kept garden, with a playhouse, slides and swings. The Rhinog mountain range and the famous Roman Steps are right on the doorstep. Newly redecorated bedrooms are all en suite.

Open all day all wk 11-11 (Sun noon-10.30) **Bar Meals** Av main course £9 food served all day **Restaurant** Fixed menu price fr £10.50 food served all day ⊕ FREDERIC ROBINSON ◀ Robinson's Best Bitter, guest bitters ♂ Stowford Press. ♀ 10 **Facilities** Children's menu Play area Dogs allowed Garden Parking **Rooms** 5

TUDWEILIOG

Lion Hotel ♥

LL53 8ND ☎ 01758 770244
e-mail: martinlee1962@hotmail.com
dir: A487 from Caernarfon onto A499 towards
Pwllheli. Right onto B4417 to Nefyn, onto Edern then
onto Tudweiliog

The beach is only a mile away from this friendly
inn, run by the Lee family for over 30 years. The
large garden and children's play area makes the
pub especially popular with the cyclists, walkers
and families who flock to the Lleyn Peninsula.
The bar features an extensive list of over 80 malt
whiskies. A typical menu might consist of Tuscan
bean soup, Welsh lamb bake, and rice pudding.

Open all wk Bar Meals L served all wk 12-2
D served all wk 6-9 Av main course £8.25
⊕ FREE HOUSE ◀ Purple Moose Brewery Ale,
Boddingtons. ♥ 6 Facilities Children's menu Play
area Family room Garden Parking

ABERGAVENNY

Clytha Arms ♥

Clytha NP7 9BW
☎ 01873 840209 📠 01873 840209
e-mail: theclythaarms@tiscali.co.uk
dir: From A449/A40 junction (E of Abergavenny)
follow signs for 'Old Road Abergavenny/Clytha'

Andrew and Beverley Canning This former dower
house is heavily involved with the Welsh Cider
Festival in May and the Beer and Cheese Festival
in August. Hardly surprising then that the bar
offers Weston ciders and the Clytha's own perry,
as well as local beers from the Rhymney Brewery
and Crow Valley – at least four are always on
offer. Whisky, gin and vodka come from the
Penderyn Distillery just 20 miles away. As for
food, the menu offers treats for every taste,
from rabbit and cider pie to bacon, laverbread
and cockles. Treacle pudding and home-made
custard to finish is a must.

Open noon-3 6-mdnt (Fri-Sun noon-mdnt) Closed: 25
Dec, Mon L Bar Meals L served Tue-Sun 12.30-2.30
D served Mon-Sat 7-9.30 Av main course £10
Restaurant L served Tue-Sun 12.30-2.30 D served
Mon-Sat 7-9.30 Fixed menu price fr £16.95 Av 3
course à la carte fr £25 ⊕ FREE HOUSE ◀ Felinfoel
Double Dragon, Rhymney Bitter, 4 guest ales (300+
per year) ♻ Westons Old Rosie, Westons Perry, Clytha
Perry. ♥ 10 Facilities Children's menu Play area
Dogs allowed Garden Parking

LLANTRISANT

The Greyhound Inn △ ★★★ INN ☗

NP15 1LE

☎ 01291 672505 & 673447

📠 01291 673255

e-mail: enquiry@greyhound-inn.com

dir: M4 junct 24, A449 towards Monmouth, exit at 1st junct signed Usk. 2nd left for Llantrisant.

A traditional 17th-century Welsh longhouse, once part of a 400-acre farm, and an inn since 1845. Today, after 27 years in the same family's hands, the Greyhound has two acres of award-winning gardens, a four-acre paddock, accommodation and an array of restored outbuildings. The regular menu ranges over old favourites such as prawn cocktail, home-made curries, pies and lasagne. It is complemented by a daily specials blackboard offering unusual and seasonal dishes: chicken veronique; local pheasant; pork roberto; and Usk salmon. The vegetarian selection, with eight choices, is particularly notable. Home-made sweets include hazelnut meringue gateau.

Open all day 11-11 **Closed:** 25 & 31 Dec, 1 Jan, Sun eve **Bar Meals** L served all wk 12-2.15 D served Mon-Sat 6-10 Av main course £11 **Restaurant** L served all wk 12-2.15 D served Mon-Sat 6-10 ⊕ FREE HOUSE ◖ Interbrew Flowers Original & Bass, Greene King Abbot Ale, guest ale. ☗ 10 **Facilities** Children's menu Family room Dogs allowed Garden Parking **Rooms** 10

SKENFRITH

The Bell at Skenfrith ★★★★★ RR ◉◉ ☗

NP7 8UH ☎ 01600 750235 📄 01600 750525

e-mail: enquiries@skenfrith.co.uk

dir: M4 junct 24 onto A449. Exit onto A40, through tunnel & lights. At rdbt take 1st exit, right at lights onto A466 towards Hereford Road. Left onto B4521 towards Abergavenny, 3m on left

A 17th-century inn with views of Skenfrith Castle, where the oak bar, flagstone floors, comfortable sofas and old settles have plenty of character. Locally sourced ingredients, many from the inn's kitchen garden, are used in regularly changing menus. One day's selection could include warm duck salad; slow braised shoulder of Talgarth lamb with pan-seared lambs' liver and mashed potato; and lemon meringue pie. The fixed priced carte offers exquisite dishes which carefully combine finely judged flavours.

Open Closed: last wk Jan & 1st wk Feb, Mon Nov-Mar **Bar Meals** L served all wk 12-2.30 booking required D served Mon-Sat 7-9.30, Sun 7-9 booking required Av main course £15 **Restaurant** L served all wk 12-2.30 booking required D served Mon-Sat 7-9.30, Sun 7-9 booking required Fixed menu price fr £19 Av 3 course à la carte fr £28 ⊕ FREE HOUSE ◖ Timothy Taylor Landlord, St Austell Tribute, Wye Valley Bitter ♻ Local cider. ☗ 13 **Facilities** Children's menu Dogs allowed Garden Parking **Rooms** 11

TINTERN PARVA

Fountain Inn ☐

Trellech Grange NP16 6QW ☎ 01291 689303
e-mail: fountaininntintern@btconnect.com
dir: *From M48 junct 2 follow Chepstow then Tintern signs. In Tintern turn by George Hotel for Raglan. Bear right, inn at top of hill*

A fire failed to destroy this fine old early 17th-century inn, and its charming character remains unspoilt. It enjoys views of the Wye Valley from the garden, and is close to Tintern Abbey. Home-cooked food includes grilled sardines with balsamic vinegar and cherry tomatoes; leek and Caerphilly sausages with onion gravy; and beef and Guinness pie. Also a good selection of steaks, omelettes, and seafood choices are available. Recent change of landlord.

Open Closed: Mon (ex BH) **Bar Meals** L served Wed-Sun 12-2.30 D served all wk 6-9 **Restaurant** L served Wed-Sun 12-2.30 D served all wk 6-9 ⊕ FREE HOUSE ◀ Hook Norton, Spinning Dog, Ring of Bells, Interbrew Bass, Hobgoblin, Rev James, Kingstone Classic, Cats Whiskers. ☐ 10 **Facilities** Children's menu Family room Dogs allowed Garden Parking

TREDUNNOCK

The Newbridge ★★★★ RR ◉ ☐

NP15 1LY
☎ 01633 451000 📄 01633 451001
e-mail: newbridge@evanspubs.co.uk
dir: *M4 junct 24 follow Newport signs. Right at Toby Carvery, B4236 to Caerleon. Right over bridge, through Caerleon to mini rdbt. Straight ahead onto Llnagibby/Usk road*

In an idyllic riverside location, with warm and welcoming decor, comfortable sofas and subtle lighting. The quality and consistency of the modern British food is reflected in exciting seasonal menus, based on local produce. Expect a typical meal of oak-smoked haddock risotto with parmesan wafer and herb oil; mustard-crusted rack of local Penperlleni lamb with fondant potatoes and carved vegetables; and banana Tatin with caramel ice cream. Dinner could be watercress, spinach and goats' cheese tart with beetroot coulis; Old Spot pork loin with potato cake, baby vegetables and buttered tarragon jus; and home-made ice cream.

Open all wk 11am-mdnt **Bar Meals** L served all wk 12-2.30 booking required D served Mon-Sat 6.30-10, Sun 6-8.30 booking required **Restaurant** L served all wk 12-2.30 booking required D served Mon-Sat 6.30-10, Sun 6-8.30 booking required ⊕ FREE HOUSE ◀ Brains Rev James, Hobby Horse, guest ale ♂ Aspalls. ☐ 12 **Facilities** Children's menu Garden Parking **Rooms** 6

AMROTH

The New Inn ♓

SA67 8NW ☎ 01834 812368
dir: A48 to Carmarthen, A40 to St Clears, A477 to Llanteg then left

A 400-year-old inn, originally a farmhouse, belonging to Amroth Castle Estate. It has old world charm with beamed ceilings, a Flemish chimney, a flagstone floor and an inglenook fireplace. It is close to the beach, and local lobster and crab are a feature, along with a popular choice of home-made dishes including steak and kidney pie, soup and curry. Enjoy food or drink outside on the large lawn complete with picnic benches.

Open all day all wk Mar-Oct 11am-11pm Closed: Oct-Mar **Bar Meals** food served all day **Restaurant** food served all day ⊕ FREE HOUSE ◀ Brains, Old Speckled Hen, Guinness, guest ales. ♓ 8 **Facilities** Children's menu Family room Dogs allowed Garden Parking **Notes** no credit cards

NEWPORT

Salutation Inn 🄰 ★★★ INN

Felindre Farchog, Crymych SA41 3UY
☎ 01239 820564 ▤ 01239 820355
e-mail: JohnDenley@aol.com
web: www.salutationcountryhotel.co.uk
dir: On A487 between Cardigan & Fishguard

Set right on the banks of the River Nevern, this 16th-century coaching inn stands in a quiet village in the heart of the Pembrokeshire Coast National Park. The oak-beamed bars are full of old world charm and country atmosphere. There is an emphasis on fresh local produce on the varied menu, including meat, poultry, fish, cheese and fruit and vegetables. Asparagus and smoked Cerwyn cheese, or rustic game pâté to start, with perhaps prime fillet of Welsh Black beef on rösti and roasted shallots to follow are fine examples of the fare. There are eight en suite bedrooms available.

Open all day all wk **Bar Meals** L served all wk 12.30-2.30 D served all wk 6.30-9 **Restaurant** L served Sun 12.30-2.30 booking required D served Sat-Sun 7-9 booking required ⊕ FREE HOUSE ◀ Felinfoel, Brains, Local guest ales ♂ Thatchers Gold. **Facilities** Children's menu Dogs allowed Garden Parking **Rooms** 8

BRECON

The Felin Fach Griffin ★★★★ INN ◎◎ ▮

Felin Fach LD3 0UB ☎ 01874 620111
e-mail: enquiries@eatdrinksleep.ltd.uk
dir: 4.5m N of Brecon on A470 (Brecon to Hay-on-Wye road)

This much-feted country inn exemplifies owner Charles Inkin's passion for 'the simple things, done well'. Food is served in rambling bare-floored rooms where original features, including an Aga, are teamed with tasteful modern touches. The all important lunchtime menu includes Gorwydd Caephilly ploughman's with home-made soda bread and pickles, or Welsh pork and leek sausages. The freshest seafood could feature wild halibut fillet with young spring vegetables and fresh creamed morels. Other mains include rack of Herdwick lamb, shepherd's pie and carrot purée, and oak roast salmon on crushed Witchill potato and spinach.

Open all day 11-11 Closed: 24-25 Dec **Bar Meals** L served Mon-Sat 12.30-2.30, Sun 12-2.30 Av main course £11 **Restaurant** L served Mon-Sat 12.30-2.30, Sun 12-2.30 D served Mon-Sat 6.30-9.30, Sun 6.30-9 Fixed menu price fr £15 Av 3 course à la carte fr £35 ⊕ FREE HOUSE ◀ Breconshire Breweries, Wye Valley Butty Bach ♉ Thatchers. ▮ 20 **Facilities** Children's menu Dogs allowed Garden Parking **Rooms** 7

COEDWAY

The Old Hand and Diamond Inn

SY5 9AR ☎ 01743 884379 📄 01743 884379
e-mail: moz123@aol.com
web: www.oldhandanddiamond.co.uk
dir: 9m from Shrewsbury

Set in beautiful countryside close to the River Severn and the Welsh border, this 17th-century inn retains much of its original character. Open winter fires crackle in the beamed interior, whilst outside you'll find a children's play area and a beer garden with plenty of seating on the patio. You can enjoy a pint of Woods Shropshire Lad and Stones Station Bitter. Local produce underpins the extensive restaurant menu, offering dishes like braised haunch of venison with juniper berry and sloe gin, and whole sea bass filled with crab, soy and honey.

Open all day all wk 11am-1am **Bar Meals** L served Mon-Thu 12-2.30, Fri-Sun 12-9.30 D served Mon-Thu 6-9.30, Fri-Sun 12-9.30 Av main course £10.95 **Restaurant** L served Mon-Thu 12-2.30, Fri-Sun 12-9.30 D served Mon-Thu 6-9.30, Fri-Sun 12-9.30 Av 3 course à la carte fr £22 ⊕ FREE HOUSE ◀ Worthington, Shropshire Lad, guest ales. **Facilities** Children's menu Play area Dogs allowed Garden Parking

CRICKHOWELL

Nantyffin Cider Mill Inn �

Brecon Rd NP8 1SG

☎ 01873 810775 🖷 01873 810986

e-mail: info@cidermill.co.uk

dir: *At junct of A40 & A479, 1.5m W of Crickhowell*

Originally a drovers' inn, located at the foot of the Black Mountains between Crickhowell and Brecon, the Nantyffin dates from the 16th century. It became well known for the cider it produced in the 19th century and the original cider press, fully working until the 1960s, has been incorporated into the Mill Room Restaurant. These days the Nantyffin is renowned for its successful pairing of traditional pub values with acclaimed French bistro-style food. The bars are full of character and offer a range of ales, draught and bottled Welsh ciders, and a comprehensive wine list. Menus are based on locally sourced produce such as beef, pork, lamb and poultry from a farm only six miles away.

Open noon-3 6-11 Closed: Mon (ex BH), Sun eve Oct-Mar **Bar Meals** L served Tue-Sun 12-2.30 D served Tue-Sun 6.30-9.30 **Restaurant** L served Sun 12-2.30 booking required D served Fri-Sat 6.30-9.30 booking required ⊕ FREE HOUSE ◀ Reverend James, Rhymney Best Bitter, Felinfoel Stout Ö Stowford Press, Taffy Apples. 壹 12 **Facilities** Children's menu Dogs allowed Garden Parking

HAY-ON-WYE

Kilverts Inn ♑

The Bullring HR3 5AG

☎ 01497 821042 🖷 01497 821580

e-mail: info@kilverts.co.uk

dir: *From A438 take B4351 to Hay. Turn right after bridge, left towards park and left again*

In the summer months, be sure to visit this pub's lovely garden, with its lawns, flower beds, pond and fountain. Indoors, there's a timber-framed, olde-worlde style bar offering a range of local beers. Expect robust, generous food, with worldwide influences – typical dishes include grilled goats' cheese with a pesto crust; Kilvert's famous home-made steak and pudding; home-made fisherman's pie and chilli con carne. At the bar there's an impressive selection of ales and ciders. There is an annual beer festival too.

Open all wk **Bar Meals** L served all wk 12.30-2.30 D served all wk 6.30-9 Av main course £8.95 **Restaurant** D served Fri-Sat 6.30-9 ⊕ FREE HOUSE ◀ Wye Valley Butty Bach, The Reverend James, Pedigree, Guest Ales Ö Westons Old Rosie. 壹 8 **Facilities** Children's menu Family room Dogs allowed Garden Parking

MONTGOMERY

Dragon Hotel ★★ HL ◉

SY15 6PA

☎ 01686 668359 📠 0870 011 8227

e-mail: reception@dragonhotel.com

web: www.dragonhotel.com

dir: *A483 towards Welshpool, right onto B4386 then B4385. Behind town hall*

In a small quiet town amidst the stunning countryside of the Welsh Marches, this family-run black and white timber-framed coaching inn offers a friendly welcome. An enclosed patio has been created from the former coach entrance. The hotel prides itself on its use of fresh local produce in the kitchen too. In addition to daily blackboard specials and soups, the bar menu includes warm ciabattas; beef, chicken or vegetarian fajitas; and home-made fish pie. The carte may start perhaps with leek-laced Welsh cakes topped with a Perl Las cheese sauce, and continue with breast of local pheasant wrapped in prosciutto, with blackcurrant jus and honey-roasted vegetables.

Open all wk noon-2 6-11 **Bar Meals** L served all wk 12-2 D served all wk 7-9 Av main course £8 **Restaurant** L served all wk 12-2 booking required D served all wk 7-9 booking required Fixed menu price fr £25 Av 3 course à la carte fr £29 ⊕ FREE HOUSE ◀ Wood Special, Interbrew Bass, guest. **Facilities** Children's menu Dogs allowed Garden Parking **Rooms** 20

NEW RADNOR

Red Lion Inn

Llanfihangel-nant-Melan LD8 2TN

☎ 01544 350220 📠 01544 350220

e-mail: theredlioninn@yahoo.co.uk

dir: *A483 to Crossgates then right onto A44, 6m to pub. 3m W of New Radnor on A44*

Old habits die hard here: this ancient drover's inn still provides water, though nowadays it's for hosing down the bike. The inn has a lounge and a locals' bar, two small restaurants and a sun-trap garden. A broad menu draws extensively on local produce, including herbs from the garden. Mussels, usually served as a starter in white wine, garlic and cream, come from the River Conwy up north. Main courses might include game terrine with Cognac and grape preserve; Welsh Black beef fillet with béarnaise sauce; organic salmon fish cakes; and leek, wild mushroom and chestnut gâteau. Round off with Welsh cheeses and home-made walnut bread.

Open noon-11.30 (Sun noon-7.30) Closed: Tue **Bar Meals** L served Mon-Sat 12-3, Sun 12-7.30 D served Mon-Sat 6-11.30, Sun 12-7.30 ⊕ FREE HOUSE ◀ Guest Ales ○ Thatchers. **Facilities** Children's menu Family room Dogs allowed Garden Parking

REYNOLDSTON

King Arthur Hotel ▮

Higher Green SA3 1AD
☎ 01792 390775 📄 01792 391075
e-mail: info@kingarthurhotel.co.uk
dir: *Just N of A4118 SW of Swansea*

A traditional country inn, with real log fires, in a village lying at the heart of the beautiful Gower Peninsula. Eat in the restaurant, main bar or family room, choosing main menu or specials board dishes including seasonal game, Welsh Black beef, locally caught fish and vegetarian options. Try whole trout with cockle and laverbread sauce; crisp garlicky chicken Kiev; or tuna and bean salad.

Open all day all wk **Closed:** 25 Dec **Bar Meals** food served all day **Restaurant** L served all wk 12-2.30 D served Sun-Thu 6-9, Fri-Sat 6-9.30 ⊕ FREE HOUSE ◀ Felinfoel Double Dragon, Worthington Bitter & Bass, Tomas Watkins OSB, King Arthur Ale. ▮ 9 **Facilities** Children's menu Family room Garden Parking

COWBRIDGE

Hare & Hounds ▮

Aberthin CF71 7LG ☎ 01446 774892
e-mail: nicholasmassey@hotmail.com
dir: *1m from Cowbridge*

Transformed from a run-down boozer to a popular dining pub, this 15th-century former mint stands in the pretty village of Aberthin. The bar remains a cosy traditional haven with an open fire, while the dining room sports a contemporary look, with a warm decor and modern furnishings. Local diners now beat a path to the door for hearty food prepared from Welsh ingredients, local and organic where possible. At lunch, tuck into chicken liver parfait with plum chutney or quail's egg and bacon salad for starters or a light bite, or a main dish like cottage pie and gammon, egg and home-made chips. More imaginative evening dishes may take in pan-fried venison with fondant potato and roasted pear jus; braised pork belly with cider apple jus; and wild mushroom risotto with basil dressing. On fine days dine alfresco by the stream in the garden.

Open all day all wk noon-mdnt (Mon 4-mdnt Fri-Sat noon-1am) **Bar Meals** L served Tue-Sat 12-3 **Restaurant** L served Tue-Sun 12-3 booking required D served Tue-Sat 6-9 booking required ⊕ MARSTONS ◀ Ringwood Best, Pedigree. 4 guests Ŏ Thatchers Gold. ▮ 11 **Facilities** Children's menu Family room Dogs allowed Garden Parking **Notes** no credit cards